PROF

The Life of Frederick Lindemann

PROF

The Life of Frederick Lindemann

Adrian Fort

JONATHAN CAPE
LONDON

Published by Jonathan Cape 2003

2 4 6 8 10 9 7 5 3 1

First published in Great Britain in 2003 by
Jonathan Cape
Random House, 20 Vauxhall Bridge Road,
London SW1V 2SA

Random House Australia (Pty) Limited
20 Alfred Street, Milsons Point, Sydney,
New South Wales 2061, Australia

Random House New Zealand Limited
18 Poland Road, Glenfield,
Auckland 10, New Zealand

Random House South Africa (Pty) Limited
Endulini, 5A Jubilee Road, Parktown 2193, South Africa

The Random House Group Limited Reg. No. 954009
www.randomhouse.co.uk

A CIP catalogue record for this book
is available from the British Library

ISBN 0-224-06317-0

Papers used by The Random House Group Limited are natural,
recyclable products made from wood grown in sustainable forests;
the manufacturing processes conform to the environmental
regulations of the country of origin

Typeset in Ehrhardt by Palimpsest Book Production Limited,
Polmont, Stirlingshire
Printed and bound in Great Britain by
Clays Ltd, St Ives PLC

For Claire, Viola and George

CONTENTS

Illustrations

1. Frederick Lindemann
2. Royal Aircraft Factory BE2e (*Royal Air Force Museum; P 9456*).
3. Scientific staff of the Royal Aircraft Factory outside the Chudleigh Mess in 1917 (*by courtesy of Quinetic*).
4. Lady Elizabeth Lindsay (*by courtesy of the Earl of Crawford and Balcarres*).
5. Lindemann lecturing at the Clarendon Laboratory, drawn by his pupil William Merton (*by courtesy of William Merton, Esq.*).
6. Lindemann on board the *Sona* (*Birkenhead Papers; by courtesy of Lady Juliet Townsend*).
7. *Tea at Chartwell*, painting by Winston Churchill, 1928 (*National Trust Photo Library/Mark Fiennes*).
8. On board HMS *Prince of Wales*, August 1941 (*Imperial War Museum, A 4987; reproduced by permission of the Imperial War Museum*).
9. Churchill and Lindemann watching an anti-aircraft demonstration (*Imperial War Museum, H 10306; reproduced by permission of the Imperial War Museum*).
10. 'Window': cartoon in the *Daily Mirror*.
11. Magdalen Bridge, Oxford, photographed by Lindemann.
12. Drawing of a vase, by Lindemann.
13. Brigadier Lindemann and Franz Simon (*by courtesy of Mrs Kathrin Baxandall*).
14. Lindemann's servant, Harvey.
15. Lindemann with Dorothee Simon (*by courtesy of Mrs Kathrin Baxandall*).

Every effort has been made to trace and contact copyright holders. The publishers will be pleased to correct any mistakes or omissions in future editions.

ONE

Family Origins

Frederick Lindemann, Winston Churchill's close friend and scientific adviser, died on 3 July 1957, in the spacious set of rooms overlooking Christ Church Meadow in Oxford that he had occupied for half a lifetime. His death brought to a close a career that was far removed from the roll of common men. As a child he lived in attractive and peaceful surroundings in Devonshire. The important years of his education were spent in Germany, and in Berlin as a young man, in the early years of the twentieth century when science was on the threshold of momentous advances, he achieved international recognition as a physicist. At the onset of war in 1914 he returned to England, where he contributed remarkably to the development of aeronautics and, through experiments in which he calmly put his own life at risk, discovered the scientific method of escaping from aeroplane spin.

When peace returned he settled at Oxford, where his reputation as a physicist had won him the chair of experimental philosophy, and in the ensuing twenty years he nurtured the study of science at Oxford from moribund beginnings to world renown. In the 1930s, as England drifted towards the peril of another war, he entered the political arena, standing for Parliament himself, and campaigning in the face of ministerial hostility and official apathy to alert the country to the neglect of its defences. He also brought to England, and safety, some of Germany's leading Jewish scientists, who were to prove invaluable in the struggle that lay ahead.

The renewal of conflict with Germany, the country of his forefathers, drew him straight to the centre of power, where, as personal and scientific adviser to the Prime Minister and as a member of the Cabinet, his influence and advice directly affected the conduct of the war and came to have far-reaching consequences for the nation. In the post-war years he combined his work as the head of Oxford physics with that of Opposition spokesman on economics in the House of Lords, until he was called once again to serve as a Cabinet minister, becoming responsible for the course and direction that Britain was to take as an atomic power.

These are the main divisions of his life, but the thread that bound the years of his influence was the friendship of Winston Churchill, to whom he became counsellor, confidant and closest companion. His personal charm and love Lindemann reserved for a few; to the multitude he was largely indifferent, but very ready, if obstructed, to draw on an armoury of both wit and invective, disdain and contempt. Between raillery and mockery he steered a delicate course, buttressed by obstinacy, by exceptional intelligence and by unshakable confidence in the rightness of his opinions.

Along the course of this extraordinary journey he became a Fellow of the Royal Society, a Companion of Honour, a Privy Counsellor and a viscount. Both in science and in politics he climbed to the summit, and at his funeral the long reach of Christ Church Cathedral was full, the mourners ranging from loyal and affectionate servants to the greatest statesmen in the land.

Lindemann had travelled far from his origins. Because of his natural reticence, and perhaps because he kept his door closed in the face of enquirers, he was clothed in a certain mystery that he did little to dispel. In fact his background was colourful, its brightness contrasting with the severe persona that he usually presented to the world. His father had wanted early in life to be an explorer, but became instead a successful entrepreneur and a talented scientist. His mother was half-Russian. She was brought up in America and at the age of seventeen had married a banker twenty-eight years her senior, whose ward she was. Her second marriage was to Adolf Lindemann, with whom she had four children. Of these, Frederick Lindemann was the second, born on 5 April 1886.

The earliest detailed record of the Lindemann family is of a Captain Lindemann, serving in the Imperial Army in Strasburg in 1641, and by the end of the seventeenth century the family had settled in the Palatinate – that land of medieval cathedrals, steeply rising castles, thickly wooded hills and vineyards in the valleys of its two great rivers, the Rhine and the Moselle.

For successive generations the Lindemanns served on the estates of the Wittelsbach family, who were long dominant in the Palatinate and were Dukes of Zweibrücken, a duchy that was absorbed by the kingdom of Bavaria after Napoleon's downfall. The Lindemann family was not then rich, but was well established and locally respected. Their homeland had long been a border territory, vulnerable to the designs of France from the west and to Germanic influence from the east. Its population was among the four million people who changed rulers during the Napoleonic Wars, the land becoming for a time the French department of the Sarre, but after France's final defeat in 1815 being included in the German Federation.

While parts of the family may have settled further south, in the French territory of Alsace, Frederick Lindemann's immediate ancestors came from Germany. However, in the twentieth century it was not always politic to emphasise German connections, and after the Great War, when anti-German feeling had become virulent, members of the family – with the notable exception of Lindemann's father – maintained that they were Alsatian and not German, a notion never dispelled by Lindemann himself.

For as long as could be remembered the Lindemann family had been Roman Catholic, but in spite of that background Frederick was in his time often thought to be Jewish, something that he flatly denied. It is impossible now to be certain of the truth as so little is known of Lindemann's mother, but the notion seems to be without foundation. Although the name Lindemann could suggest a Jewish origin, as Jews in Germany were often given by their states the names of shrubs and trees (and *Linde* is the German word for a lime-tree) this is scarcely conclusive, and in the case of this branch of the Lindemann family there is no evidence of any Jewish blood. Furthermore, in the days when social communities were smaller and more transparent, and when such matters were ruthlessly investigated, members of the family from time to time contracted marriages and joined associations that would have rigorously excluded Jews. It may have been Lindemann's occasional anti-Semitic remarks that led some people to think that he must have been Jewish himself.

Despite the Lindemanns' family tradition, Frederick and his siblings were in fact raised as Protestants, at their mother's insistence. This caused annoyance among other branches of the family but, in the event, their concern was not to be shared by Frederick, who rejected both religions and, as an adult, could best be described as agnostic. Yet despite his religious scepticism he approved strongly on secular grounds of the cohesive social force of the Church of England, and thought that its traditions were all to England's good. He had a similarly temporal admiration for the Catholic Church, believing that it kept people in order and succeeded in preventing a proliferation of religions. However, he would qualify this opinion by complaining that through the Inquisition and the persecution of scientists such as Galileo, the Catholic Church had retarded the advance of science by centuries. And he was apt to be caustic about the outward forms of the Church. As Lord Chandos[1] later said:

Lindemann was a militant agnostic and regarded a large part of the activities of the Church and its doctrine as a target for amused and

3

quizzical satire; he regarded the gaiters with all the force of an anti-clerical Frenchman. Thus the Church and the Christian religion he thought of as an object of ridicule.

At the time of Lindemann's birth the head of the family was Frederick Lindemann's great-uncle, Chrétien Philippe Adolphe, the Comte de Lindemann. He was born in 1811, in what is now the Palatinate, but was at that time part of France. When he was twenty-three he moved to Paris, where he settled and married into a rich shipping family. In middle age he went out to the West Indies, first to Dominica and then to Haiti, for which country he was appointed political and commercial representative to the Kingdom of the Two Sicilies.

He arrived in that kingdom when it was in the last throes of its existence before the Bourbons of Naples were swept away by the revolutionary tide unleashed by Garibaldi. On 6 February 1861, having stayed by the side of the Bourbon king, Francis II, in the embattled fortress of Gaeta, Chrétien Lindemann was given the hereditary title of count, for his loyalty to the Neapolitan dynasty. In 1869 he was appointed San Salvador's ambassador to the North German Union, and two years later Costa Rica appointed him ambassador to Italy. At length he decided to return to his native country, which after the fall of Napoleon had been reacquired by Bavaria, and in 1874 he became a Bavarian citizen.

Chrétien's younger brother, Karl, Frederick's grandfather, was senior forester to the King of Bavaria, a position that, in view of the economic significance of timber in those days, was of considerable importance, involving the management of wide areas of forest and a large workforce. He had a son, Adolf, born in Bavaria in 1846 on the small estate of Langenberg, a short distance north of the border of Alsace and not far from Karlsruhe, across the River Rhine.

From an early age Adolf Lindemann displayed both interest and ability in many aspects of science, especially in astronomy, for which he showed unusual talent. He often said that one of the proudest days of his life was when, at the age of fourteen, he set a star in his home-made equatorial and found it exactly upon the cross-wires. That a teenage boy could build and align a telescope so accurately is an indication of unusual theoretical and practical talent.

Having first gone to school at Speyer, on the banks of the Rhine, Adolf studied engineering in Nuremberg. His wider interests in natural sciences were such that he originally intended to become an explorer, at that brief moment in history when it was a recognised way of life. With this in mind he gained expertise in the design of scientific instruments, working for

T. Ertel & Co. in Munich. However, he had to abandon hopes of exploration when he contracted typhoid. Although he made a complete recovery, he believed that he would always be at risk of compromising his expeditions by falling ill while deep in the wilderness.

Adolf's well-being suffered also in a more dramatic manner. While living in Munich he was involved in a duel, in which he was wounded sufficiently seriously to prevent him from being called up to fight in the Bavarian Army in 1866 when Prussia, in the first of its expansionist wars, launched an attack upon Austria.

Around the time of the Franco-Prussian War, Adolf Lindemann abandoned Germany for England. There is no clear evidence as to why he did so, but it is likely that, in the modern description, he was an economic migrant. He left Ertel & Co. in April 1870 and settled in London that summer. In March 1872 he was offered a post at the firm of Siemens Bros. The electrical industry was at this time becoming international in character, and although Siemens was a German firm, it had set up a branch in Woolwich to manufacture cables. Adolf flourished at Siemens, where he stayed for three years, and was befriended by the manager, a remarkable industrialist called Georg von Chauvin, who later became godfather to his son, Frederick. By 1874 he had been given an important position in making and laying the first transatlantic cable, which opened the way for the revolution in communications between Europe and America.

He took readily to the work, and it was conveniently close to the Observatory at Greenwich, where he could pursue his interest in astronomy. He joined the Royal Astronomical Society in 1872, and in later life also became a Fellow of the Royal Geographical Society.

With some families it is possible to pinpoint quite closely a moment when fortune either smiles or frowns upon them and imposes a radical change in their status. Adolf Lindemann's family was one such, and the origin of the events that made it rich lay in a holiday that Adolf spent near his family's home in Germany.

Adolf had retained close contact with his homeland and frequently travelled there. In the summer of 1876, during an expedition to look for fossils, he stayed at Pirmasens, a town some forty-five miles north of Strasburg, and soon after his arrival he gave a lecture to the local Natural History Society. His subject was 'beetles', but in his introductory remarks he talked of his hotel and of his dismay when, arriving hot and dusty in the town, he had been told that he could not have a bath until the following day. Water, it seemed, had to be brought up from the valley below the town, which explained the exorbitant charge of two guilders for a bath. However, his talk was interrupted by his listeners exclaiming, 'We couldn't care less about your hotel room: if you're so clever, then give us water.'[2]

This presented Adolf Lindemann with a problem that exactly engaged his interests in natural science and engineering, and he decided to rise to the challenge thrown down at Pirmasens. By the end of the year he had secured a concession from the local council for the supply of water to the town, and he set about buying and installing, at his own expense, the water pipes that would, he believed, transform the community. Unfortunately, as is common with building work, delays and difficulties soon arose and, despite his enthusiasm, after eighteen months the scheme appeared to have stalled. Lindemann became the butt of unfavourable comment from local people, and his financial embarrassment threatened his stay at the hotel, where he had run up considerable bills.

Luckily his father, living not far away at Zweibrücken, had been keeping a kindly eye on Adolf and now offered help. As a result of his ideas and contacts, an agreement was reached with a civil engineer from London who, together with some English backers, formed and financed the Pirmasens Water Company, and to this organisation Adolf Lindemann assigned his rights and became a consultant. By 1879 the whole system was up and running, and a few years later similar work was started in Speyer, the medieval city some forty miles away on the banks of the Rhine where Adolf had first gone to school. Before very long the newly watered town of Pirmasens began to prosper. Its population increased eightfold over the ensuing two decades, and the town is now Germany's leading manufacturer of footwear.

Adolf began gradually to build up a holding in the company, and as the years unfolded the flow of dividends increased and the value of the business rose. By 1911 he had acquired nearly all the shares in the company, and in that year Pirmasens Town Council, which had long regretted not taking a greater financial interest in the water works, agreed to buy the company for over two million marks (about £5 million in today's terms). Adolf had reached the uplands of wealth, on which his son Frederick was to walk, without financial care, all his life.

In the early years of the business Adolf had become a friend of Benjamin Davidson, a partner in Rothschild's Bank, for which he had worked in Russia and California, before moving in 1862 to France and subsequently to England. Davidson was popular at the bank and was fondly described by members of the Rothschild family at that time as 'Benny the Bachelor'.

Davidson had a friend called Gilbert Noble, a successful civil engineer of Scottish origin, who had also worked in Russia but had eventually settled in America. Noble was married, and although his wife's origins are unclear, it was believed in the Lindemann family that she was Russian and of aristocratic blood. She and Gilbert had a daughter, Olga, who – according to the 1881 British census – was born in New York in 1850, but who was more generally believed to have been born in New London, Connecticut, in January 1851: that, at least, is what is inscribed on her gravestone. The truth of her birth and ancestry remains obscure, partly because of her strong discouragement of enquiries on the subject.

In due course Noble arranged with Benjamin Davidson that Olga would become Davidson's ward, should her father die. When he did so, Olga came to England and moved into Benjamin's house. Further information about her early life is scarce, and a confusing detail emerges from the British census of 1871, in which the Davidson household contained a spinster called Olga O'Brien. In any event, the relationship between Davidson and his ward flourished, and at length they were married.

At first Benjamin and Olga lived in London, where they had three children. The two eldest were girls and were happy living in the city, but the third child, Gilbert, had delicate health, so the family moved to the south coast, and eventually to Devonshire, which they thought would offer pure and soft air that would be good for their son. Accordingly in 1876 they settled in Sidmouth, in a house called Richmond Lodge.

Benjamin Davidson died just two years later, at the age of fifty-five, but Olga remained in Sidmouth. By 1881, according to her census return, she was living at Richmond Lodge with her three young children, attended by nine servants. Four of them were German – an unusual circumstance in south Devon at that time, but perhaps Olga had by then become receptive to the ideas of Adolf Lindemann. He had become a family friend in the years following Benjamin's marriage to Olga, and after Benjamin's death he had remained close to his widow; so much so that in 1884, a week after his thirty-eighth birthday, Adolf Lindemann and Olga Davidson were married. So Adolf came permanently to the Davidsons' house, which he and Olga renamed 'Sidholme', perhaps to mark the start of their new life together.

For all the later success of his business enterprises, at the time of his marriage Adolf had no money to speak of. Davidson had provided for his wife and children in his will, but for some years Olga's second marriage was to prove a strain on her finances. When she began to give Adolf money with which to build a stake in the water companies, economies became necessary: her horses and carriages were sold and the three young children had to give up their ponies and other such pleasures. Moreover, for about fifteen years there were long absences from Sidholme, while the family stayed abroad in order to save money.

Whatever the attractions of these intervals spent on the Continent, Sidholme must have seemed a peaceful anchorage: solid, spacious, with plenty of mahogany furniture and an atmosphere of Victorian opulence. Some of the rooms were notably attractive; others could at least be described as interesting. Olga had a sitting room with walls lined with feathers from the peacocks that strutted around the garden, and the main drawing room was large, imposing and lined with books. Most striking was the music room, which had been added in 1848 as a private chapel. This impressive room was enlivened by murals, and below the ceiling, which was hung with cut-glass chandeliers, ran panels illustrating musical instruments. There were two marble fireplaces and rococo mirrors, and on a dais stood a carved and decorated organ. The garden was attractive and, rambling uphill with fine trees and winding paths, its border marked by iron railings, it flourished under Olga's enthusiastic care.

Adolf and Olga's first child, born in 1885, was called Charles. Frederick Alexander Lindemann was the second, born a year later. His birth actually took place in Baden-Baden, where his parents were staying at the time. That he was born in Germany and not in England, the country for which he was to develop an intense patriotism, was to cause him inconvenience and annoyance in later life, and it was one of a number of resentments that were to colour his character. However, soon after Frederick's birth the family returned to Sidholme, and in that comfortable and welcoming house, set in a south-coast bay, with a backcloth of the red cliffs and green hills of Devonshire, Frederick Lindemann was to spend a happy childhood.

In his earliest days his world was naturally circumscribed by the activities of his immediate family, and in this he was fortunate. It was a lively household: the three children of Olga's first marriage were, at the time that she married Adolf Lindemann, aged thirteen, eleven and eight respectively, and there were to be four more children by Olga's second marriage: Charles and Frederick; Linda, born in 1887; and Septimus, in 1891.

Septimus was born while Olga was staying at Bad Homburg. Known as 'Sepi', he was 'the Benjamin of the family', coming a relatively long time after the others, and was greatly spoilt by his mother.

Frederick and his elder brother were to remain intimate and devoted friends throughout Frederick's life, but Linda, the only daughter of the marriage, seems to have been a rather difficult child and apt to fall out with her brothers. However, for one who at an early age became interested in literature, she may have felt undervalued in a family in which science was paramount. Later in life she became a respected novelist, but her temperament remained volatile, and in time she became completely estranged from her brothers, partly as a result of her marriage.

In 1916 Linda married a barrister, Noel Vickers, whom all the family liked. The marriage was tragically short, lasting for only a few months before

Vickers was killed fighting on the Western Front. Although Frederick was later to sustain a permanent animosity towards his sister, his letter to her after Noel's death displayed a tender side:

> I cannot tell you how horrified I was by your telegram. This news so brutally final, is really too cruel. To anyone who knew him well, as I did, who was privileged to recognise the truly loveable character beneath the incisive manner, the shock of losing poor dear old Noel gives some faint conception of what you must feel . . . The hardest part, my poor child, is yours to 'carry on'. If I can be of the slightest use to you in any way, you know that you can rely on me.[3]

Two years later, however, Linda married again, and this was deeply unpopular with her family. Linda had been left a lot of money by Vickers and the family thought that her new husband, Ian Kirkpatrick, was a fortune-hunter. Matters were not helped by Linda informing her family of the marriage only after the event; nor by the news being conveyed by telegram rather than in person. Nevertheless, in 1918 Olga attempted to improve relations and invited the couple to Sidholme. It was a disastrous encounter: the animosity became so intense that Frederick and Kirkpatrick fell to blows, and Linda and her new husband were ordered out of the house. Linda was told by her mother that, while she herself could return to Sidholme, she could never again bring Kirkpatrick. Even these emotions might, with most people, have faded in time, but for the rest of his life Frederick never offered friendship to his sister, and he never met his nephew – the son that she had by Vickers.

Frederick's stubborn tendency to bear grudges long after most people would have let matters drop was also demonstrated in his relations with Sepi, who turned out very differently from his elder brothers, and chose to live the life of a playboy in the South of France. Frederick strongly disapproved, and for years had a glacial opinion of this cheerful idler. It was only after the Second World War that he came to regret his severity, when he ruefully discovered that Sepi had displayed great bravery during the German occupation of France and had moved around the country disguised as a French officer. Characteristically Frederick tried, in his will, to make amends for his behaviour towards his younger brother.

However, when the children were young, the family was happy and close. Olga was a forceful woman but she was devoted to all her children, giving them much love and affection, which was happily supplemented by their father.

When Frederick was very young his two half-sisters, Dora and Blanche, began to call him 'Peach' because of the colour and smoothness of his complexion. The name stuck and was for many years used by the family and very close friends. Frederick always detested it, but his Christian names – Frederick and Alexander – were for him risky alternatives, as they could all too easily be shortened, and from early in life he considered abbreviations to be, as he later put it, 'the height of vulgarity'. His brother Charles always called him 'F. A.', which he much preferred. At school he was chronically nervous that his nickname would be discovered, and when he arrived at Oxford as a professor he remained equally insistent, for fear of ridicule, that it should never be used. According to Charles, no letter to F. A. starting 'Dear Peach' would ever be answered.

At Sidholme, however, he was known to all as Peach. There, in the full and busy household, with its numerous family retainers, there were plenty of indoor occupations and a wealth of things to do in the garden and in the surrounding countryside. Olga was an excellent pianist and encouraged her children to play; she also had a lovely voice and would spend hours in the music room, accompanying herself, either on the piano or on the harp. Her friendships included Liszt and Paderewski, the celebrated Polish pianist and patriot, who was reputed to have come to Sidholme and to have played on its painted organ.

With this background it is not surprising that Frederick himself was soon drawn to the music room, and to its organ, which he learnt to play with skill. Despite an unwillingness to practise, he also became a first-rate piano player, and his sister recalled him – when 'brooding and restless' – consoling himself by playing Beethoven sonatas. Yet as he grew older his reticence meant that he would not play even in front of close friends. The story is told of how a Christ Church undergraduate in the rooms below Lindemann's was heard to hack his way painfully through a mazurka by Chopin; when he had finished, the same piece could be heard being played upstairs by Lindemann, faultlessly but without any subsequent acknowledgement that he had done so.

There was also a billiard room at Sidholme, and Frederick would play for hours with his father. He took naturally to ball games, and in time became not only good at squash, but also excellent at golf and a champion of international standard at tennis. At Sidholme the children had an assorted pack of terriers, and children and dogs would set off in search of rabbits, rats and stoats. They were also encouraged by their father to fish for trout in the River Sid, although they were told that they had to use a fly, on the grounds that it was unsporting to use worms. When they grew older, and as money began to flow more freely from the companies in Bavaria, Olga encouraged her children to ride, and Frederick would happily mount up and explore the surrounding countryside.

Most exciting of all for the children were the observatory and laboratory near the top of the garden. These had been constructed by their father, whose love of astronomy had continued unabated after his move to Devonshire. Adolf Lindemann had remained a close friend of the celebrated astronomer Max Wolf, who had come to inspect Lindemann's observatory while on a visit to England. So well known would Adolf become in astronomy circles that he would in time have a minor planet named after him: planet 828, '*Lindemannia*'. This was first observed in 1916, from Vienna, and its discoverer dedicated it to 'Herr Lindemann, who unselfishly and generously supports astronomical research'.[4]

Adolf spent long hours in his observatory working on the design of a novel form of telescope, and he also made a 'most ingenious chronograph, and a revolving eyepiece, the first of its kind to be constructed'.[5] It must have given him great pleasure that his two eldest sons showed such interest in the science that was close to his heart. When the children were young there was no more feared punishment than to be told they would not be allowed to go to the observatory.

This colourful and self-contained family must have contrasted with many of their neighbours, the quintessentially English people who lived in Sidmouth in the 1890s, and one of the few links that the children had with other families was tennis. Charles and Frederick both became good players, and matches with neighbours were frequently arranged. Although motor cars were still relatively rare, the Lindemanns had acquired one, together with a chauffeur to drive it, and would motor over to their friends for tournaments. On these occasions there was fierce rivalry on court, and matches would continue for hours until twilight forced the close of play.

These were the busy but contented scenes in which Frederick spent his childhood – a childhood that was to foster in him a deep and enduring self-confidence.

It soon became clear that he had inherited great intelligence, and was also blessed with the unusual combination of analytical strength and instant recall, not just of figures but of anything that he read. When quite young, Frederick was able to reel off from memory whole pages of books and large numbers of recondite facts. A 'party piece' was to quote 'pi', the ratio of the circumference of a circle to its diameter, to 300 decimal places – a remarkable performance, although how many of the visitors to Sidholme had the stamina to sit through this is not recorded.

Frederick also began to demonstrate a certain wilfulness and an antagonism when thwarted. Examples of his strongly competitive character as a child were later recalled by his sister. She wrote of her brother's air of troubled arrogance and unhappy determination, and recalled him at the schoolroom tea table eating with silent concentration, going from the bread and butter to the cake stage before the others. In telling phrases, Linda spoke of difficult scenes and 'something like a silent battle of nerves running through tennis matches, stamp collections, swimming trophies, school prizes'. She also remembered his papers littering the study:

> All figures and lines and symbols. Not to be removed or destroyed or laughed at. Peach at luncheon shining with quite appalling general knowledge which made all conversation a nightmare of pitfalls. Peach determinedly playing chess, playing tennis, playing the piano. Poor Peach, never really playing at all.[6]

Although one must bear in mind that Linda in time fell out spectacularly with all three of her brothers, this description gives a compelling image of the young Frederick, his incipient brilliance sparking the impatience of a child.

When he was about ten, a tutor was engaged for the children – a Swiss called Dessin. He seems not to have left an indelible mark. Charles Lindemann recalled only that he was a Socialist, and that despite being Swiss he was fluent neither in French nor in German. He was followed by a more engaging tutor called Rosenstock, who had been educated at Oxford and was a keen naturalist and ornithologist, and had published in 1895 a translation of *Heligoland as an Ornithological Observatory* – in its day a much sought-after work. Rosenstock encouraged the boys' love of nature, and would cheerfully take them out with butterfly nets or follow the noisy terriers in their hunts for rats and stoats.

As was the custom, the time eventually came for tutors to depart and the schoolroom to be closed, their place usurped by school trunks and the poignancy of departing trains. So Charles and Frederick were in due course sent away to boarding school, their parents selecting one near Falkirk, in Stirlingshire, which specialised in training boys for Sandhurst and the army. The school, Blair Lodge, was an unlikely choice, for reasons both of geography and educational purpose, and it appears to have been selected because Olga and Adolf had been impressed by the headmaster, a friend of theirs. It is now many years since the school put up the shutters, but a picture emerges of a minor public school, somewhat akin to the better-known Fettes or Loretto, promoting 'muscular Christianity' – organised games during the week and four church services on Sundays – within a framework of formality and a conventional syllabus.

At this establishment the thirteen-year-old Frederick arrived for his first term. Despite the distance from home and family, and the contrast with the relatively comfortable life at Sidholme, he seems to have been content at Blair Lodge, although some of its requirements (such as the wearing of a kilt, which he detested) offended his sensitivity. His letters home, perhaps unusual in that they were always addressed to his father rather than to his mother, were written in attractive and finely formed handwriting, and affectionately display schoolboy enthusiasms and anticipation of the approach of the holidays:

Dearest Papa,
I am getting on pretty well with my work being top of my arithmetic, Algebra and Euclid forms. I ought easily to be top for the term if I can keep it up. The boy who used to be top of the arithmetic form hates me and is always trying to do me a mischief, but lately when there was a proper fight I seized him by the throat and flung him under the lockers and he has been quite decent since except when I can't hit him and am wrestling with other boys. My slide-rule is the only one in the school and all the small boys wonder what it is, except the big boys who do not properly understand it. One of the masters wants me to lend it to him to show to his class . . .

I have got about 30 new stamps and the same number of postcards for about 10 of my stamps. It will not be very long to the holidays now, only about $4\frac{1}{2}$ weeks and the time passes very quickly here with so much to do. It will be fine to go to Sch. Langenberg first and as we have from July 27th to October 1st we might go to Blankenberge afterwards. With love from C. L. and myself I remain
        Your affectionate son
        F. A. L.

At Blair Lodge, Frederick excelled at maths and won prizes for Latin, made easy for him by his remarkable memory. He was allowed to take up golf, and quickly became good enough to play with the masters. This pleased him partly because it excused him from various lessons, and he soon won several medals. Long-sighted in one eye and short-sighted in the other, he also excelled at shooting – a skill that is often enhanced by abnormal eyesight. It also seems that, like any schoolboy, Frederick was ready to dodge the rules when faced with childish temptation. He would, for example, surreptitiously lay out chocolates on the ledge of his pew in church, so that when bidden to pray he could place them unobserved in his mouth: an early indication of a love of chocolates that was to last throughout his life. However, one aspect of Blair Lodge to which he never got used was having to get up at, for him, the early hour of seven, and he would compensate for this in the holidays by lying in bed all morning. Throughout his life, except where his political work prevented it, he would be a late riser.

It might have been expected that the boys would stay at Blair Lodge until they were eighteen or nineteen, when they would have been ready for university or for entry into the army. However, this was not to be the case for either of them. Indeed, they each stayed at Blair Lodge for only one year. There is a suggestion that by then they had learnt as much as the school could teach them – Frederick's mathematical ability in particular rivalling that of the masters. At all events both boys left early, their parents' decision being perhaps in keeping with Adolf's continental origins, or with his belief that science, which was not on offer at Blair Lodge, was the proper bedrock of education.

Even in the nineteenth century the scientific community was international and Adolf had kept up his friendships with scientists in Germany. One of these was an eminent chemist in Darmstadt, who encouraged Adolf to send his sons to its Lycaeum, which at that time had a good reputation and offered, besides a thorough German education, plenty of tennis.

So, at the age of fourteen, Frederick Lindemann finished the British part of his schooling and went to Germany. It was there that he would receive the rest of his education, and where his intellect would be keenly sharpened; and it was in Germany that he was to spend, with great distinction and success, much of his young adulthood.

TWO

Schooled in Germany

In 1900 Lindemann arrived in Darmstadt and was enrolled in the Lycaeum. Although it was far from home, he would have the company and support of his brother Charles, who had gone ahead of him to Germany, and later of his younger brother Sepi. There would also be friends of his parents to whom he could turn, and he would have the excitement of being in a new country, albeit one of which he had at least some knowledge from spending holidays there with his cousins.

It was probably a welcome move for the young Frederick. As he grew from childhood to youth he had become increasingly aware of the nuances of the social world around him, and had begun to feel some resentment at having been sent to a Scottish school of no particular standing. He was to attach the blame for this failing, as he saw it, to his mother, and it was to be one of the causes of a gradual cooling in his relationship with her.

Olga proved reluctant, as her children grew older, to relinquish the hold that a mother naturally exercises over her offspring when they are young, and to Lindemann she increasingly began to seem bossy and critical. She had fits of pique, and she also believed in teasing her children. Lindemann did not respond well to this, despite the fact that he himself had no reservations about teasing others. Adolf Lindemann, however, made little effort to quell his wife's temper. He adored Olga, and he also detested rows and did not care to have his peace disturbed.

Although the emotional distance between mother and son began to widen, one bond that did remain was their taste in music. They both liked the lighter Wagner operas, and composers of easy melodies such as Mendelssohn and Johann Strauss, and Chopin – who was Lindemann's favourite. They also shared a dislike of modern music, which was to be one of Lindemann's lifelong prejudices; he would sneer at composers such as Debussy, Ravel and Stravinsky. Instead, like many mathematicians, he was greatly drawn to Bach.

It was predominantly Adolf Lindemann's decision to send his sons to Germany for the rest of their schooling: for a man of his outlook, the idea of a German education would have had obvious merit. By the turn of the century Germany was at the forefront of the teaching of science and technology, and the fostering of scientific learning was considered to be of paramount importance. The study of physics and chemistry was strongly encouraged in institutions of higher learning, and even in lower schools the teaching of science was far in advance of that in America, Britain or Germany's neighbours in Europe.

The schooling at the Lycaeum in Darmstadt was rigorous. The 'main purpose was the unrelenting provision of staggering quantities of factual knowledge',[1] and the school buildings had imposing exteriors, matching the atmosphere in the schoolrooms. Many of the teachers had doctorates, and standards were high. It was a regime that suited Lindemann, and his reports show that he excelled at Latin, English and maths and shone at chemistry. He quickly proved to be precociously advanced, and was even moved into a higher class than his older brother.

Holidays were spent at his beloved home in Devonshire, or at the houses on the Continent rented by his parents. Yet there is no evidence that any of the three brothers suffered from the identity crisis that so often afflicts children whose upbringing is divided between two countries. However, as one event proved, the family was careful not to overweaken their children's links with England. While the Lindemann sons were at the Lycaeum, both Frederick and his elder brother reached the age at which the German Army regarded the sons of the Fatherland as ready for military service. Their parents did not want them to be conscripted; nor, no doubt, did they. One way of avoiding it was for Adolf to become British. As his step-daughter Dora recalled: 'We were thoroughly alarmed, and strings were pulled to get him British nationality.'[2] Accordingly, in 1904, when Frederick was eighteen, Adolf became a naturalised Englishman.

At the end of his time at the Lycaeum, Lindemann passed his *Maturum*, with great ease, and in 1905 moved up to the Grand-Ducal Technical High School, also at Darmstadt, where he was to study for three years in the division of *Electrotechnik*.

Such institutions could more properly be described as technical universities. The teaching was of a high standard, the professors being in several cases Nobel Laureates. The German enthusiasm for science meant that a doctorate from a *Technische Hochschule* received more respect than a philosophy doctorate from a university – very different from the values that prevailed in England, which was something that in later years Lindemann fought hard to change.

In Germany, successive leaders of the country had made the connection between technological development and material prosperity, and support for technology complemented Germany's political ideals. Victory in the Franco-Prussian War had charged the Hohenzollern Reich with a confidence bordering on aggression, and by the turn of the century the atmosphere in the country had become heady:

> Manufacturers on the Rhine built factories to supply the eastern territories of Prussia and the coal of the Ruhr valley furnished them with power and soon with chemical raw materials. The huge indemnity which France had to pay after the war provided capital for the development of industry and the building of railways. The sleepy German towns of Saxony, the South, and particularly the Rhineland, began to be seized by a wave of new enterprise.[3]

Yet despite its steep ascent to power, Germany remained conscious of the industrial might of its competitors, and felt the need to find and develop ways of supplementing her indigenous raw materials, which (apart from coal) were in short supply. Advances in science were thought to be the sure way to meet that need. This was particularly true in the field of chemistry; as a result, Germany's chemical industry had become a giant on the world stage, with its leaders becoming influential in German society and politics. Accordingly, German industry placed far more emphasis on scientific research than did other countries, and this was to reap large dividends. Germany lacked nitrates, for example, for fertilisers and for explosives – both of which were considered desirable by the Germans – but it had been discovered that they could be produced through chemical processes. It was the same with the dyestuffs industry: startling growth was seen in firms such as BASF, Bayer and Hoechst, later to combine to form the giant I. G. Farben, and the key to their success was the scientific expertise that had been fostered in schools and universities. In the last two decades of the nineteenth century the world's production of dyes had doubled, with Germany at length supplying over 80 per cent of the market.

So by sending his sons first to school and then to technical university in Germany, Adolf Lindemann had launched them on a flood tide, and it swept them swiftly along a course that entirely suited their nature. At the High School Lindemann demonstrated an unusual insight into physics and chemistry, but it was also during his time there that he began to make his mark on local society.

The city of Darmstadt now sprawls adjacent to the bleak industrial estates that stretch to the horizon south of Frankfurt, but in the early years of the twentieth century it was an attractive town of 30,000 inhabitants. The leader of its society, and the main landowner, was the Grand Duke Ernst-Ludwig of Hesse, and his inspiration had begun to lift Darmstadt well above the run of most German cities.

He was the owner of a hilltop park called Mathildenhöhe, where in 1899, with one eye on the potential benefits to the local economy, he invited selected German and Austrian artists to found an artists' colony. That soon flourished, and by the time Lindemann arrived in Darmstadt the city had become the world centre for Art Nouveau. The artistic atmosphere was matched by the city's architecture, embellished by the rococo Prinz Georg Garden and by the Orangerie, a lovely park in the baroque style enclosing an eighteenth-century castle.

Darmstadt society basked in the reflection of Ernst-Ludwig's high position in the European social firmament. He was a grandson of Queen Victoria, and two of his sisters (both later murdered by the Bolsheviks) had married into the Russian royal family: Tsar Nicholas II himself was Ernst-Ludwig's brother-in-law. In the Grand Duke's circle were some of Adolf Lindemann's friends, and through them his sons received a social entrée. The two young Englishmen were soon taken up, and became greatly attracted to life at the palace, Wolfsgarten. When Ernst-Ludwig took them for a ride in his Opel motor car, for instance, Lindemann was fascinated, and it was this ride that first sparked the interest in cars that would result in his later owning a long succession of opulent limousines.

Ernst-Ludwig also loved tennis and had established a tennis club at his palace. Frederick and Charles Lindemann were a formidable tennis pair, and were able to widen their circle of friends quickly by playing at this club, where an added interest was the presence of the numerous Russian nobles who attended the court of the Tsar, which moved to Darmstadt every summer to stay at Wolfsgarten.

One consequence was that, during his time at school in the city, Lindemann played tennis with both the Tsar and the Kaiser, although it is not recorded whether in this august and autocratic company he felt it advisable to moderate his game. Possibly he did, because Lindemann used later to tell with amusement of a doubles game in which his opponents had been the Kaiser and a German Army artillery major. The unfortunate officer had served two consecutive double faults when the All-Highest turned to him with a peremptory bark and said: 'You forget with whom you are playing.' Lindemann used to reflect how the poor major, as he threw up the ball for his next serve, must have thought that his entire military career was on the line.

One of Lindemann's few letters to his mother describes his tennis prowess at this time:

11, Bismarckstrasse,
Darmstadt.
Aug 11th, '05

My dear Mamma,

I am very glad to hear that you are so much better. I would have written before but I thought that I had better wait and tell you about Kreuznach. I won two firsts and two seconds there; a set of 6 liqueur glasses shaped like port wine glasses, a decanter, a cigarette case and a cigar box. A chap called Andrews got the other prizes. I am playing with him at Homburg. I shall probably go there on Monday. Please thank Rosa for her letters. I am glad to hear she is staying on at Sidmouth. Hoping to hear you are quite well again soon, I remain,

Your affectionate son,
Peach.

As Lindemann neither smoked nor drank, these prizes were on the normal plane of uselessness that characterises sporting trophies; but it was not only tobacco and alcohol that he avoided, as he had already acquired the quirky eating habits that were to remain with him for the rest of his life. When he was ten his parents, encouraged by the example of one or two leading athletes, had been persuaded that vegetarianism was one of the secrets of good health. They had therefore coerced their children into taking part in this momentary enthusiasm, but like most people they had soon tired of the inconvenience. Charles had followed his parents' example and returned to meat-eating, but his younger brother had stayed on the diet, probably as a result of an already well-developed streak of obstinacy and a dislike of change. He used later to say that he had no principled objection to the eating of meat: he just didn't like it. Even so, in his youth it must have been very tempting for him to eat and drink in the same way as his friends, and his refusal to do so is an example of the determination with which he was armed from an early age.

Salad, Port Salut cheese and the whites of egg, enlivened by large amounts of olive oil and mayonnaise, seemed to be the prominent features of this strange regime. Many years later Lindemann told his brother that 'he cursed the day when he was used for this silly experiment', but apart from the difficulties it was to cause during wartime, it seemed to provide adequate nourishment, even for a man of his large size.

Another of Lindemann's idiosyncrasies was the way he dressed for tennis: even allowing for the restrictive clothes that were customary before the Great War, Lindemann's appearance on court was unusual. His boots were made of buckskin and his trousers of flannel, and he would wear his shirt buttoned to the neck and to the wrists, as though he considered it inappropriate to display any flesh. Yet such apparel did not seem to hamper him on court, and with his brother Charles he began to play in tournaments at a high level, as he described in a letter to his father:

July 10th, '06.

My dear Papa,
Please excuse my not having written before to thank you for the M300 you sent so quickly. I was fairly successful at Strasburg and won the Akademische Meisterschaft, the second in Open Mixed, the second in the Meisterschaft von Suddeutschland and the second in handicap doubles. I beat O. Kreuzer who was considered the third-best player in Germany, and who beat Lemaire, the Belgian champion, 6–3, 6–4 . . .

For someone who was barely twenty, his tennis was proving very successful.

This letter was typical of those he wrote to his father, and they were usually also filled with scientific detail and reports of experiments that he had carried out. Science was a happy bond between father and son, to both of whom such letters clearly gave pleasure.

Lindemann's scientific aptitude quickly became apparent at the Technical High School, where it was strongly encouraged, and before long he was rewarded with a remarkable success when he developed, with his brother's help, a special type of glass for use with X-rays.

X-rays are electromagnetic waves that are about a thousand times shorter than visible light waves, with photons that bear correspondingly greater energy, and they have the ability to penetrate matter opaque to visible light. Their discovery in November 1895 by Wilhelm Roentgen was one of the revolutionary steps that led to the development of quantum theory. Knowledge of the extraordinary nature of X-rays had resulted from an experiment by Henri Becquerel in February 1896, a month after he had read a report of Roentgen's work. Thinking that X-rays might be emitted by minerals exposed to the sun, Becquerel placed various samples in the sunlight, on photographic plates wrapped in black paper. To his astonishment he then found that certain other specimens, which he had not been able to use because of cloudy weather, emitted similar rays. These other minerals were salts of uranium, which in some unknown way could generate powerful rays, subsequently given the name 'radiation' by Madame Curie.

Hearing of this discovery, Pierre and Marie Curie had set about investigating the properties of uranium. They had started with about five tons of pitchblende, the ore from which uranium is extracted, and by an arduous process of separation had isolated tiny amounts of radioactive matter. In the course of this work they had noticed that parts of their pitchblende emitted even more radiation than the uranium, and from those parts they isolated what became known as radium.

The potential for using X-rays in medical diagnosis had caused enormous excitement around the world almost as soon as their discovery was announced. In 1897, for example, portable X-ray sets for the examination of wound fractures were taken to Khartoum by surgeons accompanying Kitchener's expedition against the Mahdi. By the time Lindemann had reached Darmstadt the immense importance of X-rays had become widely realised.

X-rays are produced by means of a glass tube in which a stream of electrons is made to collide with a metal anode. The collision causes rays of energy to emanate outwards from the point of collision, just as ripples travel outwards when a stone is dropped in water. On their journey from the anode to their target (which might be a patient in a hospital), the X-rays pass through the glass of the tube, which by its very nature absorbs some of the rays and reduces their effect. Lindemann believed that he could improve on the glass then in use, and make a new type that would absorb fewer rays and thus provide radiographs of higher quality and more consistent exposure.

From the theoretical knowledge that he had already gained, Lindemann worked out that it should be possible to make suitably transparent glass out of compounds of elements such as lithium, beryllium and boron, which have the lowest atomic weights of all the solid elements. Having formulated the theory, he succeeded – with the help of his brother Charles – in making the glass in their laboratory at home in Devonshire.

This invention contributed, for a time, to the inestimable benefits that the use of X-rays was beginning to bring, particularly in the field of medicine. The invention became known as Lindemann glass, and achieved wide commercial use. Adolf Lindemann urged his sons to sell the rights to their glass before large businesses found their own ways of solving the problem. Unfortunately the brothers did not heed their father's shrewd advice, although they at once took out a patent. They therefore later suffered the loss of their invention's potential, when a research scientist with the General Electric Company in America developed an even better X-ray tube, which produced such a high intensity of X-rays that the use of special glass became unnecessary.

After three years at the High School, Lindemann had completed his formal education, although there appears to have been some abnormality about his last two terms, as his final report stated enigmatically:

The studies and exercises laid down for these two terms could not be carried out because Mr Lindemann has not pursued the normal programme under the usual professors.

He left the school at Easter 1908, yet not before he had demonstrated conspicuously, and with the proof of practical success, that he was growing into a scientist of rare ability. Meanwhile his brother Charles had been adopted, in a way permitted by French law, by his father's first cousin, who was now head of the French branch of the family, but had no children of his own. This was to mean that Charles began to spend much of his time in this cousin's various houses, in France and England, and to see less of his brother and his family at home. He was soon drawn into a rich and more worldly orbit, and in time married a beautiful Frenchwoman, Madeline de Lagotellerie.

Lindemann, however, was now poised for a major new step in his career: a move to Berlin. He might instead have gone to Oxford or Cambridge, which at that time between them formed the first league of universities; of the two, Cambridge would have been the natural choice for a man of scientific leaning and ability. Had he gone there perhaps his character would have developed differently: his sense of rootlessness might have been less pervasive, and a few years at an English university might have modified his apparently persistent desire to be accepted without question as an Englishman. As it was, he stayed in Germany and arrived in Berlin in the autumn of 1908.

By the turn of the century Berlin had established a claim to be the world centre of scientific learning. This was partly because of the Kaiser's encouragement of scientific institutions, exemplified by his view that 'the new century will be mastered by science and technical concepts, and not like the last, by philosophy'. It was also partly because the financial backing of the Prussian state had drawn the country's best minds to the capital. So by moving to Berlin, Lindemann arrived at the focal point of exciting developments while one of the great revolutions in the advance of science was taking place.

Since Newton's day, two-and-a-half centuries earlier, the established principles of classical physics had formed the path upon which scientific understanding was founded. However, new scientific discoveries had advanced knowledge exponentially throughout the nineteenth century, and now that path was crumbling fast. Yet as the century drew to a close, excitement and satisfaction became mixed with a troubled concern, as strange inconsistencies began to mar the progress that had been made:

> the edifice of classical physics that had been built during that century began to crack, in some areas, under the weight of new unsolved problems and new discoveries.[4]

It fell to Max Planck, professor of theoretical physics at the University of Berlin, to provide an answer to the fundamental problem that was emerging. Planck was well described as 'the gatekeeper of the twentieth century: the critical transitional figure, who unexpectedly and without an especially revolutionary turn of mind, opened the door to modern physics through his work on the problem of blackbody or cavity radiation'.[5]

Planck had long been intrigued by thermal radiation and his interest in it had confronted him with earlier attempts to explain the radiation from a 'blackbody', an idealised concept of the perfect absorber of electromagnetic radiation. He now turned his mind to the spectrum of blackbody radiation – in other words, the distribution of energy as a function of wavelength emitted by a blackbody.

The formula that Planck put forward is considered to represent the beginning of the quantum revolution, although it is argued that his thoughts crystallised only after Albert Einstein had in the first years of the new century taken up and elaborated his ideas, particularly the crucial suggestion that energy is emitted not in a continuous stream but in a discrete package or 'quantum'.

Einstein was at that time living in Switzerland, working as a clerk in the Patent Office in Berne, but his brilliant and iconoclastic papers – perhaps the most famous of which were those of 1905 and 1907 on the Special Theory of Relativity – were the passports by which quantum theory came into its own.

The contrast in both mind and character between Planck and Einstein is arresting. Planck's conclusions were drawn after a methodical journey along the path laid out by the great nineteenth-century scientific pioneers, while Einstein's hurricane of revolutionary ideas blew up independently from the orderly peace of Switzerland. Between them they opened the gate to the dramatic advances of the early twentieth century.

Into this arena there now came Walther Nernst, an outstanding chemist working in a field of great industrial and practical importance: the thermodynamics of chemical reactions. He was an extreme example of a type of scientist that Lindemann was later so often to complain he could see emerging from the technological universities in Germany, but not in Britain. Nernst had an eclectic scientific mind and an outstanding intellect, and was to become a Nobel Prizewinner in 1920. He also had a worldly ego and ambition.

In aspect, Nernst had something of the cartoon version of the brainbox scientist, and he was not immune to the occasional miscalculation. In 1905 he came to Berlin to take up the chair of physical chemistry at the university, and it was told with relish in scientific circles that his triumphant entry into the city was delayed for the most ironical reason: that Nernst, who had played a large part in the development of the galvanic cell, had incorrectly connected up the battery of his car.

His biographer, Kurt Mendelssohn, wryly relates another error, set much later in Nernst's career, when, during the Great War, in which he received both the Iron Cross and the coveted *Pour le Mérite*, he was entrusted with the development and testing of explosives:

Usually the preliminary tests were done at the proving grounds at Spandau . . . However, on one occasion Nernst could not be bothered to go that far and instead packed the charge into a small disused well in the laboratory court. The bottom appeared to be filled with rubble and it was open at the top. This, Nernst argued, would direct the blast skywards without doing any damage. The firing took place just after noon while Rubens gave his daily lecture on elementary physics to an audience of about 300 students. They, as well as their lecturer, were duly startled, first by a terrific bang and immediately afterwards by complete darkness. The latter phenomenon turned out to be caused by dense clouds of dust which had been blasted into the lecture room. In his haste, Nernst had omitted to investigate the original purpose of the well, which in fact was not closed at the bottom but opened into a number of ventilation shafts. This system of providing air for the lecture rooms had long been superseded by a more modern installation and the shafts were filled with dust and dirt that had accumulated in them since Helmholtz' days, forty years earlier.[6]

There are many such tales of the best-laid scientific plans meeting unexpected obstacles. At Göttingen University, for example, which had an international reputation and at which Nernst had studied, the authorities had constructed, at great expense, an entirely iron-free room for the purposes of research into magnetism. It immediately proved quite unserviceable, however, as the park in which it was housed was a favourite trysting-point for soldiers from the nearby cavalry barracks, who used to keep their spurs on while getting to know their girls.

However, beneath Nernst's genial exterior lay the incisive mind that made him the third partner, of equal standing with Planck and Einstein, in the formidable trio that stood at the apex of science as a new era of physics took shape. As Lindemann was to write:

> Walther Nernst undoubtedly possessed one of the most versatile and original minds of his generation. There was no subject in science or everyday life in which he was not interested and there was scarcely one to which he was not able to make a brilliant contribution.[7]

He had explored the border between physics and chemistry, and had puzzled and probed at the problems thrown up by the development of thermodynamics.

> . . . practically the whole of his time in Berlin up to the world war Nernst devoted himself to elucidating the one question not yet solved by classical thermodynamics, a problem attacked without success by many of his eminent contemporaries, namely the calculation of equilibria from thermal data . . . with characteristic boldness Nernst enunciated his theorem, which has since become known as the 'Third Law of Thermodynamics', in 1906.[8]

Nernst's theorem concerned the atomic status to be expected in a solid if it could be cooled to the absolute zero of temperature. Its significance was on a level with the revolutionary concepts being put forward by Planck and Einstein. In particular Planck's quantum hypothesis and Nernst's heat theorem were to some extent mutually dependent, and experimental evidence for the one would be a prop for the other. Yet these were still only theories, and they needed practical experiments to back them. Nernst at least had a laboratory that was capable of such work.

Lindemann's abilities had been brought to Nernst's attention by a friend of Adolf Lindemann, and as a consequence Nernst invited the young man to study and work in his laboratory. He was to prove exceptionally able both as a theoretician and an experimenter.

Lindemann arrived at the university in October 1908. In a long letter to his father he gave an enthusiastic, if slightly arrogant, description of his lectures and the professors. Clearly excited at the prospect before him, he wrote of what was to be an extremely successful and happy working partnership:

Nov 4th, '08

My dear Papa,

. . . I have started work at the university properly now so can tell you something about it. The arrangements in the way of 'Horsale', instruments and so on are not nearly as good as Darmstadt, but the professors seem much better. They all strike one as being remarkably young. Planck and Rubens only seem about 45 . . . Warmetheorie is also very good, still very elementary of course . . . Nernst is very 'unscheinbar',[9] small with a big head, bald, with a moustache and a little napoleon. At present his physical chemistry is also very elementary. I am afraid it was a mistake going in for Fischer's chemie and Rubens' Physik . . . I thought the lectures would be more advanced . . . Rubens' physics are the same, he is the best lecturer of any of them, perhaps I should say the best teacher. I find his static electricity quite interesting, though of course it is all well-known things . . . Tomorrow I am going to do my first phys. chem. practicum with Nernst.

With hindsight we can see that Lindemann was describing with youthful confidence some of the world's greatest physicists. Nevertheless, such letters remain attractive examples of a son reaching out with pleasure to a father whom he knows will understand and enjoy the details of his daily life.

The initial impact of Lindemann's arrival must have confirmed Nernst's confidence in him, and Lindemann wrote to his father three weeks after his earlier letter:

26b, Essener Strasse,
Berlin N.W.
Nov. 26th, '08.

My dear Papa,

Very many thanks for your letter. I saw Nernst and he seems quite willing for me to do a Doktorarbeit in his laboratory, and gave me my choice of measuring the specific heats of gases by a new system of his own, or measuring the temperature co-efficients of electric batteries. He said he needed the data of the latter to test a new law which he discovered.

At Nernst's suggestion, the work on which Lindemann embarked for his doctoral thesis concerned measurements of the specific heat of a wide range of solids, from the lowest achievable temperature up. In the event, his thesis, which was published in 1911, was a critique of Einstein's formula for explaining the decrease in the specific heat of diamond.

Lindemann's outstanding ability was soon apparent, even on the rarefied plane occupied by Walther Nernst; yet the other pupils were also exceptional, bidden to the feet of the master only when he detected someone of the highest potential. As Professor Sir Thomas Merton, FRS, who was later to work for Lindemann at Oxford, put it:

> Nernst's pupils were all rather pleased with themselves. They were supposed to be rather selective, and Nernst absorbed most of their time. Lindemann didn't attend many lectures elsewhere.[10]

Among those that he did attend, however, were Planck's epoch-making lectures on quantum theory.

Other Englishmen in the laboratory included A. S. Russell, who was subsequently recruited by Lindemann for work at Oxford, and H. E. Watson, later Professor Emeritus at University College London. Both men recalled Lindemann's flair and originality in designing instruments, which later enhanced his contributions during the First World War. Watson also spoke of Lindemann's dexterity at glass-blowing, a great advantage in his work for Nernst:

> Lindemann would often sit down to a blow-pipe and at once become the centre of an admiring crowd. His favourite demonstration was making very small vacuum vessels, a comparatively simple but very delicate operation.[11]

Nernst had also invited Charles Lindemann into his laboratory in the Bunsenstrasse. Like his younger brother, Charles had shown that he was a scientist of ability and an able experimenter. Accordingly he was set by Nernst to measure the expansion co-efficients of the substances of which the specific heats were being measured in his laboratory – an essential part of the process.

The work on which Lindemann himself was engaged was exciting, but the circumstances of his daily life were also unusually agreeable. When they first came to Berlin, Lindemann and his brother leased a flat in the Ludwigkirchstrasse, which was looked after by the housekeeper whom they had brought with them from Darmstadt, who fed them and made it a comfortable home. Their time at Darmstadt had given the brothers a taste for an active social life, and they now responded enthusiastically to the effervescence of Berlin.

Lindemann was by now a first-rate pianist and went to many concerts, especially those given by his parents' friend, Paderewski. He was tall, fit and good-looking, and soon entered into a series of flirtations. The two brothers would bring back to their flat the girls they had taken out, whether to skate, play tennis or share the other pleasures of the city. They also frequented the theatre at a time when actresses had a certain reputation and often generated feelings that, supposedly, marriage was designed to quell. In Charles Lindemann's words, they lived 'in happy bachelor disorder' with many girlfriends:

> It was not unusual for them to stay the night. F. A. was usually courting some girl or other. When we moved to the Adlon to be near our work, of course, we had to give up this charming promiscuity. I think that, in the continental manner, it never occurred to F. A. that girls were not intended for sleeping purposes.[12]

It had not been long before the brothers had moved to the Hotel Adlon. It was Berlin's best and newest hotel, having opened the previous year on the Unter den Linden, directly opposite the Brandenburg Gate. Word of its attractions had soon spread. Rich families began to prefer its suites to their own draughty residences, and the Foreign Office started using it as an unofficial annexe. It must have had obvious attractions for the Lindemann brothers, but it was an unusual move. In today's terms it would be rather like a student at London University having digs at Claridges.

Although Adolf was generous to his children, he encouraged them to stand on their own feet, partly by saying that if they earnt as much as their allowance, he would double it. The family's investment in the water companies was by now bearing fruit, some of which began to fall into the children's laps. Accordingly Lindemann was given an allowance of £600 per year (the equivalent in today's money of £30,000) – a sum on which most students could jog along in considerable comfort.

For all his instinctive fastidiousness, Lindemann's lifestyle in Berlin was hedonistic, and a far cry from that of so many penurious students living off plain fare in sparsely furnished bedsitters. He would lunch or dine, frequently in female company, at the Adlon, or at other fashionable restaurants such as the Bristol or the Esplanade. Their French relations would often send French girls with letters of introduction, which helped to keep the Lindemann brothers fluent in the language. Within the confines of Lindemann's eccentric diet, his food was of the highest standard. He was, and remained throughout his life, very fond of chocolates, especially those filled with liqueurs: Charles recalled laughing with his brother on finding him one night in his room sitting in bed, sipping brandy from one of the silver cups that he had won at tennis, trying to quell the pain in a tooth.

Legend has it that in those days summers were long and hot, and winters were cold and white. The winter of 1908 was certainly a bitter one, with deep snow covering the streets of the city until the end of March. The Wannsee, the lovely lake that shimmers to the edge of Berlin, froze, and Lindemann used to go for long excursions on the ice with Henry Tizard[13] who worked for a short time in Nernst's laboratory. Like Lindemann, Tizard was many years later to make an outstanding contribution to the application of science to Britain's air defence, and one that was crucial to winning the Battle of Britain; but he and Lindemann were also to develop a mutual and notorious hostility that lasted for many years. In Berlin, however, they were for a time good friends. Tizard later wrote of Lindemann:

> There was always something about him that prevented intimacy. He was one of the cleverest men I have known. He had been to school in Germany, talked German very well – as well as he talked English – and was fluent in French.[14]

They were drawn together by their studies and by the fact of their both having homes in England. Their lifestyles were, however, very different: Tizard recalls envying the Berliners strolling in their fur-lined coats, while he would stand right up against the china stove in his bedsitter to keep out the winter's cold.

At one point Lindemann asked Tizard to share rooms with him, but the suggestion was declined. This was probably fortunate, as relations between the two cooled considerably for a time as a result of a boxing match which they had held, at Tizard's suggestion, and in which Lindemann had been entirely outclassed. This had infuriated him at the time, and continued to rankle thereafter.

Another Englishman who became a friend of Lindemann in Berlin was Alfred Egerton, known to his friends as 'Kink' or Jack.[15] He had been working at University College London, and had met Walther Nernst when he visited the college with Lindemann. Nernst had been impressed by Egerton and had invited him to work in his laboratory; Egerton had agreed to go, and in November 1913 he moved to Berlin. He too was to be one of Lindemann's recruits to the Clarendon when he began his great project, after the First World War, to raise Oxford physics to international fame.

Berlin was an attractive city and a delightful place to be a student. As befitted the capital of Prussia, it had an orderly appearance, its streets made colourful by numerous soldiers and others in uniform. An illustration of the disciplined atmosphere was later recalled with amusement by Tizard: the Kaiser had a special musical horn fitted to his car, and frequently visited his Chancellor, von Bulow, whose offices were opposite Tizard's rooms. Whenever this horn was heard all the officers in the street would turn smartly to face the roadway and stand at the salute until the All-Highest had passed. On one occasion the horn was heard and numerous officers turned and stood at the salute for some time, until it appeared that the Kaiser was not after all driving by. They relaxed, only to stiffen once more to attention when the horn was again sounded. After this had happened several times a small boy was seen at a high window with a horn in his hand. A sergeant was sent into the house to arrest the boy's father.

Given the brilliance of his work, Lindemann soon became Nernst's favourite pupil. He regularly attended the professor's dinner-parties, and in the disciplined city of Berlin no one gave him a second glance as he walked in white tie along the streets to dinner. Nernst enjoyed the material blessings of life, having made a great fortune out of selling the patents to his 'Nernst Lamp', and his dinners were formal and lengthy affairs. Even so, he often expressed disapproval of the amount of time Lindemann spent on the tennis court in summer. However, Nernst was a good-natured man and it was probably only a token reproof.

Much of Lindemann's spare time was taken up with tennis. He used to play at Berlin's 'Red-White' and 'Blue-White' clubs, often in partnership with his brother. As with Ernst-Ludwig's club at Darmstadt, tennis in Berlin was an avenue to social advancement: the Kaiser's sons and nephews all belonged to the Red-White club, as did many of the city's social elite. The game also took Lindemann away from Berlin: he played in many matches around the country and was notably successful in tournaments in Scandinavia. Many of these were arranged by the Swedish king, Gustav V, who was enthralled by the game, and who often played under the sobriquet of 'Mr G', frequently partnering the ladies' champion Suzanne Lenglen, christened 'Suzanne the Terrible' for her fiery success on court.

Meanwhile in Nernst's laboratory Lindemann was developing a second line of research, besides his work on specific heats for his thesis. This investigation concerned the relationship between the melting point of a solid and its other thermal properties. His suggestion was that the melting of a solid occurred when the vibrations of its atoms was great enough to cover the gap normally present between neighbouring atoms, so breaking up the ordered arrangement of atoms that is a characteristic of solid materials. He also related the melting temperature of a solid to the volume occupied by each atom in that solid, its frequency of oscillation and its mass. These concepts were characteristically simple and remarkably successful at the time, although now superseded by a more sophisticated approach based on statistical mechanics.

Lindemann's work on the melting-point formula was to contribute greatly to his reputation. His obituary in the science magazine *Nature* was to read:

> . . . the subject of his first independent paper was characteristic: his simple physical model of a crystal lattice melting when the atoms oscillate so violently as to hit their neighbours enabled him to relate, with a minimum of calculation, the melting-point of a material to its Einstein single frequency.[16]

His research in this field was so significant that it was soon being discussed at a gathering of the world's most eminent physicists.

In 1910, while staying in Brussels with Dr Robert Goldschmidt, Walther Nernst had met the Belgian magnate Ernest Solvay, who had made untold sums of money from the industrial manufacture of carbonate of soda. Solvay had a great interest in matters of science, although he regarded himself as an amateur, and had produced a paper on what he described as 'gravitation and matter'. When he met Nernst, Solvay told him how much he would like to bring his ideas to the attention of professional scientists, and this inspired Nernst with the grand scheme of gathering together the world's leading physicists to discuss the problems of the hour, the foremost of which were the kinetic theory of matter and the quantum theory of radiation.

Solvay was delighted with this idea, and he encouraged Nernst to prepare a detailed plan. In due course a conference was arranged, and Lindemann was chosen as one of its secretaries, a signal honour for a man of his youth and status, reflecting the widespread esteem in which his work was beginning to be held.

The Solvay Conferences, as they came to be known, attracted considerable fame and were to be held over a period of many years. The first was held at the Hotel Metropole in Brussels in November 1911 and, in Lord Birkenhead's words, which remain true to this day, 'it is doubtful whether in the history of science so much genius had been contained within the four walls of a single room'.[17]

The theme of the first conference was 'The theory of Radiation and the Quanta', and its attendees included the greatest scientists in the world: Nernst, Planck, Einstein, Rubens, Rutherford, Madame Curie, Poincaré, Sommerfeld and a dozen others of similar standing, with H. A. Lorentz, winner of the 1902 Nobel Prize for physics, as president. As secretary, Lindemann was no mere observer and taker of minutes, but was invited to share in the discussions. One of the other two Secretaries was the Duc de

Broglie, a close family friend of Lindemann, and an outstanding physicist whose brother, Prince Louis de Broglie, was to win a Nobel Prize.

Writing to his father, Lindemann gave a sketch of the participants:

Poincaré said he knew an astronomer Lindemann in London and was very pleased to hear I was his son. Lorentz is a wonderful all round man with extraordinarily quick comprehension and also a great sense of humour. Sommerfeld seems to be generally considered the best mathematical physicist in Germany. I got on very well with him and promised to visit him when I go to Munich.

He seemed also to take to Madame Curie, after initial misgivings, describing her as 'quite a good sort when one knows her'; but he also told his father that it was Einstein who made the greatest impression on him, apart perhaps from Lorentz. His friendship with Einstein, begun at the Solvay Conference, was to prosper over the years, and in due course Lindemann was to persuade Einstein to accept a Studentship at Christ Church and to give a celebrated series of lectures in Oxford.

At this first Solvay Conference, Lindemann's 'melting-point formula' was considered, and his contribution to the debate was described in the report of the conference:

. . . He also discussed the case of diamond . . . for which a diffraction pattern could be observed all round the crystal. However, the same phenomenon was not observed for the pyrites, substances having the same constitution as diamond. Lindemann explained that this discrepancy was certainly due to the great difference between the inter-atomic distances of the two substances.[18]

These proposals were certainly characteristic of Lindemann, containing a difficult proposition, lucidly expressed and of great practical use. He played a successful part at the proceedings – so much so that he was also asked to act as co-secretary of the second Solvay Conference, to be held in 1913.

Meanwhile the research on specific heats that Lindemann had carried out for his thesis was published, jointly with Nernst, as the first of his many papers that were to appear over the next decade. These publications were to prove of great value in spreading knowledge of how the thermal properties of materials could be understood in terms of quantum theory. Together Nernst and Lindemann proposed modifications to the Planck–Einstein formula and extended it from solids to gases.

Lindemann's enthusiasm was not confined to this important subject. From his earliest contact with science his mind had ranged widely and deeply, and his work with Nernst was soon to stimulate papers on such varied subjects as the electrical conductivity of metals, the stability of radioactive nuclei and astrophysics.

However, his paramount interest was in the specific heat of a substance – a subject of the greatest significance, and a crucial guide to analysing the structure of matter. At the time that Lindemann began to work on specific heat, it was described as the amount of heat required to increase the temperature of one gram of a substance by one degree centigrade. From the comparison of specific heats at various temperatures an understanding could be derived of the atomic structure of the substance, at that time largely unknown. Low temperatures were of great importance because it was only by using them that the new theories could be tested.

As Lindemann put it, the purpose of achieving extremely low temperatures was that they create conditions in which the thermal agitation of molecules does not interfere with the study of their arrangement or with the action of intermolecular forces; and if the temperature is low enough, nuclei can actually be orientated and their properties studied much more closely.

Absolute zero is about minus 273 degrees centigrade, at which temperature it was thought that materials would be entirely lacking in heat energy. It was known to be an unattainable goal in that no practical device existed that could cool material all the way down to absolute zero. Despite that obstacle, Nernst suggested that knowledge of the behaviour of specific heats of substances at extremely low temperatures would be needed in the fields of both physics and chemistry. It was on the search for these methods, and on the measurements themselves once substances had been sufficiently cooled, that Lindemann began to work.

He proved to be brilliant at the job, as was described by C. H. Collie, who was later to work with Lindemann at the Clarendon Laboratory:

> . . . to carry out these simple measurements at low temperatures was a matter which required outstanding technical ability and considerable resources.
>
> Of all the pundits aware of the great importance of the issue only Nernst, head of a great and real experimental institute, had the necessary means at his disposal, and in Lindemann he found a man with the technical skill and courage and single-mindedness to make use of these means.[19]

Earlier experimenters in this field, notably two Frenchmen, Dulong and Petit, had been able to take measurements close to the freezing point of water. Lindemann succeeded in measuring substances at very much lower temperatures than had been possible before. His task now was to measure the discrepancies between the actual specific heats of materials – especially solids – and the predictions of classical physics.

To cool substances sufficiently to test his theorem, Nernst devised, largely with Lindemann's help, a simple but effective calorimeter that could be used with the liquefied hydrogen and helium which they produced for their experiments. This calorimeter was a wonderful example of Lindemann's skill as a designer of equipment: it was innovative in its use of a very high vacuum as a measure of reducing heat loss, and in the way it used electricity to supply very small and accurately measurable amounts of heat to the material being examined.

As they began their measurements they made a very strange discovery: that specific heats begin to fall dramatically as low temperatures are reached, approaching zero in the vicinity of the absolute zero of temperature. This phenomenon did not at all fit the tenets of classical physics, as had been postulated by Dulong and Petit.

In 1906, a year after Nernst had set out his Heat Theorem, Einstein had, entirely independently, published a paper that also postulated the vanishing of specific heats at absolute zero. He had already published a paper on light, which explained the 'photo-electric effect' on the basis of Planck's quantum theory. Nernst's biographer described what happened next:

He now took a further step in applying the same considerations to the vibration of atoms in a solid . . . As the temperature is lowered and the heat energy of the substance decreases, the stage must be reached when there is not sufficient energy available to provide each atom with an appropriate quantum. This means that less energy can be taken up by the solid; its specific heat therefore decreases . . . With his theory of the specific heats, Einstein had demonstrated the applicability of the quantum concept to a completely different field of physics and thereby emphasised its universal significance . . . Nernst himself and his pupils, in particular F. A. Lindemann, immediately compared the Einstein formula with their results. They found that while doubtless the theory was basically correct, small discrepancies existed. For these they, in turn, proposed a quantum-theoretical correction, and thereby testified to their own belief in the quantum theory. Inevitably, physicists all over the world began to be interested in these new ideas.[20]

Professor Derek Jackson, FRS, a celebrated spectroscopist who was later to join Lindemann at the Clarendon Laboratory, described the significance of Lindemann's work in the light of the quantum theory:

. . . the first and originating object of the theory was to give a mathematical relation as a function of the temperature of a solid body which would describe exactly the distribution of energy throughout the spectrum . . . All attempts to find such a relation which relied on classical physics had failed completely . . . the formula proposed by Planck gave a distribution which was in agreement with the experimental results to the limit of the accuracy of measurement. This was a wonderful discovery. It had but one serious flaw. It required the assumption that the exchange of energy from the form of kinetic energy or potential energy to the form of radiation energy could occur only in discrete units [quanta]; the size of these units was finite, and exactly proportional to the frequency of the radiation.

When the quantum theory was first proposed, this assumption alarmed or horrified many physicists schooled in the classical electromagnetic theory of Maxwell, for which anything other than a continuous interchange of energy between the two forms was impossible. It was therefore of the greatest importance to investigate other consequences of the quantum theory, and to make experiments to test these. This was precisely what Lindemann did . . .

. . . Lindemann's enthusiastic acceptance of Planck's quantum theory, and the lucidity with which he was able to explain its success in predicting and explaining phenomena far removed from the distribution of energy in the continuous spectrum at the most important conferences of physicists at this time, played a large role in the general acceptance of the quantum theory.[21]

Jackson also made a point that is crucial to the proper appreciation of Lindemann's merit as a scientist – his writings do not properly reflect the exceptional ability that was obvious to those who heard him speak:

Indeed his success in conferences was one of his more important achievements, a fact which cannot be realised by studying his published papers. Consequently a generation of physicists, who neither attended these conferences nor had the chance of talking with the leading physicists of that time [Einstein, Planck, Sommerfeld, Born, Rutherford, von Laue, Poincaré, Wien, Jeans, Eddington] have no means of understanding the importance of Lindemann's contribution to physics . . .

The starting point for Lindemann's work was the assumption that the thermal energy of a solid, embodied physically in the mechanical vibrations of individual atoms, could be increased only by the addition of small quanta of energy, as stated by Planck and developed by Einstein. Lindemann's experiments showed that Einstein's theory could account well for the variation of the specific heats of metals with temperature, but that the thermal properties of materials such as sulphur were not in agreement with the theory. This weakness led Lindemann and Nernst to modify Einstein's theory by making new assumptions about the size of a quantum of energy so that there was greater agreement with the thermal properties of solids. Lindemann was also able to show that the size of energy quanta should be related to certain optical properties of materials, thereby demonstrating the essential unity of physical phenomena.[22]

In 1912 Lindemann was invited to address the British Association at a conference in Dundee attended by the leaders of the scientific establishment in Britain, including J. R. Strutt[23] and Ernest Rutherford. The paper that he presented was on the atomic heats of solids, and 'was of considerable importance in the development of physics, since it contributed to the accumulation of evidence for the universal application of the principles of quantum physics. It was partly through this paper that his reputation in his own country was established.'[24]

In the same year he spent some time working in France. The Duc de Broglie, his co-secretary at the first Solvay Conference, had previously suggested to Lindemann that he should come to Paris to work with him in his private laboratory. Lindemann now took up the invitation, and with de Broglie resumed his work on X-rays. As a result, at the beginning of 1913 he was elected to the Société Française de Physique in Paris.

By now he was twenty-six. He could properly be described as cosmopolitan, both at play and at work, and his reputation of exceptional ability had widened the choices that lay before him as to how and where he might make a career.

A few days after his election to the Société Française, Lindemann received an invitation to give a series of graduate lectures at the University of Chicago. He was told that he could choose any subject he liked. The principal of the university, R. A. Millikan, had been in Berlin in the summer of 1912 – as had the poet Rupert Brooke, who, sitting in the Café des Westens in the Unter den Linden, had written his ode to 'The Old Vicarage, Grantchester'.

In Berlin, Millikan had met Lindemann and had thought so highly of him that he offered to make way for his lectures:

If you wish to cover pretty thoroughly quantum theories in this course, I shall be very glad indeed to change the subject of my course and come into your course as a student.[25]

As many of Lindemann's notes, lectures and articles were connected with explaining and gaining acceptance for Einstein's theories among the general educated public, it is not surprising that he agreed to go. He chose to speak on 'The Transition from Newtonian to Modern Physics', and in June set sail for America on board RMS *Olympic*, whose sister-ship, the *Titanic*, had been sunk by an iceberg a little over twelve months earlier.

From America he sent several letters and 'picture post-cards' to his parents. He described his excursions – for example, to the Grand Canyon – with exact geological detail, but hardly mentioned his lectures. Whether at that early age his delivery was as notoriously inaudible as it was later to become is unclear, but there was no doubt about the merit of its content. His friends in Germany followed his progress with interest, and in August Nernst wrote to him of events in Berlin and of successfully enticing Einstein to the capital: 'Einstein will move to Berlin at Easter. Planck and I were in Zurich the other day, and the Academy has already elected him. We have great expectations of him.'[26]

At the end of the summer Lindemann returned to Europe, and in the autumn a new possibility arose. It had become known that the chair of physics at Oxford would soon become vacant. The incumbent, Robert Clifton, had been *in situ* for nearly fifty years and had finally concluded that it was time for a change – an opinion that had begun to enjoy widespread support.

Lindemann's erstwhile friend from Berlin, Henry Tizard, then began to do some lobbying on Lindemann's behalf. In November 1913 Lindemann travelled to Oxford, from where he wrote to his father about the possible appointment:

. . . Oxford is very fine as regards the buildings, and the people are very nice. Tizard would like to come down early in January. Can I invite him definitely? The professorship in question is for physics, the Clarendon Lab. The present 'encumbrance' is Clifton. He has been there since about 1870. They chose him in preference to Helmholtz, who wanted to come. Tizard thinks I might get it, I can hardly believe it. Townsend, who is the other physicist there, is very nice. I lunched with him today. He is one of Carson's Ulstermen. Clifton says he is going to retire next September.[27]

Tizard's view that Lindemann might be appointed to this post was not shared by many in the scientific world. The favourite for Clifton's chair was

Harry Moseley, an exceptionally able scientist who was considered to be the most promising of all the English physicists of his generation and was expected by many to win a Nobel Prize. Lindemann's work on X-rays had led him, in the closing weeks of 1913, into a typically waspish discourse with Moseley. *Nature* magazine, the long-established forum for scientific debate, published the two men's claims and rejoinders. J. L. Heilbron, Moseley's biographer, wrote of Lindemann:

A practised juggler with numbers, he took an immediate dislike to Bohr's theory,[28] which he conceived to be nothing but numerology, and when Moseley asserted that X rays, on which Lindemann now fancied himself an expert, confirmed the obnoxious atom, 'F. A.' slashed out at him in the pages of *Nature*.[29]

Moseley replied, but for all his brilliance 'his defence failed to persuade', and he ended rather less confident than he began, saying: 'Either Bohr's theory or my interpretation of it requires modification.'[30]

However, greater events were soon to intervene, and Moseley would not live to develop his theories. He was a young brigade signals officer at Gallipoli when, early on the morning of 10 August 1915, 30,000 Turks, 'calling upon the name of God', streamed down a hill towards the British lines. The action was later described by General Sir Ian Hamilton:

. . . our men stood to it, and maintained, by many a deed of daring, the old traditions of their race. There was no flinching. They died in the ranks where they stood.[31]

The ranks included Harry Moseley. His death was in time to have a great impact on Lindemann's future career. With Moseley gone, the prize was in due course to fall to him, something that, as Heilbron noted, 'would have irritated Harry immensely'.

Lindemann was willing at least to contemplate a move to Oxford, but he was contented and successful in Berlin and was engrossed in the work of Nernst's laboratory. The importance of his research, and evidence of his enquiring mind, is captured in a letter to his father:

Berlin. 22.2.14

My dear Papa,
Just a line in great haste to thank you for your letters and the *Natures* and to tell you that there was every appearance of artificial radioactivity

today. An electroscope charged itself 100 volts per minute when connected with the electrodes of my tube in which uranium had been bombarded. It is difficult to think of any other explanation. The radioactive substance produced, if really there, seems to have been a gas, for on opening the tube and examining the walls and electrodes nothing was to be found.

Nernst was frightfully excited and said he would not go to South America. He afterwards suggested I should come with him and continue there. If the effect is real, which I still doubt, I shall stay here until I have more or less settled it . . . I hope to give you definite news soon.[32]

Nevertheless a move from Berlin was a possibility, so he asked Nernst for a testimonial; it was glowing, and must have given Lindemann satisfaction, even discounting the usual hyperbole of references:

Berlin 1.3.14

I hereby certify that Mr F. A. Lindemann has, since 1908, with short interruptions, worked in my laboratory with great zeal and extraordinary success. Mr Lindemann's experimental and theoretical research is so well known and has everywhere aroused such extraordinary interest that any further recommendation from me would be superfluous; I should only like to take this opportunity of expressing my warm appreciation of Mr Lindemann personally.[33]

However, Lindemann's plans were to be interrupted by the swift and unheralded approach of war, when – at the height of his success as a physicist, having achieved a high reputation and considerable acclaim – he would be forced to leave Germany. For under the midsummer sun the mood and the sounds of Berlin began to alter rapidly. The scene, as it faded, was redolent of Lewis Carroll's haunting description, written some fifty years earlier, of the end of a dream:

. . . the grass would be only rustling in the wind, and the pool rippling to the waving of the reeds; the rattling teacups would change to tinkling sheep-bells, and the Queen's shrill cries to the voice of the shepherd boy.[34]

And so the shouts and laughter of Lindemann's friends, and of the young men in Berlin, turned to the staccato commands of officers; the clink of beakers in the laboratories to the ring of swords; and the clatter of plates at fashionable parties to the echo of cavalry, as Europe caught the beat of a German army on the march.

In this growing tumult Lindemann was to abandon Berlin and his laboratory and cross the sea to England. There his unfolding career was to bring him a reputation for cool bravery and was in time to open the door to politics; and that in its turn would lead towards the unique role that he was to play at a critical moment in the history of Britain.

THREE

War And Wings

He put his craft into a spinning nose-dive. Those watching him
held their breath. It seemed certain death. But his theory worked.

Winston Churchill

Although he had no idea of the ferocity of the onslaught that was to come,
Lindemann firmly believed that a climax of some sort was approaching. His
fourteen years in the country had given him an insight into German attitudes, and he could sense the aggression that had tainted the atmosphere
in Berlin through the early months of 1914. As Lord Birkenhead expressed
it, 'he had already winded the Prussian menace seeping like the smell of a
sewer across the North Sea'.[1]

When he had stayed with Robert Millikan in Chicago, Lindemann had
discussed the German situation, and Millikan had commented on the widespread talk of *Der Tag*. Lindemann had agreed that the Germans would
start a war just as soon as they could, and had added:

Of course they plan to attack. Of course that is why they voted the
expansion of their military forces last summer. And, what is more, if
I had been one of them and a member of the Reichstag I would have
voted in the same way.[2]

Yet he saw no reason to alter his summer plans, and in July he travelled
to Zoppot, on the Baltic coast of Germany, where he was to take part in an
international tennis tournament.

As it happened, Lindemann was to have an unexpected glimpse of the
Kaiser himself, whom the unfolding crisis was to lead to Zoppot before the
month was out. Following the assassination of the heir to the Austrian throne
on 28 June 1914, there had been a rapid increase in the political temperature throughout Europe, but the German Chancellor, Bethmann-Hollweg,
had urged the Kaiser to keep to his plans for a summer cruise in the Baltic,
for fear of exacerbating an increasingly delicate situation. *The Times*'s corre-
spondent in Germany reported his departure:

41

Berlin, July 6th. The Kaiser, accompanied as usual by a large suite and some specially invited guests, left here today for his cruise in Northern waters. His Majesty arrived at Kiel this afternoon and proceeded on board the Imperial Yacht Hohenzollern.[3]

The starting point of this holiday was the regatta at Kiel, at one end of the famous canal that had been enlarged to give the German Navy an outlet to the North Sea. For the German High Command the widening of the Kiel Canal was a factor of the greatest importance. It had been due to be finished at the end of June 1914 and its completion was a prerequisite without which Germany could not risk a war. As the Kaiser arrived at Holtenau Locks, the gateway to Kiel harbour, he made a rousing speech, full of nationalist fervour and ending with the words of his former Chancellor, Bismarck: 'We Germans fear God and otherwise absolutely nothing, and no one else in this world.'

Meanwhile, despite growing unease in the chancelleries of Europe, there was little disturbance to the everyday life of the populace, and in Zoppot the streets were filled with holidaymakers and the tennis tournament was in full swing.

Yet the catastrophe was inexorably approaching, and developments in Austria-Hungary far to the south were reducing the chances of continued peace almost by the hour. On the afternoon of 24 July the Cabinet met in London, to continue its long search for a resolution of what until then had been the paramount political difficulty facing the country: Ulster's rejection of the Home Rule Bill. In the event the meeting was to be interrupted by momentous news. Winston Churchill, by then First Lord of the Admiralty, later recorded the fateful moment in *The World Crisis*:

The discussion had reached its inconclusive end, and the Cabinet was about to separate, when the quiet grave tones of Sir Edward Grey's voice were heard reading a document which had just been brought to him from the Foreign Office. It was the Austrian note to Serbia. He had been reading or speaking for several minutes before I could disengage my mind from the tedious and bewildering debate which had just closed. We were all very tired, but gradually as the phrases and sentences followed one another, impressions of a wholly different character began to form in my mind. This note was clearly an ultimatum; but it was an ultimatum such as had never been penned in modern times. As the reading proceeded it seemed absolutely impossible that any State in the world could accept it, or that any acceptance, however abject, would satisfy the aggressor. The parishes of Fermanagh and

Tyrone faded back into the mists and squalls of Ireland, and a strange light began immediately, but by perceptible gradations, to fall and grow upon the map of Europe.[4]

Far away in Norwegian waters the Kaiser concluded that he must return to his capital, and on 27 July, as the momentum of events gathered pace, he set sail for Kiel.

In Zoppot, Jack Egerton and his wife were watching Lindemann's progress in the tournament. Ruth Egerton recorded in her diary how she and her husband were staying at Zoppot when the Kaiser's boat, *Hohenzollern*, made an unexpected appearance there. When they heard of the arrival of the gleaming, three-masted yacht Lindemann and Egerton went down to the pier and watched the Emperor disembark. This was the first indication that they had of the seriousness of the situation, but at the appearance of newspaper placards announcing Russia's mobilisation,[5] they were left in no doubt that they should at once return to England. Egerton telephoned Professor Nernst, who told them that if they went back to Berlin they might be interned. It was a timely warning: in the event, as is recorded in Ruth Egerton's diary,[6] 'the *pension* in Berlin in which they had been staying had already been visited by Prussian officials demanding to know Egerton's whereabouts.

So the Egertons made a hasty departure from Germany, boarding a crowded train and reaching London on 2 August. With great regret, as he had reached the finals of the tournament, Lindemann also abandoned Germany and set out for home.

Some time earlier he and Egerton had agreed that if war came they would make a joint approach to the War Office. Accordingly, on 8 August Egerton submitted the letter that they had prepared, setting out their skills and offering their services. This letter shows how, right from the start, Lindemann was turning his mind to the way in which science might play a part in war:

> They would be willing to drive and be responsible for a motor-car . . . and equip it either with (a) apparatus for generating electricity for X-ray purposes etc. or (b) with water pumping and purifying apparatus, whichever may be most useful.
>
> Lieut Egerton knows German and some French, and can drive and look after the motor-car. He has also acted as a company commander in the University of London OTC two years ago. Mr Lindemann knows German and French perfectly (like a native) and is an expert in electrical matters, especially in X-ray work.

We have made this offer in view of the fact that the Royal Flying Corps require motor-cars and those who speak French and German are also required.[7]

The authorities probably never even considered these tempting offers. At such a moment of hectic activity they would have had enough to attend to with more orthodox applications. In any event there was no response.

To judge by his correspondence with his father, it may have been at around this time that Lindemann began to feel that his German name – and in this case Egerton's reference to him speaking German like a native – might tell against him. Nevertheless, his determination to play a part was undiminished, so he turned his mind to his own special abilities and to how his scientific knowledge could be put to use.

He wasted no time. On 13 August 1914 he had an interview at the Admiralty, and followed it up by submitting his first proposal, addressing it to the Naval Construction Department:

Dear Sir,   13.viii.1914
Your remark in our interview this morning about the desirability of any apparatus capable of indicating the approach of submarines emboldens me to ask whether a microphone has been tried for this purpose. Sunk in the water to a depth of some thirty feet, so as to be rid of surface effects, one might possibly notice the beat of the screw or even the hum of the dynamo at a distance of several miles. The apparatus could be tried very quickly and easily but the idea is so obvious that no doubt you have done so already. If not I need hardly say that if desired I would be very ready to make the experiments if you would give me the necessary facilities in the way of permits.[8]

However, the Admiralty, no doubt bombarded by requests and suggestions, and having to cope with the frenetic pace set by its indefatigable First Lord, Winston Churchill, declined to spend any time on Lindemann's offer.

At length, after several other approaches, and after trying without success every opening that he could think of, he went home to Devonshire. There, encouraged by his father, he turned again to pure physics, and set to work on a paper on the theory of the metallic state. It was an important contribution to contemporary understanding of the subject, and was published the following year.[9] He also worked with his father on research in astronomy and, using the observatory at Sidholme, produced another paper, entitled 'Note on a number of dark stars'.[10]

As the months passed and the fighting on the Western Front intensified,

Lindemann did not let up in his offers of help and ideas, or in his quest for a commission. On 1 February 1915 he wrote to the Master General of the Ordnance with a suggestion for a method of locating a hidden gun and determining its range. The memorandum, signed by 'F. A. Lindemann, PhD, FRAS', proposed locating guns by means of the sound waves generated when they were fired, using telephone wires from three different points. In his letter he set out the necessary formulae, and added that Sir Ernest Rutherford or Sir James Dewar would vouch for his knowledge of the relevant physics and mathematics.

Although on that occasion too he was rebuffed, he was at last about to meet with success, and in the spring of 1915 received the offer of a full-time role, albeit as a civilian rather than as a commissioned officer. It was a job, however, that was ideally suited to his talents, and was to lead in due course to achievements of great importance in the development of aeronautics.

At the beginning of the war the attitude of many of the military authorities towards scientists seemed to be one of patronising ignorance. Geoffrey Taylor, soon to become a colleague of Lindemann (and later Professor Sir Geoffrey Taylor, FRS) recalled how, as a young meteorologist at the outbreak of war, he went to the War Office to volunteer for the army:

> I suggested to the War Office that if I could be given telegraphic facilities I might set up a weather forecasting service for the army in the field. The officer to whom I made this suggestion did not seem to doubt that I could tell exactly what the weather was going to be – as he might very well have done – but thought the knowledge would be of no value to the army in the field. 'Soldiers don't go into battle under umbrellas, they go whether it is raining or not' was his comment.[11]

Fortunately, this attitude was less entrenched among technically minded soldiers, many of whom were joining the army's flying wing in the growing belief that aeroplanes would have a significant role to play. Taylor continued:

> Shortly after my interview this officer happened to meet Major Sefton Brancker who was at that time, before the creation of the Royal Flying Corps, in command of the flying wing of the army. He told Brancker of my visit and asked if he had any use for scientists in his department. Brancker replied that he could use as many as he could lay his hands on, and that evening he sent a messenger to tell me that the Royal Aircraft Factory at Farnborough would employ me as a scientist if I would offer my service in that capacity.[12]

The sceptical attitude towards boffins was soon to change, and as the war developed there would be a much greater use of science than in any previous conflict, exploiting the enormous accumulation of knowledge during the nineteenth century. In Britain the crucible in which this was to take place was the Royal Aircraft Factory at Farnborough.

R. B. Haldane, when Secretary of State for War in 1909, had reconstructed what had formerly been His Majesty's Balloon Factory at Farnborough and had given it the shape that it had acquired by 1914. It was by then under the supervision of a well-known engineer, Mervyn O'Gorman, described by the pioneering aircraft designer Geoffrey de Havilland (himself for a time at Farnborough) as 'a far-sighted and brilliant administrator who did great work for British aeronautics during his brief reign as superintendent at Farnborough'. At the beginning of the war O'Gorman was *en poste* as the supervisor and, recruiting particularly from the universities, gathered at the Royal Aircraft Factory a prolific group of scientists of the highest calibre.

It was O'Gorman who in 1915 agreed to employ Lindemann. He informed him by letter on 28 March that his references were satisfactory, and invited him to commence work as a temporary technical assistant, with pay of £3 per week, starting after Easter.

The question of references illustrates the doubts that attached to Lindemann's name. The superintendent had written to Lindemann's brother-in-law, the barrister Noel Vickers, on 22 March:

Mr F. A. Lindemann has applied to me for a temporary position during the war, and has referred me to you for testimony as to his nationality, etc. I understand that Mr Lindemann's father is a German, and Mr Lindemann has himself spent many years in Germany leaving only at the outbreak of war. You will readily understand that I have to make the most careful enquiries in cases in which there may be the slightest possibility of doubt; so would you kindly let me know what you can with regard to him?

To this request Vickers had replied:

In my opinion you can thoroughly rely on Mr F. A. Lindemann's loyalty, honour and integrity . . . Lindemann's father is by birth a Bavarian who has been resident in England over 40 years . . . I believe Mr Lindemann sen. never served in the German Army, having been wounded in a duel which prevented him from fighting in the Bavarian army against Prussia in 1866.[13]

The fighting that Vickers referred to was the war in which Bismarck had established Prussian hegemony in central Europe, and it might have coloured the superintendent's view if, however long ago, Lindemann's father had fought in the army of what was now the enemy.

Such doubts must have been discouraging for Lindemann, and may have contributed to the reticence and defensiveness about his background that he rapidly developed, and which distanced him from colleagues and friends who might otherwise have seen him as a warmer character.

In the spring of 1915 he duly arrived at the Royal Aircraft Factory. He later wrote:

> Like other scientists with no special knowledge of aircraft, I was posted to H Department, a branch to which all sorts of odd questions were referred which did not seem to fit into any special field. What to work on was left very much to our own choice, and my investigations ranged from detecting aircraft by sound, explaining why some cylinders with cast-iron fins cooled better than others, designing and making rate-of-climb meters, sun-proof doping for wings, compasses, automatic pilots, turn indicators, bombsights, accelerometers, range-finders for the Navy, a contraption to brush aside balloon cables, to occasional excursions into aerodynamics such as the cause of spinning.[14]

Of H Department Geoffrey Taylor said:

> The asylum for theoreticians to which I was assigned when I arrived at Farnborough was called H Department. I never knew what H stood for. It might have been Heaven, or it might have been Hell, so varied were the ideas of other departments of what went on there. It tackled problems wished on it by the War Office which the engineers did not care about.[15]

In fact 'H Department' was synonymous with 'Physics Department' and was set up in 1910. Four years later O'Gorman had put together an exceptionally able team of youthful scientists, and a large proportion of those that survived the war went on to achieve eminence in their professions. They formed a mess and lived together at a house called 'Chudleigh', on the Fleet Road, which had room for eight or nine people.

As the young scientists set about their pioneering work at Farnborough they must have been constantly aware of its dangers, and of the high cost to be paid for getting the sums wrong. Casualties had occurred very soon after the Chudleigh mess had been set up, and included the spectacular demise of Edward Busk, an award-winning engineer from King's College, Cambridge, who was burnt to death in an accident over the airfield on 5 November 1914.

The group was also joined by Dr Hermann Glauert, who later experimented on aeroplane spins, and who in March 1918 was to publish, jointly with Lindemann and R. G. Harris, the definitive tract on the subject, entitled 'The Experimental and Mathematical Investigation of Spinning'. His life too was cut short. F. M. Green later wrote of Glauert:

Some time after the war he was killed by falling debris from an unexpectedly violent explosion when the Royal Engineers were engaged in blasting. Glauert had been made an FRS for brilliant work in aeronautics. He had the facility for making difficult things clear. His death was a great loss.[16]

Despite the ever-present risk of death or injury, and the natural gravitas of some of its members, the Chudleigh mess was by all accounts a happy one, full of laughter and fun, and Lindemann fitted in well, in spite of the first impressions he made on people. He was tall and saturnine, and had a rather forbidding air – 'distant' was a description that he courted all his life – and his occasionally sharp tongue did nothing to soften this brittle surface. He spoke in a mumbling nasal twang, which became harsh when animosity inflected his voice. It would not have done so for long at Farnborough, however, where the work was exhilarating and he found the atmosphere increasingly congenial.

Lord Birkenhead described the scene at Chudleigh:

There was little fear of embarrassment for Lindemann in such company. The atmosphere was that of a somewhat rowdy Senior Common Room in which violent disputes on abstruse subjects and hearty undergraduate banter were frequent, the youth of the members preventing a too solemn parade of knowledge. Aston came to the mess indignant that he had been forced to shut down a diffusion apparatus intended to separate the then undiscovered isotopes of neon, but Lindemann persuaded him that the apparatus would not have worked in any case.[17]

A further ancedote is told by Professor R.V. Jones:

In the evenings at Farnborough there was time to think about other matters, and also a few jokes to relieve the strain of the war. Lindemann happily recalled the aerodynamicist, H. Glauert, who smoked such a foul-smelling shag in his pipe that the others thought that they would teach him a lesson by mixing ebonite shavings in with his tobacco; but after a few puffs, while his expectant colleagues watched, his puzzled expression at the new aroma gradually changed to satisfaction, and he was smoking as enthusiastically as ever.[18]

At home in the mess the scientists would relax – 'three-dimensional chess' was a favourite game – and join in good-natured argument. For example, when Lindemann and Geoffrey Taylor differed on the method of packing spheres most closely, one saying that there was only one possible way and the other claiming two, the altercation was a lively one, with demonstrations using a bowl of oranges. They were cheered on by the rest of the mess, with Taylor saying, 'But don't you see, stoopid', until the matter was ended with the oranges being thrown at the contestants.

Lindemann had a trick later in life, which he would occasionally demonstrate when dining at Oxford, of peeling an orange without touching it by hand. And Dame Myra Hess, when giving musical sustenance to wartime audiences at the National Gallery, would, as a 'party piece', play the piano holding an orange in each hand, her long slender fingers overcoming the impediment without any difficulty. So perhaps oranges have a fascination for some people in their moments of relaxation.

There was also spare time away from the sheds and workshops, when the atmosphere would become redolent of the carefree life of university. Frank Aston, for instance, with whom Lindemann was later to publish a groundbreaking paper on isotopes, was a noted golfer, musician and tennis player, but was eclipsed at all three by Lindemann. On one occasion in icy weather the group went skating on Fleet Pond. Lindemann seemed rather reluctant to skate, so Aston helped him slowly and carefully out to the middle, at which point Lindemann shook himself free and proceeded to give a faultless and graceful demonstration of figure-skating. Aston's temporary discomfiture was greeted with laughter from the onlookers, but Lindemann was a firm friend once his affections had been engaged, and his obvious good nature soon dispelled Aston's feeling of slight. In another undergraduate gesture later in the war, when William Farren was getting married in Cambridge, Lindemann flew an aeroplane over the church and released – for good luck – a boot attached to a parachute, which descended gracefully just as the bridal couple were emerging.

Commenting on the ice-skating episode, Farren later wrote:

He had a similar diffidence about his other accomplishments. Three of us went golfing with him, but again he needed much persuasion, as he said he had not touched a club since he wore a sailor suit. He did the first few holes in bogey, and the rest in one over bogey, having acquired a blister on his hand.[19]

In fact Lindemann remained a golfer of a high standard for many years, although he continued to deprecate his ability. It was the same with squash: although he played very well, he tended to sneer at the game, saying that all that was needed was a broad back and a large behind.

However disappointed he may have been at not being commissioned into the army, there is no doubt that Lindemann was better suited to the company at Chudleigh and to the work at Farnborough than he would have been to the life of an officer in the trenches, with its quite different type of camaraderie. Apart from anything else, it would hardly have suited his austere vegetarian diet. As Lord Birkenhead aptly put it:

> He was to take calculated risks as great as those of any combative soldier, but he was spared the squalor of their lives and, what would have been to such a temperament as his, the terrors of propinquity and institutional life. The discipline, the compulsion of rank, the constant association with strangers, the bawdy talk and the lack of privacy – all these would have played havoc with his nervous system.
>
> At Farnborough orders were not given, but desires conveyed, and there, at ease and on an intellectual equality with his fellow boffins, he was able to grope his way by trial and error through the new problems and make a positive contribution to the winning of the war under a superintendent, Mervyn O'Gorman, whose coming inaugurated the use of scientific methods in aeronautical development.[20]

A descriptive vignette comes from another of Lindemann's companions in the Chudleigh mess, George Thomson, who later spoke of the slightly strange figure in their midst:

> He was older than most of us, but not all; and he gave the impression of being foreign – he was only recently back from Germany. He impressed us immensely because he was very much a man of the world. 'Lindemann's duchesses' were talked about. Really I think there was only one, but still – impressive. And he was a striking person to look at: tall, thin, dark. Unkind people said that he looked like Mephistopheles, but I think that this was perhaps not quite fair to him.

'I think,' continued Thomson, a future winner of the Nobel Prize for physics, 'he was the most exciting person to talk physics to that I have ever talked to, and I've met a good many.'[21]

The Factory had at this time a fourfold function: to supply aeronautical information; and to test, design and manufacture prototype engines. This varied work enabled Lindemann to embark on a wide range of different projects, and it was in the course of this that he began to develop his intense conviction of the value of science to national defence.

In his first month, for example, he extended his ideas on the detection of vessels by their radiation, based on the greater conductivity of steel than seawater. This was in response to a letter from the supervisor, O'Gorman, referring to work on the proposals that Lindemann had earlier put to the Admiralty; he now moved on to the possibility of the detection of aircraft by infra-red rays. Twenty years later the use of infra-red for this purpose was to become a hobby-horse of his, and would partly be the cause of a spectacular breach with the colleagues with whom he was then working in a new and more urgent quest for air defence.

His next idea was for incendiary packages that would catch fire spontaneously, and which he proposed 'for setting fire to stores, sheds etc.' – another suggestion that was to be resurrected in the Second World War. Prophetically, he also began to think of means of detecting aircraft at a distance – an idea that foreshadowed an immensely important development of the future. He explored several avenues, including long-wave radiation and acoustics, but decided that the latter had insufficient promise to justify continued research.

He also turned his mind to signalling methods, for use both on land and at sea, and prepared several reports describing ways of signalling without attracting attention. The methods he proposed included the use of rays other than light rays, varying the composition of an apparently constant source of light, and heat rays emitted by hot bodies. Each suggestion was meticulously detailed, explained and supported by data.

The language of his reports is a reminder that these were still the early days of flying. For instance, H Dept Report 804, entitled 'Means of communication between passenger and pilot in an aircraft', compared speech, electrical methods and the use of stethoscope ear-pieces. In his report Lindemann struck the engagingly old-fashioned note that 'the ear-pieces themselves are made interchangeable on the stethoscopes so that each user could carry his own ear-piece, which fit him, in his waistcoat pocket'. He continued: 'The unfavourable reports which have been received about the scheme are based on the alleged discomfort', so they would be 'better fitted in conjunction with some experienced military tailor'.

He also worked on a rate-of-climb meter, which had a miniature home-made vacuum flask to keep the temperature of the air constant. According to Lindemann, professional pilots always referred to this as 'the coffee-ometer'.

Perhaps not surprisingly, considering that the first powered flight had taken place only a dozen years earlier, quite a number of the ideas that the scientists at the Royal Aircraft Factory pursued now seem faintly ludicrous. Geoffrey Taylor gives an example:

The French had been dropping steel darts called 'flechettes' on troops from the air. It was found that these whirled when dropped even though they would point into the wind when suspended at their centre of gravity, and we were asked to design one that would fall straight. We pointed out that a bomb which would project its fragments horizon-tally would have a much better chance of hitting standing men than darts dropped vertically, but it seemed a matter of prestige that we should have our own dart, and that it should be better than the French dart, so we designed one.

Finally we were asked how the darts would spread if a bundle of them were thrown from a plane. To answer this we got a pilot to throw a few hundred of them over a field from a few hundred feet. When this had been done Melvill Jones and I went over the field and pushed a square of paper over every dart we could find sticking up out of the ground. When we had gone over the field in this way and were looking at the distribution so revealed, a cavalry officer came up on his horse and asked us what we were doing. We explained that the darts had been dropped from a plane. He looked at them and, seeing a dart piercing every sheet of paper, remarked: 'I should never have believed it was possible to make such good shooting from an airplane'.

Having finished that job the darts were never used; not, we were told, for the reason we had originally put forward against them, that they would be inefficient, but because they were regarded as inhuman weapons which could not be used by gentlemen.[22]

These darts were a rather barbarous weapon, a seven-inch steel rod machined out at one end like the feathers of an arrow. Apparently the objec-tion to them was that, when dropped from a great height, they were silent and so swift that they could neither be seen nor heard in time for the victim to get out of their way. Unlike a mortar bomb that could be heard, or a bomb that could be seen as it was dropped from an aeroplane, darts did not give the enemy a chance, and therefore met with official disapproval.

Despite the many rejections of his ideas, Lindemann – embodying the expression 'it's dogged as does it' – continued to submit a wide range of proposals for, as he saw it, increasing the efficiency of the war machine. He was not satisfied by the lukewarm reception of his paper on the location of steamships by long-wave radiation, which he put to the naval authorities in April 1915 and did not let the matter rest. By July his proposal had reached the Prime Minister, Mr Balfour. A nod from the latter at least persuaded the Admiralty to discuss the matter, even if nothing came of it.

Success in the war at sea, and especially the defence of shipping against submarines, was to be vital to the country as the conflict progressed, and therefore many of the proposals emanating from Farnborough, including several of Lindemann's, were devised for use at sea rather than in the air. One example was his paper entitled 'Secret signalling by infrared rays', which he submitted at the beginning of 1916. His reports at Farnborough demonstrate a skill for which he was to be noted all his life: his ability to illustrate complex scientific ideas by relating them to everyday objects. In this case, he explained how a simple charcoal brazier would be suitable for sending signals, if used with a metal screen to cut off heat rays, and an ebonite screen to block visible light. The receiver would use a sensitive thermopile, and messages could be coded by means of figures, allowing the rays to travel for such time as corresponded to each digit.

On several occasions he was invited by the navy to demonstrate his ideas at sea. For instance, he conducted an experiment with a light polariser to help detect objects underwater. His purpose was to discover whether it was refracted light or the waves of the sea that prevented one seeing through seawater except from directly overhead. That experiment was not a success. 'Unfortunately,' he reported, 'the water in this part of the channel is so turgid that it is impossible to see any objects below the surface.' That apart, he was quite sure it would work, and recommended its use for enabling aircraft flying over water to spot the submarines that were all too soon to become a deadly threat.

He also made a detailed suggestion for the use of coloured lights for steering torpedoes from an aeroplane. He was a ready source of ideas involving the properties of light, and at Farnborough successfully carried out experiments on the use of protective paints not visible to a selected part of the spectrum. His colleagues there used to recall how his aeroplane was frequently coated in some exotic colour or pattern with which he was experimenting.

At the beginning of 1916 he once again put forward his suggestion for the location of guns by their reports, but was again unsuccessful and received a letter from the Ministry of Munitions informing him that his 'communication doesn't add to the information already at the disposal of the Authorities'.[23] In so many of these cases it is difficult to dispel the picture of a reservoir of bright ideas from the Factory scientists lapping fruitlessly against the stolid dam of the War Office mind.

Although by now well ensconced at the Royal Aircraft Factory, Lindemann still yearned for a commission in the army. This may have been reinforced by the suspicion that, with his cosmopolitan air, many people did not regard him as completely British. Perhaps to counter this he gradually became, as he was to remain throughout his life, a paramount example of the expression 'more royalist than the king'.

Too much can be made of this, but it was a view quite widely held, as described by the physicist Kurt Mendelssohn, who was later to work for Lindemann at Oxford:

> It was inevitable that most people with whom he now came into contact should regard him as a German and some of them were convinced that he was a German spy . . . He became withdrawn to avoid exposing himself to slights and insults. Secretiveness about his personal life developed into a mania and he discouraged personal approaches by a stand-offishness which was easily mistaken for arrogance.[24]

Yet their surname had proved no obstacle to either of his brothers, both of whom joined the army, and this may have rankled with Lindemann. He clearly felt that despite his brothers' successful applications, he needed to dispel misapprehension about his ancestry, and raised the issue with O'Gorman in November 1915, saying that 'the point which may well arouse misgivings is the enemy origin suggested by my name'. He was quite unequivocal on the point:

> I never was German, however, not even technically, for my father had lost his German nationality long before the time of my birth (1886) . . . in view of these facts I venture to hope that my name will not debar me from obtaining a commission.[25]

In fact we know this was not the case, whatever Lindemann may have believed at the time. Although his father had come to England in 1870, Adolf was not actually naturalised until 1904, and then only in order to protect Charles and Frederick from call-up by the German Army. Prior to his naturalisation he would, by English law, have retained his German nationality, which would have been passed on to his children.

Undeterred, in January 1916 Lindemann again wrote to the supervisor asking for his support in his application for a commission, and this time he received a more encouraging reaction. O'Gorman replied that he didn't want to spare him, but that the matter could be arranged. His doubts remained, however, and Lindemann told his father: 'I hardly expect he will do anything.'

By now he may have thought that O'Gorman was taking the view – as well he might – that his scientists were of greater value at Farnborough than in other branches of the services. However, the Factory scientists were about to be given a significantly expanded role, and in Lindemann's case this was to result in the celebrated stories that, denied or otherwise, were ever after to be associated with his name.

With the continual development of ideas for improvements in aeronautics and aeroplane technology, and with the growing activity and importance of the war in the air, it was becoming increasingly unsatisfactory that none of the civilians at Farnborough was permitted to fly. The professional pilots were of little help in diagnosing problems in the air: they did not understand the physical causes of the behaviour of their aeroplanes, and they could not speak in scientific terms. Instead they tended to refer to the 'feel' of an aeroplane, and this became too haphazard a description as the war developed. For their part, the scientists needed first-hand knowledge of the various problems of flight which they were being asked to solve. The lack of proper understanding between designer and airman was beginning to hamper the supply of reliable aircraft to the airfields in France.

At all events, in March 1916 the Army Council appointed a committee to inquire into whether the Royal Aircraft Factory was being efficiently managed. The upshot was that Colonel O'Gorman was 'moved sideways' to the War Office, and his place temporarily taken by his deputy, S. Heckstall Smith. These changes presented the scientists with an opportunity to renew their campaign for permission to fly, and it was Lindemann who spearheaded their cause.

William Farren, who was at Farnborough at this time, later wrote:

In 1916 there was a strong and growing feeling at the Factory amongst the engineers and scientists that it would be a great advantage if they could fly themselves as pilots, partly in order to be able to experience at first hand what flying an aeroplane is like, and so to understand something about it, partly in order to be able to do specific experiments either on the aeroplane itself or on equipment, gadgets etc. Largely as a result of Lindemann's pressure permission was given for five or six to be chosen to go to the Central Flying School at Netheravon and Upavon.[26]

Lindemann also described what happened:

> In those times experiments were much less carefully organised than today. Flying was considered more an art than a science and the professional pilots were at no pains to dispel this idea and often exhibited all the allures of the prima donna or of the then fortunately non-existent temperamental film star. It was only when the first Air Board was formed that some of us at last obtained permission to learn to fly, thanks, I like to think, to a somewhat journalistically phrased application concocted by myself.[27]

Perhaps it was in response to this pressure that the War Office finally relented, with the result that in the summer of 1916 the first scientists arrived at the Central Flying School, which was run by Henry Tizard, Lindemann's friend from his Berlin days. Among the first batch from Farnborough were Lindemann himself, George Thomson, William Farren and Keith Lucas, although their enthusiastic ranks were depleted within a short time of their arrival, when Lucas flew his aeroplane into another pupil's, in mid-air, with fatal results.

Although they were now in a military institution, Lindemann at once demonstrated his independent outlook. He would arrive for each flight in civilian dress, meticulous – among all the uniforms – in his habitual Melton overcoat, bowler hat and umbrella. These he would place neatly in his cockpit before donning flying clothes. He would then reverse the process before emerging from the aeroplane. No one complained. As Farren noted:

> He was six years older than I was in years, but many more in experience, both of the world and of science. But I doubt whether anything about him impressed me quite so much as his complete indifference to the difficulties of arriving at an RFC Station in a bowler hat and carrying an umbrella. Lucas and I were in khaki, and therefore relatively inconspicuous, for which we were thankful. Lindemann was unperturbed and, to our surprise, so was the RFC. Their instructions were to teach us to fly, and presumably did not extend to what particular kind of clothes we wore. Nevertheless, we felt it rather unfair that, purely because of our uniforms, we had to attend parades, and drill like soldiers, whereas Lindemann was naturally excused.[28]

Some of Lindemann's other idiosyncrasies were likewise ill suited to military life. Farren continued:

The catering at an RFC station in those days did not provide for vegetarians, and Lindemann was living largely on tinned apricots. Lucas said: 'If you go on doing that you will be ill', and sure enough Lindemann *was* ill, and eventually had to stay in bed. But as usual, in some way which seemed characteristic of everything he did, he got the better of circumstances, and was restored to activity.[29]

In one respect Lindemann must have been apprehensive that his efforts to be allowed to fly would fail at the last obstacle: he had to be passed physically fit. One of his eyes was so bad that, in the context of flying, it was effectively useless (not that this had affected the standard of his tennis) and he knew that with his weak eye he would be unable to see any of the letters in his eye test. How he passed the medical test for flying is a story that later received widespread circulation. When he was asked what happened with the army doctor, he said:

> I took a 50–50 chance. I went in, and he sat me in the chair, and whilst we were chatting I used my good eye to memorise the letters on the side of the card which I could see. When he started the test I knew he would either leave it that way round, or turn it over. He turned it over, so I shut my bad eye and read the new side without any difficulty. He then turned it the other way round and I looked at it with my bad eye and read out the letters from memory. Of course, he might have insisted on which eye I used first, but I had to risk that.[30]

Lindemann seems to have done well on his course at the flying school, and his instructor sent him a friendly letter after his departure saying: 'I wish all the so-called "Huns" were as satisfactory and pleasant to teach.' On 16 September 1916 he completed his first solo flight, which lasted five minutes, and on 25 October received his graduation certificate and was pronounced qualified for service in the Royal Flying Corps.

Doubts persisted, however, over his name. Some people held that after Lindemann received his pilot's licence, the ground staff never quite abandoned the suspicion that if they put too much fuel in his aeroplane he might abscond back to Germany. There was a popular (but probably mythical) story that on one occasion the authorities at Dover Castle telephoned Farnborough to report that someone with a German-sounding name and wearing a bowler hat had run out of fuel and made a forced landing nearby, and that this man was actually claiming to be from the Royal Aircraft Factory.

For the pilots and observers in aeroplanes, machine failure was a recurrent hazard. The pressing demand for new aeroplanes meant that the aircraft being sent out to France were receiving only a minimum of testing before despatch: enough to prove their airworthiness, but with little or no simulation of fighting conditions. The machines therefore got their baptism of fire when almost new, and the RFC pilots had no certainty as to how the aeroplanes would respond to the stress and strain of tortuous battle action. Some of these aeroplanes became notorious: the DH2 and the FE8, for example, and the Sopwith Two-Seater Scout, better known as the 'Spinning Jenny'.

One of the worst uncertainties for pilots was finding themselves entering a spiral dive or, as it became more widely termed, a 'spin'. As Constance Babington Smith put it:

> The spiral dive was a mysterious terror, an Act of God which, if it came to you, for no known reason, like lightning, meant disaster to you and your machine.[31]

The danger usually came through loss of speed, when the aeroplane might stall. A pilot would fly more and more slowly, until suddenly, without warning, the wing would dip below him. Before he knew it, the nose in front had collapsed and he would be facing vertically downwards, staring at the void between him and the ground. The earth would start to spin before his eyes as he hurtled towards it, and he would lose his sense of where he was. He would be buffeted in his seat and the wind would shriek in the struts; the dials on the instruments would vibrate and crazily turn, but he would not see them. He would pull back the stick, to no effect; then again, this time with all his might, as far as it would go. He would pitch it left, then right; he would press on the pedals, now right, now left, and kick on them again and again, in a desperate attempt to gain control of the aeroplane, spinning at seventy miles an hour towards the ground. Then, sharp and sudden, fear would bite his stomach, as he realised at last that he had only seconds to live.

With their aeroplanes being suddenly and for no known reason gripped by spin, the pilots' resentment was directed, for want of any more proximate target, at the designers. The problem was magnified in the autumn of 1916, after a number of squadrons in France had been equipped with the FE8, a new single-seater, or 'scout', designed at the Factory. Almost at once these fighters fell prey to a series of fatal spinning accidents. The tale was repeated in the spring of 1917 – April of that year for ever after being known as 'Bloody April' – when similar disasters befell the RE8, a reconnaissance two-seater also designed at the Factory and known, in rhyming slang, as a

'Harry Tate', after a contemporary music-hall performer. In Lindemann's own words:

> In 1916 many pilots were killed flying our recently designed RE8s by spinning into the ground. Although various people had succeeded in getting out of a spin, nobody quite knew how, nor indeed how or why aircraft spun at all.[32]

Nor did anyone seem able to give comfort to the pilots. Major J. A. Chamier, a highly experienced pilot who had become a staff officer, did his best to help by issuing guidance notes for those flying the RE8:

> The chief thing to remember is that the machine gives very little indication of losing its speed until it suddenly shows an uncontrollable tendency to dive, which cannot be corrected.[33]

Not greatly encouraging to those reading the notes.

At Farnborough, concern was mounting rapidly, and Lindemann therefore turned his mind to unravelling this appalling difficulty, aware that it had become the cause of despondency in England, and of death in France.

It is often held that a spin is the only condition of flight that is completely natural to an aeroplane, in that it is moving according to its own state, beyond the control of the pilot, rather like the bolting of a horse. Richard Southwell[34] described it at the time:

> A spin occurs at the stalling of the wings, which is followed by the tendency of one wing to drop and by the initiation of a spiral motion. Any tendency of the aeroplane then to rotate will be seized upon by the wings; and the aeroplane will descend, steadily turning, in a state outside the pilot's power of control.[35]

Although the pilots were well aware that there were certain conditions, such as lack of speed, that at any height they should avoid, the viciousness of the spin lay in its unpredictability. This remains a factor even today, as was neatly expressed in the words of a test pilot: 'Attempting to make a general rule about spinning is like making a rule about a shark: there is no rule.'[36] In 1917, however, flight itself only had a short history, and experience of spinning was extremely scarce. There had certainly been incidences of people recovering from a spin but, as Lindemann said, none of them knew how or why.

The grave losses of Factory-designed aeroplanes led Frank Goodden, the chief test pilot at Farnborough, to confront the problem head-on. He duly took an aeroplane up and put it into a spin. Remembering the story of a pre-war occasion when a pilot had managed to escape from a spin by desperately pushing the control stick forward, and not back (as logic suggested), Goodden found his aeroplane entering a nosedive from which he was able to regain control.

Even if a pilot had discovered what to do to put a particular aeroplane into a spin and recover from it, there was still the risk that other aeroplanes might not respond in the same way. Above all there was a lack of clear scientific analysis, without which all spins would remain empirical and the threat would not be lifted. Having survived a spin, Goodden was able to contribute valuable knowledge towards answering questions about the cause of spins; yet his actions did not provide a scientific basis of understanding on which future pilots could rely.

It was now that Lindemann came forward – as different from Frank Goodden, in Constance Babington Smith's words, 'as a ponderous raven from a flashing swallow' – and it was he who was to make the breakthrough. As the official report of the Advisory Committee for Aeronautics sets out:

> The first scientific experiments on the behaviour of an aeroplane in a spin were carried out . . . by Dr F. A. Lindemann with a BE2E aeroplane. Previously very little definite information had been available as to the behaviour and attitude of an aeroplane in a spin, or as to the effect of the control surfaces. The analysis of the results obtained gave full information as to the path and attitude of the aeroplane, and established the continuity of the spin with a normal spiral glide. Valuable information was also obtained as to the stresses involved in the manoeuvre.[37]

When Lindemann began his analysis of the problem, after further severe losses of RE8s, Goodden was no longer there to offer his experience, having been killed in a test flight at the beginning of 1917. Lindemann, however, could now fill the gap and could combine, as had never been done before, practical experience with scientific understanding.

His approach was coldly methodical. He would apply rational analysis to the facts, and would scientifically deduce from them both what caused an aeroplane to spin and what was happening while it actually was spinning. Having done so, it would, he thought, be possible to take the necessary steps to stabilise the aeroplane. With a series of such experiments, he believed, data could be built up and recorded, providing for the first time a clear explanation of the spin, and at last removing its terror.

Lindemann had been considering the problem in 1916 before he went to the Central Flying School. He had drawn some theoretical conclusions from watching others tragically spinning out of control and, working on his ideas, he carried out a series of model tests in one of the balloon sheds at the Factory. Now that he was allowed to fly, he was able to go a step further. What he needed was data, so in June 1917 he began a series of tests.

He took his aeroplane up and deliberately put it into a number of spins. In the Flight Log of the Royal Aircraft Factory about a dozen of the flights Lindemann made between June and August are specifically described as spinning tests – sometimes solo, sometimes with an observer – although it is probable that others that he made around the same time had the same purpose.

Even with today's safety measures and aeronautical knowledge, spinning requires a good measure of care and concentration and is not entirely free from risk. Nearly ninety years ago the matter was hazardous in the extreme, since the aircraft were primitive, often unreliable and – part of the problem to be solved – unpredictable. The danger was all the greater because at that time parachutes were not issued to pilots. It was popularly believed that this was because the authorities feared that pilots might bale out of their machines unnecessarily or prematurely if they were equipped with parachutes, leading to an unacceptable loss of aeroplanes.

These were the conditions in which Lindemann carried out his tests. He was to memorise a series of detailed measurements that were to be the key to the problem, while contending with cold, high wind, penetrating noise and with his aeroplane twisting, turning and buffeting as it rushed, nearly vertical, towards the ground. Besides showing great courage, he noted and accurately remembered, under conditions of enormous stress and physical difficulty, at least eight vital measurements. He saw that the answer was to speed up the downswing of the wing, and point the nose sharply down so as to pick up enough flying speed to pull out of the spin; and he realised that the great stresses on the machine were not at the rotation stage but in pulling out of the ensuing dive.

Most daunting of all, Lindemann was dealing with the unknown. He was confident that he was correct, with the calm conviction of the physicist, but must nevertheless have had, somewhere in his mind, the knowledge that if he was wrong there were only 3,000 feet of swirling air between him and oblivion. His unique achievement was to have combined three factors: the ability to work out a theory from observing other people's flights; to put an aeroplane into a spin, with no hope of survival if his theory was wrong; and, invaluably, to record his findings clearly. He himself was typically self-deprecatory, writing in later years:

The only merit I can claim in carrying out these experiments is that (unlike the professional pilot, who had usually not got a very good head for figures) I was able to remember the readings of the airspeed indicator, the bubble, the angle of incidence on the two wings (measured by tapes on the struts), the height of the beginning and ending of the spin, the time taken and the number of turns, and to write them down in my notebook when I had straightened out the plane again.[38]

It is not surprising that word of his achievement soon spread and gathered a momentum of its own. The light in which Lindemann began to be regarded by so many was expressed by Henry Tizard who, long after the war, wrote to A. L. Hetherington:

Another yarn of how a non-combatant did remarkable service in the war is furnished by the story of the spiral spin of the aeroplane. In the early days of the war an aviator, if his plane got into what was known as a spiral spin, was doomed to destruction. A certain eminent physicist sat down and worked out on paper the mathematics of the business and proved to his own satisfaction that if all controls were released, the plane would automatically get out of the spin. He thereupon laid his proof before the powers that be. The reply was naturally made: 'But, while that may be all very pretty on paper, how do you propose to prove it in practice?' 'By trying,' was the reply, 'I will go up in a plane, get into a spiral spin and come out again; my calculations are correct.' He did so, and there were no more losses in the air due to this particular cause. It was a brave thing to do.[39]

A feat of such courage and ability needs no adorning, and in due course it reached the ears of Winston Churchill. He had a particular interest in the matter because in July 1917, as Minister of Munitions, he became responsible for the design, manufacture and supply of all the aircraft and air material needed for the war. Churchill was always a great admirer of courage and intelligence, and in later years would no doubt have had many opportunities to ask Lindemann for the plain facts. All his life Churchill cherished the story of Lindemann's spin, and his description of it was infused with a touch of characteristic poetry. Lord Moran, Churchill's doctor, wrote of Lindemann in his memoirs, describing how Churchill used to speak of him:

And here was the Prof, who had a 'beautiful brain' – he was a Fellow of the Royal Society – and yet he was apparently without nerves, and was capable of the most astonishing adventures. Winston would recount to me once more the Prof's exploit in his stalling aircraft:

'You know, Charles, I was very worried at that time, we were losing some of our best pilots. Their aircraft would stall and go into a nose-dive, and the pilot was always killed. The Prof, with his mathematics, worked it all out on paper. To come out of the spin safely, the pilot must pick up enough speed in a vertical dive. No one took him seriously. So the Prof learnt to fly, and then one morning before breakfast he went up alone, wearing his bowler hat.'

Winston made some guttural sounds of mirth.

'He put his craft into a spinning nose-dive. Those watching him held their breath. It seemed certain death. But his theory worked. It is a terrific story. I did admire him so much.'[40]

And in the words of R. V. Jones:

His courage in undertaking systematic spinning, involving continuous spins of anything up to a dozen turns, has been widely recognised, but to anyone who has flown it is, to say the least of it, astonishing that he should have undertaken such an arduous and difficult, not to say dangerous, task after so little experience as a pilot.[41]

Meanwhile, by the summer of 1917 the outcome of the entire war had been thrown once more into doubt, with the Allies in acute difficulties in several theatres of the conflict. Although the German submarine offensive was posing a grave threat to Britain's food supplies, it was the war in the air that called loudest for the genius of the Factory scientists, now under intense pressure to sustain the flow of new designs and aircraft components.

As the scientists themselves tested their ideas in the air, considerable hardiness was required of them. For instance, Lindemann described working with the meteorologist G. M. B. Dobson[42] on what was probably the first automatic pilot. Although this was no doubt constructed using meticulous calculations, Lindemann recalled that 'my real faith was placed in a wire cutter I carried in my pocket with which I could cut the cables leading to the rudder if all else failed'. In his case it never did, and it pleased him that the very first of these devices flew the plane in a straight line, and about twice as accurately as a good pilot.

For others, however, all else did fail, with death and disaster the result. Undeterred by the risks, the scientists pressed on with their experiments. Thrown about by wind, often in extreme cold, in noisy, turbulent machines, hampered by engine smoke and with their goggles plastered by hot oil, they persevered with the trials that were so vital.

Lindemann also experimented with turn indicators. The perfection of these instruments was vital for alleviating a serious problem: flying through clouds without the pilots losing their sense of the vertical and the horizontal. It was only too easy for them to emerge from clouds thinking that they were flying horizontally, but finding that they were in fact flying straight towards the ground in a steep dive.

Another problem concerned the inaccuracy of bomb-aiming. As was to happen during the Second World War, many bombing missions were flown in the First World War in which lives were lost without the targets being remotely threatened, because bomb-aiming was so primitive. Lindemann took part in the design and testing of bomb-sights and carried out a number of trials. By modern standards these were very haphazard. He related how, on one such occasion, at the testing ground on the coast at Orford, he dropped his stop-watch through the floor of his aeroplane. As he manoeuvred and tried to reach his watch, which took some time, his colleague on the ground, waiting to plot the fall of bombs, thought that he had abandoned the trial and went for a swim. Lindemann continued:

As I had to jettison the bombs before landing and they unhappily straddled him in the sea, he took the whole performance somewhat amiss, although they were only twenty pounders.[43]

During 1917 a new menace had arisen to confront the people of England: the twin-engined Gotha aeroplanes that the German Air Force had begun to receive from their workshops. By the standards of the time these were enormous aircraft and could fly at up to 18,000 feet. It meant that the bombing of England by aeroplanes had become a deadly reality. As a consequence a new and better form of anti-aircraft barrage was established: it was inspired by the method devised for the protection of Venice, which had been surrounded by barrage balloons secured to rafts on the water below.

This principle also made sense to the Germans, and their version was a line of balloons hoisted all along the German frontier, which was taking a severe toll on Allied aircraft. Once more the designers at Farnborough were called on to help, and Lindemann joined his colleagues in the search for an answer.

His solution was to equip his aeroplane with thin rods and stout cables arranged in a V at the front of the machine, and to experiment by flying it into a balloon cable. He explained to the RFC pilots that an aeroplane must be at the electric potential of the air that it is passing through, while a balloon is at the potential of the earth, to which it is connected by cable. The difference of potential at a height of 3,000 feet may be in the order of

FOUR

Fresh Wind in Oxford

Oxford to him a dearer name shall be,
Than his own mother University.

John Dryden

Before the war Lindemann had thought hard about moving to the United States. His work for Nernst had marked him out as a future professor, and Millikan had tempted him with the attractions of academic life in America. Now that the war was over, he was accordingly sounded out for a chair in Chicago. The prospect probably had some appeal: in later years he was often to draw comparisons between the stability of America and the threat, as he saw it, of social disintegration in Europe, and to express the wish to move across the Atlantic. Yet although the end of the war had pitched Germany and Russia into revolutionary ferment, and although even in England the existing social order was being called into question, for Lindemann there was another prize in view, with a stronger allure even than America. He remained at Farnborough until February 1919, but from there he turned to Oxford.

At that time Oxford was evocative of ancient wisdom, wreathed in noble tranquillity, extolled in verse and prose alike: 'Cuckoo-echoing, bell-swarmèd, lark-charmèd, rook-racked, river-rounded',[1] it was depicted with characteristic grace by Evelyn Waugh when he wrote:

> Oxford, in those days, was still a city of aquatint. In her spacious and quiet streets men walked and spoke as they had done in Newman's day; her autumnal mists, her grey springtime, and the rare glory of her summer days . . . when the chestnut was in flower and the bells rang out high and clear over her gables and cupolas, exhaled the soft vapours of a thousand years of learning.[2]

Even the ludicrous imagery of the last clause does little to detract from this vision of an Oxford hardly changed since the late nineteenth century and the romantic atmosphere of *Zuleika Dobson*.[3]

Lindemann's fondness for Oxford had developed before the war. He had greatly enjoyed his stay in the university in 1913 and was now enthralled by the prospect of winning the chair of what Oxford calls experimental philosophy, known to the rest of the world as physics. In 1915 the incumbent, Robert Bellamy Clifton, had finally stepped down, but the university had postponed seeking a replacement until the end of the war.

Clifton's fifty-year reign had not been an unqualified success: he had not encouraged research, which he believed 'betrayed a certain restlessness of mind' – an unfortunate conception for a science professor – and had used his post exclusively for teaching. True to his beliefs, he was not prey to restlessness himself, producing only one significant paper in half a century.[4]

For decades, therefore, the only activities in the laboratory had been lectures and a little practical work, and the occasional acquisition of instruments for demonstration purposes. Such apparatus was exhibited in glass-fronted cases in the laboratory's front hall, and some of it even pre-dated Clifton: in its showcase, for example, a Zamboni pile, made and installed in 1840, drove unceasingly a small metal ball from one bell to the other and back again. In many instances considerable detective ability was needed to determine the use of these pristine objects.[5] They were kept 'jealously under lock and key, taken out from time to time to be dusted and cleaned, possibly to be used in a lecture, but entrusted never to the careless handling of a student of physics'.[6] It was perhaps surprising that in *Who's Who* Clifton gave his recreation as 'Work'.

He did, however, persuade the university to build him a laboratory. The money came from the accumulated proceeds of *The History of The Great Rebellion*, the Earl of Clarendon's famous chronicle of the Civil War. It was originally hoped that this money would be used for a riding school; however, the years passed and nothing was done, and the trustees eventually decided that a riding school was not needed and that the alternative suggestion of a swimming bath would be 'injurious to health'. By a process of logic peculiar to themselves, they lighted upon a physics laboratory as the nearest equivalent. Clifton designed it himself and in 1872 the first purpose-built physics laboratory in Europe was completed.

It was 'a building of dark little rooms, winding corridors, and unexpected corners'.[7] Kathrin Baxandall, the daughter of Sir Francis Simon, Lindemann's successor at Oxford, caught its atmosphere:

It was like a medieval alchemist's den, with one room with sort of workshops all the way round. I don't even remember any windows. There were things like retorts which made me think of alchemists, and all sorts of old-fashioned things but I don't remember any people there at all, except the mechanic.[8]

From this alchemist's den the only work of any importance that had emerged in half a century was C. V. Boys' measurement of the gravitational constant G; that was in 1895 and, important though it was, it was done at the Clarendon only because Boys' laboratory in London shook with vibrations caused by the London Underground.

So, by the end of the First World War, with little significant work done within living memory, and without so much as a professor, physics in the Clarendon Laboratory had sunk quietly into a trough. Lindemann's own words, written later when he was applying for funds for his laboratory, succinctly portray the inheritance that he was seeking:

> Up to the year 1870 Oxford and Cambridge were of approximately equal standing in the physical sciences. In 1865 Professor Clifton was appointed to the Chair of Experimental Philosophy and the Clarendon Laboratory was built seven years later. At about the same time the Cavendish Laboratory was built in Cambridge. In the Cavendish Laboratory a large amount of fundamental research was carried out and by 1918 the Cambridge Physics School was the best and largest in England. My predecessor, Professor Clifton, did not encourage research, the Physics School dwindled, despite the erection of the Electrical Laboratory at the beginning of this century, and in 1918 the reputation of the Department had sunk almost to zero.[9]

In these circumstances, and with the coming of peace, there arose in Oxford a feeling that a new impetus was overdue, and that a professor should be appointed with despatch, before the best candidates were taken by other universities. Accordingly, an election was set to take place before Easter 1919. The prospectus stated that:

> the duty of the Professor of Experimental Philosophy, who will have charge of the Clarendon Laboratory, will be to give instruction chiefly on mechanics, sound, light, and heat.

Drawn by this prospect, Lindemann put his name forward:

To the Registrar of the University of Oxford

Dear Sir,
I learn that the professorship of Experimental Philosophy is vacant and beg to offer my services in that capacity. My experimental work has dealt mainly with the properties of solids at low temperatures, X-ray

spectra, and photo-electric photometry. I have also published papers on the Kinetic Theory of Solids, photo-electricity, the structure of the atom, the life of radioactive substances, as well as a number of astro-physical problems.

On Lindemann's behalf, Tizard, it was said, 'pulled every string as only Tizard knew how'. His support may have been fuelled by a grievance that he held against the other candidate, G. P. Thomson (formerly Lindemann's colleague at Farnborough, but now at Cambridge) whom he believed had appropriated one of his inventions, and whom he regarded as a 'pushing Cambridge man'.[10] So Tizard sent in Lindemann's application for him; such was Lindemann's reputation that his referees included some of the greatest names in science, including both Rutherford and Rayleigh. Even so, and despite the confidence of his champion, Lindemann remained unsure that he would be chosen.[11] Writing to Jack Egerton, he said: 'My plans are of course still vague but I have taken rooms at Cambridge so as to have some place of refuge if all else fails.'[12]

He need not have worried: he was duly elected and on 1 May 1919 entered his new kingdom. The opposition faction was disappointed, but Thomson wrote a friendly letter from his college:

Dear Lindemann,
I feel I ought to congratulate you but I don't much want to! The high table was very gloomy when I announced the fact last night, though they ask me to congratulate you.

I am afraid you will rather be in the position of a Jesuit father sent to minister to the Iroquois, though the vengeance of the unconverted is more likely to take the form of an attack on your digestion than the cruder persecutions of the American Indians.

Anyhow, in your efforts to wake Oxford up you will have the most sincere good wishes of all physicists . . .[13]

Tizard's determination not to let a Cambridge man take the post reflected the rivalry between the two universities in those days. Oxford took gentle pleasure in Baedeker's celebrated advice to travellers who had not time to visit both universities, to 'omit Cambridge altogether'. The prejudice was often fuelled by ignorance: some years before Lindemann's appointment, Raymond Asquith, the son of the Prime Minister and later killed on the Somme, recalled with pleasure his Oxford servant saying to him: 'What sort of place *is* Cambridge, Sir? Something in the Keble line, I should imagine.'[14]

After he had been appointed, and with slightly more information at his disposal, Lindemann wrote to Ernest Rutherford, the leader of Cambridge physics, saying that he hoped to work in the closest co-operation with Cambridge and with other schools of physics, believing 'that there is no stimulus to new ideas like personal intercourse with other workers in allied branches'. However, although Rutherford had agreed to give his name as a referee, Lindemann had probably already burnt his boats with him, as the previous year Rutherford had been exasperated by Lindemann querying his celebrated work on the disintegration of the nucleus, and referring to 'a possible alternative explanation'. 'I do not of course suggest,' Lindemann had written, with faint praise, 'that your interpretation is not the right one; I only put the possibility before you as I think you will agree that the more epoch-making the discovery is, the more closely should all alternatives be examined.' Rutherford did not agree.

So into the firmament of Oxford there now swam a strange star 'like a new planet from his own obscure realm of astrophysics': confident, determined, brisk and exact, and ready to meet on his own terms the hallowed ways and easy customs of Oxford society. Lindemann was well aware that his new domain had many of the qualities of a white elephant, yet he was resolved to transform it entirely and to lead Oxford to the world stage on which he thought it belonged.

To achieve this objective he would need a bright vision and an unswerving purpose, but these were qualities with which he was well endowed, and to which he added an enriching dose of contempt for his opponents. He had a clear aim: to instigate promising lines of research, and to attract good men both by the importance of the work to be done and by the lure of funds – which he would have to prise out of a reluctant university. He knew that to succeed he would have to cajole an institution with a predilection for arts and the classics, firmly entrenched and sanctified by the custom of what at Oxford were referred to as 'recent centuries'.

Lindemann also knew that it was not just Oxford's preference for the humanities over science or mathematics that would pose a problem, expressed as it was by the adage 'Oxford is for manners and marmalade; Cambridge for sausages and sums'. The university's finances were in such poor health that it had avoided financial collapse at the end of the war only through an emergency short-term grant from the Government. To achieve his aims, Lindemann would have to seek funds from beyond the city walls: from industry and private benefactors. For people and equipment he would look to the service departments, and to the armaments industry that had been poised so recently to take the great offensive into Germany for the campaign of 1919. So he formed his plans and prepared his approaches.

Almost at once he ran up against the mores of Oxford, which were rather different from those he had experienced so far in life, and which to Lindemann looked very like cobwebs hanging from his colleagues' gowns. His first brush concerned the surroundings in which he was to reside.

The chair of experimental philosophy was attached to a Fellowship at Wadham College, the early home of English science, where the Royal Society of London had been conceived by, among others, Robert Boyle and Christopher Wren. After his election, Wadham had welcomed Lindemann with the offer of rooms in the college. To Wadham, these seemed perfectly acceptable, but not to Lindemann, who at once dismissed them as uncomfortable, inconvenient and undesirable. Although he had to a certain extent become used to 'roughing it' at Farnborough, that had been in wartime, and the bare walls and threadbare carpets in the mess at Chudleigh had been softened by the warmth and good fellowship of his scientific comrades. Prior to that he had been accustomed to the plush of the Hotel Adlon and to the solid comfort of Sidholme.

If in general his surroundings in Wadham seemed dim, his particular objection fixed upon the college's reluctance to provide him with what he regarded as a necessity, namely washing facilities 'en suite'.

For most of the dons such a deprivation would probably have seemed unimportant. Lindemann was different. For him it was a matter of dissatisfaction and must be put right. His strongly developed desire for privacy made him recoil at the prospect of crossing quadrangles, clad in towels and exposed to view, in order to have a bath. The exchanges he now entered into with the college authorities project today a faintly humorous picture of easy-going dons of the old school reeling before the icy blast of the determined newcomer in their midst.

Lindemann laid his case before the warden, the amiable Dr Wells:

I shall presumably stay in whatever rooms I move into for a very considerable number of years and am therefore anxious to make them as comfortable as possible. Since I am somewhat liable to colds I should like to make my suite self-contained.[15]

Here was a novel proposal indeed. Dr Wells reacted with consternation, rather in the manner of Dickens' Circumlocution Office,[16] vouchsafing on behalf of his colleagues all manner of reasons why it could not be done; and of how, among those things that *could* be done, this did not number: 'You would find Oxford opinion,' said the warden, 'strong against such a change in old buildings.'

Lindemann took a jaundiced view of this, discerning instead the pettiness of lesser men, in this case the college builder and his poodle the bursar, whom he described as an 'inefficient old dodderer'. Although at length Lindemann did get his bathroom, and a comparatively fine sitting room (now a Wadham common room), the affair rankled. 'In twentieth-century England,' he would protest, 'I do not expect to be denied the elementary luxuries of Minoan Crete.' The other Fellows were puzzled by Lindemann's brisk requirements, one of them expressing the considered opinion that he could not understand why there should be such a fuss about washing arrangements, with the term only lasting for eight weeks.

So the new arrival at once set off a fluttering in the Wadham dovecotes, and while the matter remained unresolved, he moved into the Randolph Hotel. From there he wrote to his mother, who was proposing to decorate his rooms for him:

My dear Mamma,   June 12th, 1919
Ever so many thanks for your perfectly charming letter and the vests which arrived here yesterday . . . I expect to get into Wadham on the 15th of July but I have not yet seen the rooms or decided on them . . . young Thomson[17] is coming here for a few days on Monday to stay with me . . . I have got a grant[18] of £1200 for putting in electricity, extending water supply, equipping workshop etc. and hope this will be completed in a couple of months. A grant for apparatus etc. is more or less promised for next term. In addition I hope to get a number of things from the Air Force & the university has decided to accept the Government's offer so that we may get some work done soon . . . P.S. I should of course be delighted to see either you or Papa here if you cannot come together, but the hotel is bad. How is your new cook? I hope she will be a success. Is there any parlour-maid in the offing?

A fortnight later he wrote to his father, switching from the ridiculous to the sublime with apparent unconcern:

I know very little about the rooms at Wadham which are not yet vacated . . . If it were not for the servant difficulty I should try and find a modern house as no flats are available. The college will probably be most comfortable in the meantime especially as I do not mind a small bedroom. What I object to is having to go right across the quadrangle to the baths and lavatories . . . I am writing a note on the theory of magnetic storms.[19] It started by a criticism of Chapman's theory but I fancy I have now an idea which will account for them. Chapman's theory is quite impossible . . . I saw the people who came down for their honorary degrees. Joffre[20] is getting very shaky. There was an awful crowd and the Latin speeches dragged on too long, especially as Curzon[21] did not know his part. I had a talk with Sir Henry Wilson[22] at the Wadham Garden Party about the importance of encouraging science here, and hope it may do some good.

Lindemann's letter to his mother shows that he had wasted no time in applying for money to begin his work for the Clarendon. In the stringent circumstances that prevailed, other professors might have been pleased to obtain such grants as he had received, but Lindemann preferred to believe that at Oxford science was viewed with a certain suspicion, if not with patronising detachment, which would obstruct any proper support for its development. He was later venomously to recount his irritation with the wife of Dr Pember, the warden of All Souls, who had demonstrated this outlook at a cocktail party when she said to Lindemann, who had been expressing his dismay at the lack of scientific knowledge in the country: 'Don't worry, professor, anyone who has a First in Greats could get up science in a fortnight.' Lindemann had instantly riposted: 'Well, what a pity that your husband has never had a fortnight to spare.' The encounter rankled.

The traditionalists and classicists tended to think of all branches of science as a single entity, and viewed it rather as a turgid and impenetrable backwater of the River Cherwell as it flowed gracefully under Magdalen Bridge. Engineering, for example, they considered, even years after Lindemann's arrival, as:

an appropriate subject for illiterate artisans, and that academic engineers were men with oily rags stuffed into the pockets of denim overalls, who were ill-suited, metaphorically as well as literally, to enter the senior common-rooms of the colleges.[23]

With his own wide knowledge of subjects other than science, Lindemann resented this attitude. He became quick to defend his subject at every opportunity, and whenever his humanist colleagues displayed ignorance of elementary matters of science, he would round upon them:

'You do not realise,' he would say, 'what abysmal ignorance that shows; it would be as though a scientist did not know the significance of the Battle of Tours.' No doubt he had it in mind that the humanist himself might not be so sure about that battle.[24]

Almost as soon as Lindemann arrived, his efforts to achieve a rebirth of physics in Oxford led him into controversy. He seemed to hold what were seen as arrogant opinions, and he was apt to express them with a rather sneering impatience. It was not in his character, or what he had absorbed in Germany, to be emollient or gentle, edging forward with grace. In consequence opposition began to form, and the adjectives used to describe him multiplied and soon included prickly, eccentric, arrogant, opinionated, sarcastic and uncooperative. Yet a slight turn of the prism, in respect of those whom he befriended, released a picture of charm, kindliness, humour, affection and loyalty.

Perhaps it was Lindemann's unwavering determination to achieve his aims at his chosen pace that did not at first match the gentle and somewhat circuitous ways of Oxford. It certainly led to his becoming increasingly unpopular in many Oxford circles, something that was not lessened by what his colleagues perceived as an infuriating air of superiority. He displayed considerable wit in conversation, but the border between that and remarks that bit and wounded was narrow, and Lindemann did not appear to mind the effect his comments had. 'I should like to castrate him,' he said after one contretemps with a colleague, adding in a discouraged tone, 'not that it would make any difference.'[25]

Ensconced in the Randolph, however, he set about the Herculean task of raising the dead weight of Oxford physics, and building it up into a department worthy of a great university. He had a threefold task: to make the Clarendon Laboratory suitable for fostering the important work that he envisaged; to acquire the apparatus necessary for research; and to attract research workers.

As he drew aside the Victorian veils and laid bare for the university the stark condition of the Clarendon, the authorities began to react. In Clifton's time no electricity had been laid on, the staff had consisted of one assistant with a foot-lathe and one part-time demonstrator, and the laboratory had been closed for three days a week. In such circumstances teaching had barely aroused awareness, still less enthusiasm, among undergraduates.

Although Lindemann's vision for the Clarendon was in time to be realised, finance from the university was at first so tight that the building itself swallowed whatever meagre resources were available – so much so that in both 1922 and 1923 he donated a part of his own salary to the income of his department. There were other examples of his altruism in his early years at Oxford: for some time he waived his dues as a Fellow of Wadham, besides paying the college fees of one of his pupils and guaranteeing an overdraft for a member of his staff.

He had also received a significant fillip to his credentials for the task: his name was put forward for a Fellowship of the Royal Society, the body that has for centuries fostered scientific excellence, and which occupies the highest plane in the world of science. In recognition of his remarkable contributions to physics, Lindemann was elected a Fellow in March 1920 – a great honour at the unusually young age of thirty-three.

His next step was to begin determined attempts to tap university funds, and to seek supplies from the military authorities. In this he gained an early ally in the form of I. O. Griffith, who during the war had worked with Tizard testing bombs and aeroplanes, and who was now to prove adept at university politics and was to provide invaluable administrative support.

Lindemann had an instinct for the most useful people to approach, and he directed his first enquiries to the Department of Scientific and Industrial Research (DSIR), whose Advisory Council he was later to join, at Tizard's instigation. He persuaded them in due course to fund several of the researchers that he was to recruit, besides his own research into instrument design. He also put his case to the Royal Air Force, and his requests came to the notice of the Air Council, with the result that from Air Force stores he soon began to receive all manner of essential equipment: drills, wheels, milling tools, lathes and – cutting through some tangled military red-tape, – valuable German compressors from the Occupation Authorities.

While at Farnborough he had developed several contacts with industry and, promoting the link between academic research and the needs of industry, he now turned to powerful firms such as Metropolitan Vickers.

He appealed successfully to the Royal Society, and wrote to companies such as English Electric, British Thomson-Houston, and to ICI, whose research council he was later to join. He also went to businesses with Oxford connections, such as Morris Motors and Pressed Steel, whose association with the university might be expected to attract them to his cause.

In his new role Lindemann discovered a flair for administration, which he combined with an eye for the most promising areas of research and the selection of appropriately able people to carry it out. He soon found that he no longer had the time both successfully to plan and develop from on high the reawakening laboratory and to do good research himself. As the Clarendon began to grow and prosper, his own research and practical work dwindled, but in giving priority to the former he did Oxford a great service.

He started from a small base: in 1920 a mere six undergraduates took the physics course, and there were only two research students. It was necessary to bring the course up to date, both in terms of examinations and practical work, much of which he set directly himself. His associative turn of mind also came to the fore, and in 1923, together with J. B. S. Haldane and Julian Huxley, among others, he pressed for a new degree course, to combine science and philosophy. Sadly, this imaginative idea was extinguished by Oxford's ruling body, on the somewhat circular argument that it would be difficult to find suitable people to teach it, or suitable undergraduates to take it. In this his adversary was H. W. B. Joseph, one of Oxford's leading philosophers – 'a powerful race of men who assumed intellectual jurisdiction over others' – and who was himself renowned as 'a ruthless pricker of half-truths and pretentious verbiage'.[26]

Just as Lindemann was beginning to meet and correspond with people of influence beyond the university, he had a stroke of luck, which probably contributed as much as any other single factor to his future happiness.

Dr Matthew Lee, a successful doctor in the reign of George II, had left a large amount of money in trust to Christ Church, where he had been educated, and one of his bequests was for funds to provide instruction in experimental natural science. As a result of some tortuous manoeuvres that followed the recommendations of a Royal Commission into the ancient universities, Lindemann assumed the engaging title of Dr Lee's professor of experimental philosophy. Christ Church also offered him a Studentship (the equivalent of a Fellowship), but without a seat on the Governing Body, as he was already on Wadham's. More importantly, with Wadham's agreement, Christ Church offered him somewhere to live – an offer he accepted with alacrity. He moved into a large and attractive set of rooms, which included a bedroom, a drawing room, a dining room and a separate area from which a servant could keep things in good order. He also installed – without opposition – a bathroom.

His rooms overlooked Christ Church Meadow and had a fine prospect of Magdalen Tower and Bridge. Outside, the breeze would rustle the leaves in the tall elms, the long grass would sway in the meadow, and the sun would sparkle on the nearby Thames. Lindemann must have felt a glow of pleasure at such an elegant solution to the problem of his accommodation. His rooms in Christ Church became his home, and he was to keep them for the rest of his life.

From this secure and attractive base, and with his plans for the Clarendon beginning to take shape, he was to add a new dimension to his life and swim into the warm and buoyant waters of English society; in due course these would lead him into the realms of high politics.

In the meantime, he was also a professor in charge of a department, and consequently he had to give lectures – twenty-eight a year was the requirement. He delivered them weekly, at 12.00 – he had not learnt to love early rising – and on the appointed day, shortly before twelve, his Rolls-Royce would draw up outside the Clarendon. Formal in dark coat and bowler hat, Lindemann would step down and briskly enter the building.

His subjects included the kinetic theory of gases, atomic theory and relativity. Although it was suggested by his detractors that his lectures never varied, their content was accepted as being of the highest quality. Unfortunately the conclusions of the great mind were delivered almost inaudibly; he spoke in a low, rather monotonous voice, with his hand in front of his mouth, and frequently with his back to the small audience as he wrote on the blackboard. Lindemann was the subject of a maxim popular at that time among Rhodes scholars – that to be an Oxford lecturer in physics three qualifications were necessary: that he should speak in such a low voice that only the front row could hear him; that he should write on the blackboard in such small letters that only the front row could read them; and that he should rub them out so quickly that not even the front row could get them down.[27]

However, it has to be said that even audible lectures were not in those days a great draw at Oxford: Egerton, for example, was once found standing disconsolately outside his lecture room vainly waiting for a single person to turn up. Lindemann's lectures, because of his status, were more or less unavoidable. One of his undergraduates, Douglas Roaf, who was later to carry out valuable wartime research at the Clarendon, recalled: 'You paid a pound extra to go to the professor's lectures – which he pocketed; it was really pretty much compulsory to go.'[28]

It is not surprising that when, some years later, he was asked by the chancellor of another university to deliver a 'popular' lecture on splitting the atom, Lindemann was told by a friend that: 'However popular you may or may not be at the beginning, I am prepared to bet that you will be less popular at the end.'[29]

Rather than set an example of arduous research at the laboratory bench, Lindemann's method in these years was to select researchers, choose a promising topic for them and then let them sink or swim. Like Sir Thomas Beecham, he believed in appointing or appropriating those whom he regarded as the best people and letting them play.[30] In a revealing remark to Jack Egerton and his wife, who had questioned him about why he did not explore his own lines of research more deeply, he said: 'I can understand and criticise anything, but I have not got the creative power to do it myself.'

While Lindemann would not, and increasingly could not, give exact advice as to how particular technical problems could be overcome, his sympathetic encouragement led his researchers to persevere and find solutions for themselves. He ensured that he knew exactly what each person in the laboratory was doing, and he would 'look in' on their work, always equipped with what almost became his trademarks: a pocket slide-rule, a miniature Galilean telescope and a pocket torch.

In both his own research and as a supervisor Lindemann's speciality was the flash of intuition rather than the steady flame.[31] The cost of this approach was that it led researchers up a number of blind alleys, whose walls were reached only after expense in time and money. This was balanced, however, by the pursuit of certain outstanding lines of enquiry, notably in low-temperature research.

Lindemann's move from direct research to a role as supervisor and fundraiser was a gradual process. In his first years at Oxford, certainly up until 1924 when his last paper was published, he not only remained in the top rank of researchers, but covered an unusual breadth of subjects. At the same time, and as he moved away from the workbench, he became something of a Socratic oracle with postgraduates and colleagues alike.[32] For example, some of the most important research in chemical kinetics done by Cyril Hinshelwood[33] was inspired by Lindemann's contribution to a Faraday Society discussion, while Lindemann's ideas on the ozone layer set in train immensely important research in that field.

He chose his first researchers from people whom he had known during the war. Among the earliest to arrive was Gordon Dobson,[34] who had been in charge of scientific research at the Central Flying School at Upavon. Lindemann now proposed Dobson as demonstrator in meteorology. However, he had to overcome the initial reluctance of the university to fund the post, and before he knew that he had done so he turned to industry and to the Air Ministry for support. He was already clear in his view that it was essential to retain clever people in order to enable important research to be carried out, and that doing so would have the supplementary benefit of attracting undergraduates. In a logical extension to this argument, he held that both industry and the Government should welcome a pool of young talent from which to draw and should therefore be more willing to provide funds.

Once Dobson had been appointed, he and Lindemann began to study the upper atmosphere, particularly by implementing Lindemann's theory that observation of meteor trails would be a guide to the density of air at various heights. They confounded previous theories by showing that above 50km the temperature of the upper atmosphere begins to rise, and Lindemann found the explanation for this in the absorption of solar ultraviolet radiation by a layer of ozone.[35]

They drew further support for their theories from the fact that sound waves from explosions 'skip' to long distances – which explained, for example, a puzzling phenomenon that had been noticed during the Great War when children in East Anglian schools would find their lessons disturbed by the sound of heavy artillery and shelling, which those much nearer the battlefront did not hear.[36]

The importance of Lindemann's research at this time was described by the nuclear physicist James L. Tuck, who was to become Lindemann's scientific assistant during the Second World War, before he moved to lead a team at the Los Alamos atomic project in America:

Lindemann was an old-fashioned all-round physicist, somewhat too far ahead of his time perhaps to be fully appreciated, and certainly very maladroit at getting other scientists to agree with him . . . By theory and experiment he deduced that meteors were much smaller than had been thought, that ablation increased their ballistic coefficients so that the atmosphere was less dense than had been believed, and hence adduced that the upper atmosphere was hot. All this was new and revolutionary once, though commonplace in these days of nose cones and direct measurement.[37]

Tuck also referred to Lindemann's 1919 paper: 'Note on the Vapour Pressure and Affinity of Isotopes':[38]

He also studied theoretically the separation of isotopes. After going through the various possibilities – diffusion etc. – he deduced that separation in a centrifugal field had a unique advantage over the others in that the separation coefficient depends on the mass difference between the isotopes, and not so much on the mass.

The full consequence of this innocent seeming little deduction has not yet made itself felt on mankind. May it remain that way for a long time. To appreciate how original this work was, it should be realised that this paper was not published in 1969 or even in 1940, but in 1919, one year after the discovery of isotopes by Aston.

Here is no gadgeteer. His work has a great range – from basic theoretical concept to neat experiment – and always original.[39]

Dobson was later to take forward the ideas that he had first developed with Lindemann, and in due course was to establish the fact of seasonal variation of atmospheric ozone. The two men could rightly be said to be pioneers in this subject, which has become of such importance to the modern world,[40] and together they published notable papers on conditions in the high atmosphere.[41]

Another of Lindemann's early recruits was Thomas Merton,[42] a spectroscopist with a private laboratory in London. The university appointed him a professor of spectroscopy in 1923 and he then moved his research to the Clarendon, at Lindemann's invitation. There Merton began to do important work on isotopes, an aspect of nuclear physics in which Lindemann himself was very interested, and on which he had published a paper[43] with his Farnborough colleague Frank Aston, who was later to win the Nobel Prize.

Merton was a civilised man, an expert fisherman and a keen collector of Renaissance paintings, of which, when he died in 1969, he left a significant collection, including more than one Botticelli. He had also been the first scientist and inventor to be employed by the British Secret Service.[44] He placed a high value on carrying out research at first hand, and was later to say:

> There are some scientists to whom the art of experiment provides one of the keenest aesthetic pleasures in life and to whom the idea of research by proxy is about as exciting and romantic as artificial insemination.[45]

After a comparatively short time, however, the attractions of an estate in Herefordshire, with salmon fishing on the River Wye, drew Merton away from Oxford, although he continued his research in a laboratory that he established at his house. To fill the gap Lindemann, after an interval, invited Derek Jackson[46], who arrived from Cambridge in 1927, already with credentials as a potential spectroscopist of the highest order. Having heard of his talent, Lindemann had asked him to stay for a weekend at Oxford, where Jackson explained that although he had been asked to join the Cavendish at Cambridge, he was reluctant to do so because he thought that he would in effect fall under the sway of its forceful leader, Rutherford. Lindemann was impressed by Jackson's ambitions, and, as Jackson put it: 'Lindemann bought me, just as you might buy a promising yearling.'

A third early recruit was Jack Egerton, who had been with Lindemann in Berlin and later at Farnborough. He arrived at the Clarendon in 1919, having been appointed as reader in thermodynamics in succession to Tizard, who had moved to London. His work was conducted at the Clarendon, partly in the attic and partly in the cellars, which he shared with a colony of 'vicious mosquitoes'. Despite its primitive working conditions, Egerton's research group was considered the most productive at the Clarendon, and Egerton himself 'infused his research students, brilliant or otherwise, with his own enthusiasm'.[47] Even so, undergraduates were amused by the fact that in his lectures on thermodynamics he would stress the importance to any good physicist of having Maxwell's Relations 'firmly committed to memory' and would then take from his pocket a card from which he would copy the four vital equations on the blackboard.

Working in the cellar also led to some lighter moments, as offensive vapours from chemical preparations often seeped through the Ruskin-inspired rosette ventilation holes in the steps of the lecture theatre above. On one occasion ether rose into the theatre while Lindemann was lecturing, causing drowsiness and mirth in equal measure, much to his displeasure – and he could be a stern disciplinarian.

This was demonstrated in an incident some years later concerning R. V. Jones,[48] who, both before and during the war, was to work closely with Lindemann on air-defence methods. He displayed exceptional imagination and ability as a physicist and was to play a vital part in the scientific and intelligence battles against Germany, in the course of which he won the enduring esteem of Winston Churchill. In his earlier days Jones was a pupil of Lindemann, but he was also a renowned practical joker. On one occasion he put this talent to work during a lecture at the Clarendon:

> Behind the speaker in the old Clarendon lecture theatre was a large high-voltage accelerator with sundry large spheres at about head level. This was discreetly hidden behind a curtain that could be raised electronically. One day, during the lecture, this curtain slowly raised itself to reveal to the assembled class a spectacle of horrifying lèse-majesté. The spheres were adorned with gowns, faces and bowler hats. Jones was known to be the cause of all such happenings, and he was brought before Lindemann. He gravely observed that Jones could not possibly be allowed to go unpunished, for it was a most serious matter to undermine the dignity of dons. 'After all,' said Lindemann, 'some of them need all the dignity they can get.' Jones received a light sentence.[49]

Jones' practical joking did not detract from his merit as a physicist, and he was another who joined the ranks that Lindemann recruited for the Clarendon. The later record of those who worked under Lindemann is a fitting tribute to him: Egerton joined the Advisory Committee of the DSIR and the Advisory Board of the Air Research Council, and Dobson, Jones, Jackson, Merton and Egerton were all to become Fellows of the Royal Society, knighthoods being conferred on the last two.

Gradually money began to flow towards the Clarendon, partly from the university and partly from industry. The first appointments were made, and equipment began to arrive for the scientists to develop their lines of research. Work on the building started to remove the crustiest relics of the previous regime, and Lindemann's hopes for the laboratory began to move from dreamland to reality.

However, as his quest for funds gave him less and less time for direct research, his enemies gleefully said that he seemed to be losing touch with developments in theoretical physics. Yet he remained convinced that the physical significance of theory was paramount, and that physicists should not be content, as mathematicians were, with – as he put it – mere 'squiggles on paper'. His groundbreaking work in Berlin could not be faulted on that score.

In fact it was in these early post-war years that he did some of his best work, as is confirmed by the list of scientific papers that he produced, particularly in the years 1919–24. For instance, he made a consistent contribution to the discussion and understanding of quantum theory and of the theory of relativity. Although he was hopelessly bad at making himself heard, what he said was constructed with great lucidity, and the rapid acceptance of Einstein's theories in Britain was to a significant extent due to their enthusiastic promotion by Lindemann. In his lectures he discussed the concepts of time and space that had been accepted by mankind since time immemorial, saying:

Einstein preferred a more radical solution. We must try and find, he held, some method of synchronising clocks if physics is to progress. It is no good just being content with saying I know what I mean by simultaneity; we might as well say I know what I mean by the laws of physics and have done with it.

He defined the instant at which a light-signal was reflected at a distant mirror B as half way between the time it left A and the time it returned. In a sense in fact he substituted the Indefinable Velocity for the Indefinable Time.

General Relativity may be summed up by saying that we have substituted for Euclidian geometry in which bodies proceed in straight lines, unless deflected by gravitational or other forces, a non-Euclidian geometry which enables us to maintain the claim that bodies proceed in straight lines, or more properly geodesics, even in the neighbourhood of gravitating masses, though of course they may still be deflected by other forces.

The idea that the effects of gravity could be described by a change in the geometry of the space–time continuum was of course entirely original and extremely impressive. To ask, however, as some have done, whether general relativity is true or false is entirely meaningless.

Whether the physicist prefers to describe the outside world in terms of Euclidian terms plus gravity, or of non-Euclidian geometry without gravity, is a matter of taste and not a matter of right or wrong, any more than any particular way of drawing a map is right or wrong.[50]

Lindemann's work in nuclear physics also demonstrated how far-sighted were his ideas. In his first years at the Clarendon he conducted important experiments with uranium. In these he attempted to induce nuclear change by bombarding uranium with streams of electrons of ever higher energy in the hope that, when they got through the outer rings of electrons, they would be drawn into the nucleus and would produce some kind of change. In this field he did important work with his erstwhile Farnborough colleague, Frank Aston, the 'father of mass spectroscopy', and in June 1919 they published their conclusions in the *Philosophical Magazine*.[51] Their thoughts were so far advanced that twenty-two years later, when the Tube Alloys Group was considering the atomic bomb, the question arose as to whether the volume containing their research should not be withdrawn. In the event it was decided that if it were, and the fact leaked out, it might draw undesirable attention to the contents.

Lindemann also collaborated in his father's research in astronomy, and developed with him an extremely sensitive photo-electric cell, in order to detect light from stars, nebulae and comets.[52] The current produced by this cell was measured by a newly invented silica-fibre electrometer that Lindemann had designed with his father in 1919, but which in the following years he developed in collaboration with Thomas Keeley. It was produced commercially both in England and in Germany, and was described in the *Philosophical Magazine* and included in the textbooks of the time:

The Lindemann Electrometer is a most remarkable instrument; it weighs less than 3 ounces, requires no levelling and is very robust. It is designed to be mounted just behind the focus of a telescope to record the intensity of light from stars, nebulae, comets etc.

Perhaps a further example of its simple ingenuity was the fact that Keeley and Lindemann found that the best agent for drying its interior was toast.[53]

Keeley had also been at Farnborough, and Lindemann invited him to Oxford in 1919 to act as his assistant. It was to prove a superlative appointment: in time Keeley became Lindemann's *alter ego* at the Clarendon, in effect its manager, and handled with great success the administration that was to become rapidly more time-consuming and important throughout the 1920s and 1930s. Typically Lindemann showed his appreciation of Keeley's value by quietly subsidising his salary. Keeley became a Fellow of Wadham College, where it is remembered that he said nothing at all for the first six years in which he attended meetings of the Governing Body, until finally, greatly moved by a comment from one of his colleagues, he suddenly exclaimed 'Bosh' in a loud voice, to the intense surprise of everyone in the room.

The financial burden of the developments that Lindemann had set in train was to an extent offset by the fact that a number of his researchers were rich men and could themselves make a sizeable contribution to the costs of their work. Dobson had inherited land and had a rich wife. Merton was also well off, partly because some forty years earlier his uncle Wilhelm had founded Metallgesellschaft, at one time the second-largest company in Germany. Jackson was a twin son of the owner of the *News of the World*, from which he had gained a considerable fortune, and he not only accepted no pay for his professorship, but also brought with him his own expensive laboratory apparatus.

Lindemann's choice of Griffith and Keeley, who bore so well the burden of administration, and of brilliant researchers such as Dobson, Merton, Jackson and Jones, highlights an attribute that was to serve him well throughout his life: that of being able to find people of great ability to work for him. This talent was later to be seen in his rescuing German scientists from the Nazis and bringing them to Oxford, in the staff he recruited to help him in the war, and in his choice of personal servants. Lindemann was alive to the merits of all these people and, for all his dogmatic self-confidence, was fully prepared to respect their judgement.

It pleased him to choose as colleagues men of means and background, and unsurprisingly this led to charges of snobbery. However, his approach had reason on its side: such colleagues were agreeable people, kept the costs of research low and worked for the love of physics and not for money. This attitude fitted well with his gradual move, at around this time, into upper-class circles. Yet because he was seen to be straying far from the professional and scientific milieu of north Oxford, he was castigated by detractors among Oxford's scientists and their wives. Lindemann was probably unaware of such opinions, and certainly uninterested in them. Moreover, the friendships that he made beyond Oxford were to bring benefits not only to him, but also to the university.

He began to meet many rich men upon whom he would prevail to help finance the work of the Clarendon. One of his early friends in this context was the Earl of Berkeley, another Fellow of the Royal Society, who had a private laboratory just outside Oxford, but whose home was Berkeley Castle on the banks of the River Severn, the scene of King Edward II's grisly end. Lindemann often used to stay with the Berkeleys, who considered him a welcome addition to their house parties. Sometimes he went there with Keeley, who remembered arriving at the castle, where the drawbridge was lowered and the portcullis raised to admit the professor's Rolls-Royce.

It is appropriate at this point to look ahead to the later 1930s and to trace the development of the outward and visible sign of Lindemann's success in revitalising and inspiring science at Oxford. This was the building of a new Clarendon Laboratory. Although Lindemann consistently maintained that in science people were more important than buildings, his reign at the Clarendon was to be crowned by this new development, which was completed in September 1939. It would be the most up-to-date and finest laboratory of its kind in the world, a fitting home for the spearhead of low-temperature and atomic research. The impetus for the new laboratory increased significantly after 1933, when Lindemann brought to Oxford some of the world's foremost Jewish physicists, whose jobs and lives had fallen under the threat of the Nazis.

Lindemann had used his lucid and persuasive powers to good effect on the keepers of the university's purse-strings, so that by 1937 it had in principle been agreed to build a new laboratory. However, Oxford would not commit itself to financing anything more than the building itself, believing that its job was to provide teaching rather than research. Lindemann, however, felt keenly that the laboratory would turn into a white elephant if it were not properly equipped, and if there were not funds of sufficient size and duration to attract and retain the best researchers. This was particularly true in the case of low-temperature research, which was essentially a long-term project.

The waters were further muddied, in 1937 and the following years, by the donation to the university of staggeringly large sums of money by Oxford's most famous industrialist, the motor magnate William Morris, newly created Lord Nuffield. For a number of reasons, very little of this money reached Lindemann's department, while he naturally feared that the publicity about Oxford's windfall would be a deterrent to further financial support from outside the university.

Therefore, while all looked well on the surface, he was faced with the pressing need to maintain his struggle for funds for the new laboratory. His appeals both to the university and to potential private sources were a model of clarity and of cogent argument, as he now sought annual grants for equipment and, above all, for people. To do so, he explained the place and purpose of physics, conscious that, like Lord Nuffield, few people made the connection between physics research and medical advances. In a typical letter he wrote:

I think everybody will agree that physics is the most fundamental of all the sciences, in fact it may be said to be the basis and foundation of all our knowledge of nature. For unless we understand how brute, dead matter is constituted, how it acts and reacts with its surroundings, it is obviously impossible to expect to gain any real comprehension of the more complex organisms we have to deal with in biology. But although it lies at the very foundation of all knowledge, Physics, in England at any rate, is the Cinderella of the Sciences. It is regarded as too difficult and abstract by the industrialist, although all forms of production are ultimately based upon it; it is considered too remote from practical application by those concerned for the immediate welfare of humanity who support, in such large measure and so generously, medicine and the hospitals.

Yet its immediate applications are quite definite though not always realised. The X-rays, whose contribution to the relief of human suffering can scarcely be over-estimated, were discovered by physicists searching to unravel the properties of radiation. The whole wireless industry . . . owes its existence to the fact that physicists endeavouring to elucidate the properties of matter, examined the amount of electricity given off by hot substances. A hundred years ago physicists were studying the curious phenomenon that a compass needle was deflected when it was brought near the wire joining the poles of a galvanic battery . . . the whole of our electrical industry is derived from this: the existence of electric lighting and heating, the transmission of power, the telegraph, the telephone, practically all the various forms in which electricity enters into our daily lives, originated in these apparently foolish experiments.[54]

He also made presentations to the university, conscious that over half of his department's salary bill was paid by outside sources, and warned of how progress might not be assured after all.

At length the university accepted the strength of his claims, even if it did not at once unlock its coffers. In 1939 the resplendent, state-of-the-art building was opened, a visible tribute to the fact that physics teaching and research in Oxford had reached the highest international levels. It was to be the chance of war, however, that ensured that the Clarendon's potential was realised to the full.

All that lay ahead. In the meantime, Lindemann's life began to fill with interest and activity beyond the university – among peers and politicians, and in the playgrounds of the rich.

FIVE

New Dimensions

> The laws of physics are the decrees of fate.
>
> A. N. Whitehead,
> *Science and the Modern World*

One of Lindemann's colleagues at Christ Church was J. C. Masterman.[1] He was an all-round sportsman, and often arranged tennis matches at houses near Oxford. One house where the game was taken seriously was Charlton, the home of F. E. Smith.[2] 'F. E.', as he was generally known, had for long been a celebrated advocate and politician, and by this time had become Lord Chancellor and Earl of Birkenhead. He was a mercurial character, of whom the writer John Buchan observed: 'F. E. was Aristotle's Magnificent Man, the last exponent of the eighteenth century grand manner.'[3] He lived life in bright colours, with easy resort to gambling and drink, without apparent impairment of his ability in court or in Parliament, where his maiden speech had been considered the best ever delivered.

He was now a senior figure in the land, and yet retained a youthful exuberance that inspired the many guests who visited him at Charlton. F. E. was a dedicated tennis player, and at his house there were three courts, on which matches were often held against Oxford teams. Lindemann was introduced to this world by Masterman, who included him in a team soon after his arrival at Oxford, in the early summer of 1919.

Tennis at Charlton would be played all afternoon and evening, the contests often masterminded by Birkenhead's personal assistant, 'Buns' Cartwright,[4] who was known as 'the schoolmaster'. The standard of tennis was high, and leading tennis players of the day jousted with figures in the political world, and sometimes with those in the social firmament, such as the Duke of York and the King of Greece.[5] In the evening there would be supper and claret cup, while Lord Birkenhead told stories and incessantly smoked cigars.

Word of Lindemann's skill at tennis may well have preceded him. Henry Tizard, who had lobbied for his appointment at Oxford, was well aware of his friend's athletic prowess, not least after their ill-tempered bout in the boxing ring, and Lindemann's tennis before the war had been on a level with the best players in Germany and Scandinavia. Although he had hardly played since 1914, he was soon to regain his form, and in 1920 entered both the singles and doubles at Wimbledon, reaching the second round of the 'The Gentlemen's Doubles Championship'.[6]

Masterman also took Lindemann to Blenheim Palace, to play against the Duke of Marlborough's team. Lindemann responded to the colour and splendour of the house and its family. In the words of the Earl of Birkenhead, later Lindemann's biographer:

> Blenheim Palace, conveniently near Oxford, soon made him welcome, and there he encountered a duke whose knowledge of the by-ways of history were as extensive as his own, and who still held sway like a Renaissance Prince.[7]

Victor Cazalet was another well-known tennis player of the day, and an amateur squash champion who had taught Lindemann the subtleties of that game. Cazalet now introduced him to the Duke of Westminster, who often arranged tournaments at Eaton, his estate in Cheshire. Lindemann began regularly to take part in these matches, at which his skill made him *persona grata*, and warmed to the people he met. To his fellow guests it might have seemed unusual to have a science professor in the party, but Lindemann's evident wealth and obvious intelligence eased his entry into their circles.

Before long he began to receive invitations for lunch and dinner even when there was no tennis, with hostesses attracted to the idea of spicing their parties with brains from Oxford. In 1921, for example, he was invited by the Duchess of Marlborough for Sunday lunch at Blenheim, and was asked to bring with him the mathematician Professor Hardy.[8] The parties at houses such as Eaton and Blenheim were large, and Lindemann's circle of friends began quickly to expand.

W. R. Merton, whose father was then professor of spectroscopy at Oxford, and who himself became Lindemann's scientific assistant during the war, recalls how Lindemann was viewed at houses such as Blenheim:

> Lindemann had extremely good manners, especially where women were concerned, and he had lots of social graces. It was said that 'he dined at Blenheim once a week'. They all thought he was wonderful. He impressed them with his mental arithmetic, which was quite brilliant – he was the best person at mental arithmetic that I've ever met, anywhere. He could work out the most abstruse calculation in a flash. He used it to impress people, and not only scientists, who one might think might not have been so impressed, but his social friends as well. On one occasion he was sitting on a square pouffe with the Duchess

of Marlborough and they found that they hadn't much room. Lindemann suggested that they should sit diagonally. The Duchess said: 'Do you really think that will help, Mr Lindemann?' and he replied at once, 'Oh yes, it will make an improvement of 41.42%.'[9]

His letters home from this time flow with descriptions of invitations, and begin to ring with the names of well-known figures and hostesses of the day, such as Lady Londonderry, the Duke and Duchess of Portland, Mrs Ronnie Greville, Lady Cunard, Lord Balfour, and Lord and Lady Desborough.

It is a strong possibility – and was an opinion held by several of those who knew Lindemann well – that by this time he had formed a conscious desire to become involved in British politics, but realised that with his name and background he was unlikely to succeed in doing so directly. According to this view, Lindemann made the calculation that the most effective way forward would be to become a close adviser to a successful politician – and Lord Birkenhead was his first choice. However, because Birkenhead died prematurely in 1930, Lindemann transferred his attention to Churchill. He regarded himself as complementary to both these statesmen, his skills fitting well with their political ambitions.

Whatever the truth of that theory, it was at Charlton more than anywhere that he began to be drawn into the political world. He and Birkenhead took strongly to one another, and shared a biting and sarcastic sense of humour. Lindemann had also met Sir John Simon,[10] with whom he sometimes played golf and who, like F. E., was a Fellow of Wadham, a politician and a lawyer of exceptional talent. Although Simon was almost universally disliked and was generally considered to be about as warm as a graveyard under snow, he often attended convivial dinners at Wadham, where his fellow diners would include Birkenhead and Lindemann. Wadham College would always play a part in Lindemann's life. He retained a vote on its Governing Body, assiduously attended its meetings and sometimes dined there on what Maurice Bowra described as 'his unsavoury vegetarian food'.[11]

Although it was under Birkenhead's influence that he began to take an interest in politics, particularly from the scientific angle, Lindemann received no encouragement when, a few years later, he thought of standing for Parliament. It was Birkenhead who dissuaded him, perhaps in the knowledge that Lindemann was not 'clubbable', and that he might be inclined to treat too many of his fellow MPs with fastidious disdain.

Maurice Bowra, who became in time an Oxford 'figure' in his own right, presents in his memoirs a rather jaundiced view of Lindemann:

He had a name for being brilliant and amusing but, when as an undergraduate I met him, I did not like him. He had a sneering, superior
manner and made too much ado about being a scientist, as when he
told me that he could make me a Beethoven by an operation on my
brain.[12]

It would seem unlikely that Lindemann was much in earnest about
Bowra's brain. Although Bowra's intellectual calibre was respected,
Lindemann was wary of him, believing him to be rather louche and not
altogether well regarded. In any case, Lindemann's paramount interest was
in physics – a translation of the Greek for 'natural things' – and it often
seemed that to Lindemann human beings were no more than a class of such
natural things, receiving from him no especial warmth unless they could,
as a minimum requirement, be connected to friends that he already knew.
Diana Mitford, whose second husband was Sir Oswald Mosley, was one
such friend at this time:

He was really my guru when I was sixteen. One thing we loved about
him was that he treated us as grown ups. He encouraged doubt, and
in fact helped us to begin to think for ourselves. Lindemann realised,
when I was about seventeen, that I was bored, and it was then that he
suggested that I should learn German and read Schopenhauer – *Die
Welt als Wille*! – but my father forbade it. As soon as I was eighteen
and married I learnt it, and being able to read it has enriched my whole
life. I owe it all to Prof.[13]

In her memoirs Lady Mosley also referred to Lindemann's opinion of
her friends:

We used to discuss undergraduates I knew; he disapproved of all of
them. 'A dreadful person' was his usual summing-up, and of one cherished friend, Brian Howard, 'Oh, you can't like him. He's a Jew.' Unlike
Muv [Lady Mosley's mother], he definitely preferred people to be
rich, and looked upon poverty as a fault. Rich himself, he bestowed
rich gifts; he gave me a beautiful watch from Cartier made of three
different coloured golds.[14]

Lindemann's withering comments about people like Brian Howard –
although in his case they would have received widespread support – betrayed
his less charming side. His frequent generalisations when expressing distaste
understandably caused people to disparage him in return.

His contempt stretched to far horizons. He held all the coloured races in low esteem, and was to attribute the dire geopolitical state of the world after the Second World War principally to the shift of power towards the Third World. In particular, it is not surprising that he acquired a reputation for anti-Semitism. There seems little doubt that on the surface it was well deserved: he was not in general attracted to Jews. However, that did not preclude him making firm friendships with people who were Jews. They included the Rothschilds and the Mond family, whose fortune stemmed from Imperial Chemicals Industries, and the eminent German physicist Franz Simon, who came to England at Lindemann's invitation, and there achieved international fame.

The paradox of how he maintained warm relations with Jews, while being in general anti-Semitic, is consistent with the principles of his approach to his fellow men. His starting-point was a rather cold nature and a consequent lack of curiosity about other people. However, when his interest had been aroused, he was fully capable of displaying warmth and affection. He found it easier to accept someone who had been introduced by one of his friends, more specifically if they were rich and from the upper classes; if someone possessed such qualifications, being Jewish was no bar to Lindemann's loyalty. Nevertheless, he was as careful in concealing this attitude from his important friends as he was indifferent to disclosing it to others.

In the case of Bowra, acquaintance with Diana Mitford was not enough, in Lindemann's eyes, to compensate for a certain reputation that he had acquired, aptly summarised in the celebrated remark by a don who peered balefully at Bowra across the High Table and said: 'There sits the man who made buggery disreputable in this university.'

Lindemann was later to complain of Bowra who, as vice-chancellor of Oxford, said that he always slept with a work of Ovid under his pillow. Lindemann's objection to this habit was not so much the reasonable one that talking about it negated its merit, and he may even have shared the view that Ovid was both good for insomnia and appropriate to the bedroom. Rather, he maintained that Bowra would have done better to 'sleep with Kaye and Laby's under his pillow'.[15] His interaction with Bowra exemplified in a small way the friction that Lindemann both perceived and caused among what he called 'Arts men', in his desire to improve the standing of his chosen discipline.

A letter to his parents in June 1922 gives a flavour of his social life at this time, and the obvious pleasure he took in it:

On Tuesday Wadham gave a dinner to the Lord Chancellor who made the most amusing speech I have ever heard. Lady Birkenhead made me promise to lunch with them the next time I came to Town, which is awkward as I had promised to lunch with the Scarboroughs tomorrow, and have just received a long wire from Mrs Winston Churchill asking me to lunch and to go to Wimbledon with her any day next week.[16]

Lindemann's reference to Mrs Winston Churchill was the result of a friendship that had sprung up the previous summer, when both were staying with the Duke of Westminster, and which grew steadily over the following decade. In the early 1930s the friendship was to blossom and flourish, and was to alter the scale and direction of Lindemann's life, at length leading him onto the world stage.

Lindemann had referred to this new acquaintance after he and his brother Charles had travelled to Germany in the summer of 1921 to re-establish the business, interrupted by war, that the family had retained even after the sale of the shares in the water companies. Lindemann wrote to his mother:

I expect Charles has written to Papa giving him most of the business news. We had a very busy time at Francfort [sic], Berlin, Speyer and Pirmasens but I think it will bear fruit of sorts . . . I found a letter on my return, from the Duchess of Westminster inviting me formally to Eaton.

At Eaton he had partnered Churchill's wife, Clemmie, at tennis. On that occasion he had not met her husband, perhaps because Winston had been unable to play tennis since dislocating a shoulder in earlier life. Shortly afterwards, however, the Westminsters had asked Lindemann to stay in Scotland. He had declined that invitation, as he had already made plans to go home and see his parents, but agreed instead to attend a dinner party in London, and it was there that he first met Winston Churchill. He wrote to his father describing these events:

Aug 19th, 1921.

I am very glad we can come to Sidholme after all as I refused an invitation to the Marquess of Headfort and another of the Duke of Westminster to Scotland to meet Winston Churchill, on the strength of our plans. The duke was very keen on my meeting Churchill and arranged a special dinner in Town last night for the purpose. It was quite interesting but Churchill was rather distrait.[17]

Both the Duke of Westminster and Lord Birkenhead had been struck by the depth and breadth of Lindemann's mind, and were intrigued by his scientific insights. They both realised that Churchill might share their opinion, even if in more material things Churchill, a lover of good food, wine and cigars, was altogether on a different plane.

The initial meeting between the two was not momentous, but the seeds of mutual fascination were sown. Churchill's readiness to open his mind to new themes and subjects, and to blend them with his deep feeling for history, complemented Lindemann's associative faculties and his ability to relate the rules and discoveries of science to everyday experience.

Professor R. V. Jones, who came to know both men well, described what drew the two together:

The anchor points of their friendship were courage, patriotism and humour; in these each matched the other. Love of good language and prowess in sport, Lindemann in tennis and Churchill in polo, were also matters of common ground.[18]

Lindemann had received occasional invitations from Clemmie Churchill since 1923, and in 1924 he was asked to stay at Chartwell, the Churchills' house in Kent. Early that year Churchill[19] had asked Lindemann's advice on drafting an article about war:

My dear Lindemann,
I have undertaken to write on the future possibilities of war and how frightful it will be for the human race. On this subject I have a good many ideas, but I should very much like to have another talk with you following on the most interesting one we had when you last lunched here.[20]

Lindemann responded to this request, and together they surveyed the scientific battleground. He stayed at Chartwell for a week in April, and added his ideas to those of Churchill, who clothed them in his inimitable language:

As for Poison Gas and Chemical warfare in all its forms, only the first chapter has been written of a terrible book. Certainly every one of these new avenues to destruction is being studied on both sides of the Rhine, with all the science and patience of which man is capable. And why should it be supposed that these resources will be limited to Inorganic Chemistry? A study of disease, of pestilence methodically prepared and deliberately launched upon man and beast is certainly being pursued in the laboratories of more than one great country.[21]

Lindemann's hand is also evident in a prophetic passage in the article:

May there not be methods of using explosive energy incomparably more intense than anything heretofore discovered? Might not a bomb no bigger than an orange be found to possess a secret power to destroy a whole block of buildings – nay to concentrate the force of a thousand tons of cordite and blast a township at a stroke? Could not explosives even of the existing type be guided automatically in flying machines by wireless or other rays, without a human pilot, in ceaseless procession upon a hostile city, arsenal, camp or dockyard?[22]

Lindemann reacted warmly to Churchill's interest in science. He was later to say that he regarded Churchill as a scientist who had missed his vocation, and he wrote:

All the qualities, or as the humaner elements might prefer to say, the stigmata of the scientist, are manifested in him. The readiness to face realities, even though they contradict a favourite hypothesis; the recognition that theories are made to fit facts, not facts to fit theories; the interest in phenomena and the desire to explore them; and above all the underlying conviction that the world is not just a jumble of events but there must be some higher unity, that facts fit together. He has pre-eminently the synthetic mind which makes every new piece of knowledge fall into place and interlock with previous knowledge; where the ordinary brain is content to add each new experience to the scrap-heap, he insists on fitting it into the structure of the cantilever jutting out over the abyss of ignorance.[23]

From an early stage in this immensely fruitful relationship Churchill found great value in Lindemann's ability to render long tracts and papers into short, pithy notes, and to present complicated ideas in simple and lucid terms. Churchill was greatly interested in scientific thought and kept in his papers the text of one of the lectures that exemplified Lindemann's skill:

The purpose of this lecture is to emphasise the fact that though the so-called physical laws will be in general consistent with reality, there is no certainty that the indefinables employed in their statement or the particular relations they embody have any fundamental significance beyond their appeal to the mental preferences, prejudices or infirmities of the physicist.

The metaphor of the explorer lends itself readily to exemplify this statement. He might return with a contour map of his island, giving a clear account of its main topographical features; he might return with a description of its flora and fauna. On the other hand he might report that all its paths were uphill, omitting to observe that he always marched along the course of the rivers; or that the rivers were exactly one day's march apart, refraining from remarking that he always camped when he reached the banks of a stream. All of these statements would be consistent with reality, but the relative value of the first two and the last two would depend upon whether one was interested primarily in the circumstances of the island or the mentality of the explorer.

Proceeding to discuss relativity, he went on:

according to the principle of relativity each observer defines and has a right to define his own true axis. Exactly how it is to be defined is not clear unless one considers periods great compared to, say, 10^{-9} seconds, but for long periods it would presumably be given with sufficient approximation as the longest dimension of the observer . . .

Though it is obvious which way a road runs if one considers a stretch long compared to the width, it would be by no means obvious if one could deal only with a section of a length comparable with the width.[24]

His lectures, for all their intellectual content, often contained asides at the expense of academics, particularly metaphysicians, whose strictly logical habit of mind, he suggested, 'occasionally survives in universities and other secluded regions':

A logician of this type refuses, at any rate in theory, to believe that it is possible to learn by experience or extrapolate from observed repetitions. In his view the fact that the sun has risen a million times in succession does not provide any reason for believing it will rise again . . . One can imagine occasions upon which the logician might score at the expense of the physicist who frankly admits that he does not know, but finds it pays to extrapolate, e.g., at Monte Carlo, where the logician should never even be tempted to invent a system; but in the infinitely more numerous and important affairs of daily life the physicist would survive whilst the logician would perish.[25]

His discussions with Churchill, which went beyond physics and ranged over metaphysics and mathematics (in which Lindemann was expert), provided inspiration and nourishment for Churchill's boundlessly enquiring mind:

There are a great many points which I want to ask you about, and I look forward very much to our next meeting. I will only mention one now. Have the relations between music and mathematics been examined in the same way as those between mathematics and physics? Is there any sort of correspondence? If so, there will be a correspondence between music and physics other than mere sound-waves. Might there not be a notation which would cover not merely sound-waves but harmonies and discords, rhythms and cadences; and might not this notation be found in the absolute?[26]

Lindemann was also well versed in literature, history and the Bible. Churchill found him a mine of information, and often drew on him for facts for his newspaper and magazine articles, whose titles reveal the variety of subjects in which Lindemann was helpful: 'Moses: The Leader of a People', 'Women and the Future' and 'The English and American Mind'.[27]

Moreover, the two men shared a sense of humour. Churchill appreciated the contrast and the unexpected that were often brought out in Lindemann's conversation and lectures, such as one in which he said:

The trouble is of course that no guarantee that the logic based on Peano's axioms [of logic] will be suitable for describing the external world any more than any particular form of geometry or arithmetic. Thus, for instance, it takes for granted the law of the excluded middle which no scientist would consider axiomatic or indeed appropriate in drawing his map of the universe.

The case of solipsism, though not quite in this category, must be considered before we can proceed. The dogmatic solipsist says bluntly 'nothing exists except my sense-data'. Obviously it is quite impossible to prove him wrong. But what we can do, and what we do do, is lock him up in an asylum.[28]

An illustration of the combination of intelligence and lucidity that appealed to Churchill and his family is given by Churchill's daughter Sarah, writing of Lindemann as 'Prof'. This name was given to him by Lord Birkenhead's young daughter, Lady Eleanor Smith, who became a friend after Lindemann had started to visit Charlton regularly. By the late 1920s the use of it had become widespread:

Prof had the gift of conveying a most complicated subject in simple form. One day at lunch when coffee and brandy were being served my father decided to have a slight 'go' at Prof who had just completed a treatise on the Quantum Theory. 'Prof,' he said, 'tell us in words of one syllable and in no longer than five minutes what is the Quantum Theory?' My father then placed his large gold watch known as 'the turnip' on the table. When you consider that Professor Lindemann must have spent many years working on this major theme, it was quite a tall order. However, without hesitation, like quicksilver, he planted the principle and held us spellbound. When he had finished we all spontaneously burst into applause.[29]

In later years Lindemann's detractors were to claim that his knowledge of physics did not keep step with the march of discovery, and that this was disguised when he simplified scientific subjects for Churchill. However, that claim is misconceived, as can be seen from his practical and theoretical work before he took on the Clarendon. Later on, by contrast, he did not need to be at the cutting edge of new research, so much as promote to politicians the value that scientists could bring to the country, and ensure that their discoveries were properly understood by those in positions of influence.

The eclectic nature of Lindemann's interests was also evident in a course of lectures that he later gave on the philosophy of science, the relation between physics and metaphysics appealing to the associative nature of his mind. He prefaced these lectures with a dig at Oxford's philosophers:

Rather than expose myself to the devastating criticism of the philosophical faculty, I thought it better to indicate in the title that I was not poaching on their preserves. I shall make no attempt to compete with the philosophers in the profound introspective processes of ratiocination and contemplation which result in the various theories – sometimes contradictory – which are set forth in the standard works which we admire.[30]

These lectures, amusing and intellectually powerful, attracted enthusiastic audiences, despite the difficulty of hearing what was said. They were concerned with the evolution of the use of language and logic; the physicist's translating his sense data into words; the concepts of classical physics; relativity and the quantum theory, and the revolution in ideas they brought about.

Lindemann's lectures on the philosophy of science disclose his deep knowledge of history and philosophy, as well as his unquestioned mastery of physics, and were enlivened by a thread of gently sarcastic humour. Two brief excerpts give their flavour:

> Another type of fallacy is exemplified by Zeno's paradox. Reduced to its simplest terms this may be put as follows: If one animal runs twice as fast as another and starts, say, unit distance behind the other, it will never be able to catch it. For by the time the pursuer has run unit distance the pursued will have run half a unit and so on. A half of any finite quantity is finite. But there are an infinite number of these terms. An infinite number of finite terms must however be infinite.
>
> The paradox here arises from a failure to understand what is meant by infinite, which the Greeks merely defined as not finite. The ordinary person sees little difficulty in the problem. He merely has to divide one by one minus a half. The highbrow can satisfy himself by more elaborate methods.

In another passage he said:

> On a more sophisticated bracket we have the question how far we should endeavour to make the mental constructs which we call 'external objects' resemble their appearance, as it would be described in what are called commonsense terms.
>
> Commonsense terms of course is only another way of saying: 'As they were described to me when I was learning to speak.'
>
> The philosopher tends it seems to favour these commonsense terms unduly. The mathematician goes to the other extreme and is content with a lot of little black marks on a sheet of paper. The experimental physicist keeps a middle line, or tries to. He must do this in my view if he wants to think out new experiments and make new observations. But in the last resort it is a matter of aesthetics, in other words what pleases me, or as Einstein said 'a matter of good taste'.[31]

Lindemann's emergence into the social world in general, and his friendship with Birkenhead and with Churchill in particular, added a new dimension to his life. In January 1927, together with Maynard Keynes and Desmond Macarthy, he was elected to 'The Other Club', which had been founded in 1911 by Churchill and F. E. Smith when they had been expelled from a similar institution called 'The Club'. The Other Club was a lively and largely political dining club, whose rules had been composed in a typically factious and orotund style by its founders: 'Nothing in the rules of the club,' it was laid down, 'shall interfere with the rancour or asperity of party politics.'

Lindemann would happily observe such conditions. Other members at the club's dinners, always held in the Pinafore Room at the Savoy Hotel, would typically include Duff Cooper, Alfred Munnings, William Orpen, Edwin Lutyens, J. L. Garvin and Archie Sinclair. At such convivial dinners, spiced with political gossip, Lindemann widened his acquaintance with artists, economists, journalists and members of both houses of Parliament.

At the same time he played a full part in discussions and debates with his colleagues at Oxford, both on political subjects at the Oxford Union and at other more philosophical meetings. He debated with Father d'Arcy at the Christ Church Essay Society, for example, when he changed sides and ended up by agreeing with the learned priest: 'Father, your position is impregnable,' he said, 'granted the major premise, the existence of God. And what are we poor scientists to know about that?'

Often, in conversation as well as in debate, he liked to shock and to observe people's reactions. In an address to a political club at Oxford he had explained how, in order to spare the world's workers the pain of the drudgery that was their lot, it would be possible scientifically to dehumanise them – to 'take human bodies and strip them of all emotional content, so that all the hard labour became neutral to them and would not appear onerous'. His audience, with its youthful ideals, was indeed shocked.[32]

The example is also often quoted of how, asked to define morality, Lindemann gave the answer: 'I define a moral action as one that brings advantage to my friends', which drew from Clemmie Churchill the riposte: 'Doesn't Prof sometimes say *dreadful* things?'[33]. In that instance Lindemann, who was well read in classics, was doing no more than quoting an ancient definition, and one expressed in Plato's *Republic*.

Yet Lindemann's paramount preoccupation remained the cause of science at Oxford, and the generation of funds for the Clarendon Laboratory; and those who were in principle opposed to what they saw as his extravagant claims for science found him unremittingly unyielding and often prickly.

The battlegrounds that he chose, and to which he effortlessly brought disharmony, included his own college. When Christ Church invited Lindemann to become a Student, but did not give him a seat on the Governing Body, it soon led to disagreement. Lindemann was concerned that people younger and in other ways more junior than him would, over time, be appointed Students and would gain precedence over him at High Table, which would embarrass him when he brought guests to dine. He looked askance at this possibility and felt keenly that it would in future years belittle science for fresh-faced classicists and others to take precedence over him at dinner while he, venerable in the scientific world, sat with his guest in the gloom below the salt. He therefore put forward the claim that he should take precedence over subsequent appointments.

Lindemann's social life and his dismissive attitude towards some of his colleagues ensured that many of them were reluctant to give an inch to this claim. In a development perhaps beyond the imagination even of Trollope or Dickens, the higher reaches of the law were now called in, and an eminent Silk, Gavin Simmonds, was invited to opine. After due consideration he took the college's view. For Lindemann, however, the umpire's decision was not to be taken as final; he, in turn, retained Sir John Simon, a lawyer more eminent even than Simmonds – and Simon duly found for Lindemann. The dispute was in danger of gathering all the force of an orange about to destroy a whole block of buildings, so at that point the college decided to relent. Lindemann was able to feel satisfied that he had struck at least a small blow for science. Nevertheless, heads would shake and he would be darkly disparaged as an 'intensely litigious person'.

Before long he was embroiled in another argument with Christ Church, this time over the Duke of Westminster's research student. Having become a friend of the duke, Lindemann had sought to interest him in Oxford affairs. He had invited him to stay for a 'Gaudy' at Christ Church[34] and in 1923 he prevailed upon the duke to make over an annual tax-free sum for a physics research student. In practice the trustees of this arrangement, on the advice of the duke, would appoint whomever Lindemann nominated – it is doubtful whether even lip service was paid to the idea of competitive entry. A dispute now arose following the resignation of the first student, Edward Bolton King, later to become Lindemann's close friend, business colleague and travelling companion. Lindemann insisted that future students be given a seat on the Governing Body, in accordance with the newly imple-mented recommendations of the Royal Commission.

Once more the gowns swished testily at High Table, and in the common room opposing forces pressed their case, each laying claim to worthy prin-ciple and unanswerable logic. As Lindemann said of one of his opponents at Christ Church, 'he is one of those people who are always doing one down from the highest possible motives'.[35] Again, the college at length accepted Lindemann's argument.

For most people the heat in these debates would soon have been replaced by cooler reflection, but that might not have been the case with Lindemann, had he been on the losing side. He considered that a principle was at stake – that of the honour of science. His was not the Oxford way, however, and it caused ill-feeling. Lindemann brought to these matters, in the words of his colleague John Masterman, 'a rigid continental conception of hierarchy, and thought that they were highly important and reflected on his dignity'.[36]

Lindemann was of course on the losing side in some of his battles: all his scheming, lobbying and marshalling of facts and argument failed to stop the Radcliffe Trustees selling to the motor magnate William Morris land in Oxford on which an old observatory was sited, and commissioning a new one in South Africa. Lindemann opposed this, arguing that it should be built in Oxford, where it would contribute to the cause of physics. He had even promised that if it were sited in Oxford, his father would donate the necessary equipment.

He entered into such aspects of Oxford life with gusto, and it might have seemed that he was becoming set in his life as a bachelor don. But in Berlin, Lindemann had been attractive to women and had led an active sexual life; he was thirty-three when he arrived at Oxford and there is no evidence to suppose that, for all his fastidious nature, he wished always to remain single. As it happened he did fall for two girls in his early years at Oxford; one was a relation of the Vickers family of engineers and armaments manufacturers, and the other a girl who had been an undergraduate 'blue-stocking', but who later – having been married to an American and widowed – became eminent in political life in her own right, both in Sussex where she lived and in the Conservative Party nationally.

Proposing marriage and pledging eternal love requires its own special kind of nerve, especially if the suitor's ego is not proof against rejection by the one he loves. According to his brother, Lindemann did, in the case of each girl, form the intention to propose. In the first case all went well until the last minute, at which point, although his desire may have been plain, it seems he 'let I dare not wait upon I would',[37] and at the vital moment failed to pluck up the courage to put the question clearly. One way or another he did not get the answer he wanted, and he was deeply hurt.

In the second case he did get as far as making a proposal. The wife of his colleague Jack Egerton described how Lindemann brought his *inamorata* to their house in Oxford and proposed to her there. Yet on this occasion too he failed to achieve the result that he longed for and was, in Ruth Egerton's words, 'very upset for a long time'.[38] One cannot know how deeply he felt about these girls, or about their refusals. His mask did not slip. However, according to his brother Charles, it seems that he did not turn to a life of celibacy afterwards – that would have been out of character. Instead his innate disposition to secrecy, and his firmly held opinion of what was becoming for an Oxford professor, ensured that his private life remained thereafter unobserved, although in due course he was to come much closer to another woman.

Meanwhile he continued to take part in many debates and discussions in the college and the university, usually inflexible and always wholly confident in his views:

In the early days he felt a sense of exclusion from the company – an uneasy suspicion that he was not of the tribe. He assailed the philosophers with intensive relish. A pamphlet by Reade of Keble was brutally demolished; against the logician, H. W. B. Joseph of New College, he was fierce and impressively destructive, and was sometimes a disturbing element amid the nuts and wine. At times he gave offence unintentionally under the impression that he was indulging in genial banter. Such an occasion arose when, probing among the Christ Church statutes he claimed to have found a provision which enjoined celibacy on the Canons of the Chapter. When confronted with this, one of the Canons murmured something about 'certain anomalies'. 'That is all very well,' said Lindemann, 'when you do it you call it an anomaly. When I do it you call it living in sin.'[39]

Lindemann was unforgiving of other little anomalies of collegiate life. He had noticed that the postmen delivered his telegrams to the porter's lodge, whereas they took those for the dean and canons direct to their rooms. Without hesitation he took the matter on high, writing to Sir Evelyn Murray, the Secretary to the Post Office, only to receive a rather acerbic reply:

It would not have occurred to me that the telegraphic correspondence of the ecclesiastical professors, even during the flat racing season, would turn the scale one way or the other.[40]

Although in some respects he was later to mellow, Lindemann remained unforgiving of those who crossed him and brusque with those who disagreed with what he said. In one debate he was interrupted by a colleague saying: 'Since you seem to know more about it than anyone else, we will have to take your word for it.' Lindemann at once replied: 'If you know less about it than anyone else, you have no right to be here.' Such comments were not well received, and caused resentment. Some people, such as Professor N. V. Sidgwick, a particularly learned science don, referred darkly to Lindemann's origins. Although Sidgwick had supported the campaign for 'Science Greats' – he had himself taken First Class Honours in both classics and natural sciences – he was caustic when referring to Lindemann and never let slip an opportunity to deride him. On one occasion he formally proposed to the college authorities that a favourite resort of Lindemann's, Alison's Walk in Christ Church, should be renamed 'Unter den Lindemann'.

And so Lindemann retired, single, to his fine set of rooms overlooking Christ Church Meadow. He had the material consolation of plenty of money, and he had freedom within wide limits to spend his time as he wished; his work fascinated him; and he derived great pleasure from being drawn into the sociable life of the upper classes. Now, with foresight or good luck, he made an appointment that was to add immeasurably to his convenience and comfort for the rest of his life: he engaged James Harvey as his personal servant.

From time to time Lindemann employed a number of miscellaneous servants, and a few chauffeurs of longer standing, but Harvey, who came to work for him in 1926, was to remain with him for more than thirty years, until Lindemann died. The word had gone out that the professor needed a valet, his servant Thorpe having departed, and James Harvey applied for the post. He had always known Oxford; he had grown up in the town, and had sold sweets at a cinema before getting a job as a professional middleweight boxer, fighting in small-time bouts arranged by an Oxford promoter called Harry Breeze, often at St Giles' Fair. He had also played football for Oxford City. At the end of the Great War he took a job as a waiter at the Randolph Hotel, where he worked for the following eight years.

Lindemann agreed to take Harvey on, and it proved an inspired choice. He turned out to be no ordinary valet. He had a wide range of talents, quite apart from his skill in the boxing ring. Like Lindemann, he was a very good artist in pen and ink, and he was later to draw most of Lindemann's wartime staff. While at the Randolph he had taught himself shorthand, and after joining Lindemann he learnt to type. He soon became not only Lindemann's valet, but his chef, typist, private secretary, research assistant and general factotum.

He also acted as stand-in chauffeur and attended to his master's Rolls-Royces. One of these had formerly belonged to the very rich poet and architect, Edward James, reputed to be the natural son of King Edward VII, and it had a bed in the back. Lindemann also kept an Austin 12, which he used when he wanted to drive himself. However, driving did not really suit him: he was erratic and impatient at the wheel, and quick to express in farmyard language his opinions of other road users. Yet he indulged Harvey with a kindly eye. 'Once,' said Harvey, 'I told the Professor I had seen a car wrecked by the side of the road.' 'I expect they saw you coming, Harvey,' Lindemann replied.

In time Harvey had a wife and three daughters, and they were all installed in a cottage in Christ Church Meadow. Despite having a family to care for, Harvey would spend long hours devotedly attending to his master, and in time he became his trusted friend. He was slightly deferential, but not disagreeably so, and became in some respects a 'Jeeves' figure, although he did not have great physical presence, especially when set against Lindemann, who was an imposing six feet. Harvey was broad and of barely middle height, but he was over fourteen stone and by all accounts immensely strong. He was described as looking 'a little like a gorilla' – possibly the result of his having formerly been a pugilist, but more likely because he invariably wore Lindemann's cast-off clothes, which were too big for him.

Lindemann's dress, by contrast, was expensive but discreet and, well valeted by Harvey, it began to take on the nature of a uniform. Yet he never entirely shed a faintly foreign element in his appearance. He was almost always formally clothed, in dark suit and white shirt, with highly polished shoes. He usually wore or carried an overcoat made of Melton cloth (about the heaviest material known to tailors), and sometimes in winter an even weightier construction, lined in astrakhan fur. This careful attire was completed by a bowler hat, or sometimes in summer a panama. People became used to the sight of Lindemann walking firmly along the pavements of Christ Church, his stature, gait and countenance impressive but uncommunicative, followed by Harvey at a respectful distance.

Harvey always referred to Lindemann as 'The Professor', in common with the staff at the Clarendon. As his responsibilities increased, he began to take an interest in what he researched or typed, and to try to understand its meaning. He even attempted to follow his master's interest in prime numbers. Lindemann considered most forms of relaxation to be trivial and a waste of time, even such cerebral pastimes as chess or *The Times* crossword – a source of diversion to other dons. He preferred the study of prime numbers; he was in the top rank in this abstruse and esoteric subject, on which he published several highly regarded papers.[41] He explained a little of the theory to Harvey, who did his best to understand. 'I thought I discovered a significant pattern when I charted the results of my counts,' he said one day, 'but the Professor pointed out that the result was bound to be as it was.'

Lindemann must have been pleased by Harvey's intelligence: he dictated to him the whole of his book *The Physical Significance of the Quantum Theory*, and Harvey dealt successfully with its difficult formulae and language. In later years he would copy out sheets of figures and charts, often staying until the small hours of the morning to do so. 'On one occasion,' Harvey reported, 'when I ran into difficulties I said to the Professor "What about that celebrated man[42] who said, when referring to decimals, 'I never could understand those damned dots'?" The Professor replied with a smile "Yes, but he had other qualities".'

In turn Lindemann encouraged Harvey's interests: they were both enthusiastic photographers, and one of the rooms in Lindemann's set was used as a darkroom by Harvey, who would develop and print the numerous photographs that Lindemann took on his travels. Some of these, such as those that he had taken while flying over the Himalayas, adorned Lindemann's walls; they jostled with a few kitsch Victorian pictures, including one that his mother had given him of kittens tumbling out of a basket.

In his rooms there was little of aesthetic merit: Lindemann had a cabinet containing jumbled tennis cups and vases that he had won in his youth, including one proclaiming him as champion of Sweden, but most of them were in the worst type of art-deco style of the Kaiser's Germany. In one corner stood a small model biplane mounted on a wire, attached to other wires representing various axes; he had used this in his Farnborough days, when pondering the three-dimensional aspects of the spin.[43] Apart from these objects there was little save assorted piles of papers and books. His possessions hardly enlivened the sparseness of his rooms. His colleagues would pour scorn on his philistine taste in interior design and, except for his expertise at the piano, he appeared to be entirely 'without art'. When teased about this he wilfully paid no attention, and would point to the breathtaking view from his rooms and say: 'I don't have to bother.' Roy Harrod later described these rooms with donnish disdain:

> White paint was used throughout, and the undergraduates used to refer to them as 'The White City'. The contents were hideous. Among all the objects there was not one that paid the remotest tribute to the human desire for something pleasing to look at. Later he framed some good photographs, which he had taken on his travels; but even these he hung at the wrong height, so that the effect was displeasing.[44]

Harrod also recalled Lindemann's complete disregard for artistic merit, noting for instance that whether or not he liked a portrait depended on his opinion of the sitter. Bill Merton had a brother who was an artist, and Lindemann would venture into the mysterious world of the art critic: 'I like your brother's paintings,' he would say, 'they go right to the *edge*.'

Harvey proved to be a talented sculptor. He also shared Lindemann's taste in music. He liked Beethoven and especially Chopin, and he turned out to be an able pianist, although not approaching his master's high standards – which were rarely demonstrated, as Lindemann used to play only in the vacation so as to avoid disturbing the other people on his staircase.

Lindemann could not have known, when he hired Harvey as a valet, that he was acquiring such a talented man, but it is another example – as with his researchers and staff at the Clarendon, and later when working for Churchill – of how he managed to select subordinates of the highest ability. And the service Harvey gave to Lindemann over thirty years certainly enriched his own career in a way that he could never have imagined in earlier life. When Lindemann became a Cabinet minister in the war, he moved into No. 11 Downing Street, where a room was found for his faithful servant. 'At that time,' Harvey told an interviewer many years later, 'Sir Winston Churchill wouldn't go anywhere without Lord Cherwell, and Lord Cherwell wouldn't go anywhere without Harvey, and this suited me down to the ground.'[45] And so Harvey accompanied his master and Churchill to their historic meetings at Quebec, Washington, Bermuda, Potsdam and on the *Prince of Wales* for the signing of the Atlantic Charter. 'No man,' it is said, 'is a hero to his valet', but Lindemann proved an exception to the rule.

Meanwhile, Lindemann's social life continued to gather pace, and he kept his parents well informed:

Eaton,
Chester

Aug. 6th, 1925.

My dear Papa,

. . . the tournament at Tunbridge was very much spoiled by rain, the courts were sodden and the balls scarcely bounced. Mrs Churchill and I won a third prize in the handicap mixed; on hard courts we should probably have won the whole event. Winston was most interesting and amusing and I much enjoyed my visit.

As usual there is an enormous crowd here, the same people as usual with the exception of the Crosfields and Irene Curzon who has not been here for several years. There is lots of tennis and golf, and dancing in the evening. Tonight they are getting up some sort of theatricals in which I propose to take the part of audience.

This reluctance, even at a house party, was in keeping with Lindemann's dislike of exhibiting himself. T. C. Keeley recalled another such example:

The professor always put in an appearance at the Christmas party at the Clarendon 'to show the flag'. On one occasion one of the secretaries was dared to ask him to dance with her. He declined very urbanely, explaining that he had been asked to dance by all sections, by people from all ranks of society, from chorus girls to queens, and he had never yet succumbed.[46]

His interests were widening and his days were becoming full, as can be seen in a letter to his father in early 1926:

On Monday to Farnborough, where I was due to give a lecture . . .
On Wednesday I had a committee in Town; I lunched with the
Churchills, where there was a very amusing party, the Salisburys,
Eustace Percys, Amey and Ronald MacNeill . . . On Thursday I went
to Cambridge to see what I am bound to consider their very elementary arrangements for dealing with radium . . . Next week I have one
of the Grosvenors passing through on Monday, an acrimonious
meeting on Wednesday, a discussion meeting of the Royal Society on
Thursday, and the Secretary of State for Air coming to spend Friday
and Saturday, so it does not look any too restful either.

At that time the General Strike was imminent and the political temperature high, and Lindemann's own interest in politics had deepened. He was
by now supplying Churchill with political arguments as well as scientific
information, and for a debate with Ramsay MacDonald on the principles
of Socialism, he suggested the following creed for Churchill:

Socialism is an attempt on the part of the inefficient to secure wealth
without work from the efficient, by snarling and whining. Not capable
of realising, and sometimes not caring for, the brutalities and catas-
trophes their creed involves, they pervert those whose hearts rule their
heads. Society must not submit to misfits.[47]

Not surprisingly, with such opinions, he enthusiastically offered support
when the General Strike was called, and he was given the job of helping
Churchill produce the Government paper *The British Gazette*. For this
purpose he cajoled some of those at the Clarendon Laboratory to play a
part, and sent fourteen of them up to London – whether they relished the
opportunity is not recorded. Oliver Locker-Lampson, Churchill's private
secretary, had undertaken to collect as many students from the universities
as he could find, and to train them in printing processes and in the operation of presses. One of the Clarendon students recalled his role, and how
on arriving in cars at the premises of the *Islington Daily Gazette* in London
they were met by Lindemann and a couple of the non-striking operators.
They soon had the outfit running. It was obvious that Lindemann was in
charge and was enjoying himself immensely. He stayed with them until the
last copies of the paper had left the building just as dawn was breaking.[48]

Tom Jones, the faithful friend of Lloyd George, Baldwin and
Chamberlain, records in his diary how he was staying at Chartwell with
Churchill a few months after the General Strike, but while the coalminers
were still holding out. Lindemann was also there, as was Churchill's teenage

son, Randolph who was to be given a place at Christ Church – filling, as Churchill said, a 'last minute vacancy through the kindness of Professor Lindemann':[49]

> Winston plunged, into the coal business at once . . . He talked with the greatest freedom and frankness before Lindemann and the rest . . . Lindemann, I quickly discovered, regarded all miners, if not all the working classes, as a species of sub-humans. This drove me to the Extreme Left with Winston at the Right Centre . . . Winston is dictating Volume III of the *World Crisis*, and has been working out comparative figures with the help of Lindemann and the small boy . . . as I was going away [Winston] told me 'I am very glad you expounded the democratic faith last night, as the small boy does not often hear it, and it will be very good for him.' I agreed, and said that in view of what was likely to happen in the next twenty years it was desirable he should not be unduly Lindemannised.[50]

These comments illustrate not just Lindemann's politics, but also the point – important in the context of their later friendship – that however much Churchill relished Lindemann's company and warmly welcomed his advice, he was always 'his own man', and would never adopt a policy or creed unless he firmly believed in it himself. It was far from correct to suggest, as many did, that Lindemann became a form of evil genius persuading Churchill against his better judgement. Both men were decisive and confident in their own views, and it happened that they usually agreed. However, when, as a Cabinet minister many years later, Lindemann stood firm against Churchill in an argument over atomic development, there resulted a significant if temporary breach in their relationship.

Lindemann's growing interests in the wider world meant that his credibility at Oxford began to suffer. After its initial impetus the work of the Clarendon slowed up, and for a time proceeded sluggishly, and he began to have difficulty in sustaining the enthusiasm of the university, and consequently of its bursary. While with hindsight it can be seen that his tenure of the Clarendon produced outstanding results, at the end of his first few years there the situation did not seem promising. The initial work had been put in hand, the syllabus revised, and researchers and students encouraged, but momentum had been lost. There was not yet any strong advance in original research, partly because of the lack of funds and expertise to develop low-temperature work. It seemed to many that Lindemann's priorities had changed, and that politics and social life were beginning to engage the attention that should have been directed towards the Clarendon.

It was noted that he expended considerable energy in trying to arrange places at Christ Church and other colleges for the sons of his friends. Jack Morrell encapsulates this view in his book *Science at Oxford 1914–1939*:

To some he seemed idle, truculent and tiresome . . . While pursuing the life of a socialite Lindemann jousted a good deal in defending and promoting science at Oxford. He developed a chip on his shoulder about the status of science at Oxford and sometimes was paranoic about its relation to classics. He became a publicist and even a prima donna, fighting both real and mock battles on behalf of science. As a substitute for the loss of his personal experimental research drive, he gave even more attention to polemics.

On the other hand, however much Lindemann may have clashed with his colleagues at Oxford, he was kind and helpful to undergraduates, and was a generous host in his rooms: notwithstanding his own unedifying diet, he would press the finest food, wine and cigars on his guests. He did occasionally force himself to drink alcohol, as witnessed in 1928 by James Scrymgeour-Wedderburn, a fellow guest at Chartwell:

Even poor old Prof, who is really a teetotaller, is compelled to drink ten cubic centimetres of brandy at a time, because he was once rash enough to tell Winston that the average human being could imbibe ten c.c. of brandy without causing any detectable change in his metabolism.[51]

Those living on his staircase recalled that he never exhibited any interest in them or their activities, but neither did he report any of them to the college authorities for raucous undergraduate behaviour, although he occasionally despatched Harvey to request a moderation in the noise level. In the same way, he would not visit a house of friends where he knew that there would be children without taking along some puzzle or brainteaser with which to entertain them.

However, Lindemann did remain closely involved with the activities at the Clarendon, benefiting from Keeley's efficiency in administering it from day to day. A firm hand was certainly needed, as work in a laboratory can go badly wrong. The quiet leafy streets of north Oxford were blasted on more than one occasion by a deafening report from the direction of the laboratory. In one case a lecturer had proposed to demonstrate that liquid oxygen with a combustible material could be used as an explosive, mixing alcohol and oxygen in a box and exploding it by means of a spark from an

induction coil. In a preliminary experiment to determine the quantity necessary, he made a mistake in his sums. Keeley reported what followed:

> The detonation was terrific. It woke up the whole laboratory, blew out
> the windows, knocked down the great wooden shutters that every room
> was provided with, and smashed a large amount of apparatus.
> Fortunately the lecturer was not injured, although he emerged from
> the room black all over due to the dust that had been disturbed by the
> explosion.[52]

A more serious accident occurred when an American research student
was doing calculations on the waves that were produced on the earth's
surface by explosions. He set up experiments to simulate such effects, in
which the detonator was activated by an accumulator that was supposed to
be connected by an assistant. On one occasion the assistant had forgotten
that the accumulator was still connected, and did not notice that the plunger
in the switch had stuck down, so that when he came to attach the detonator, the explosive at once went off. Death was instantaneous.[53]

In 1927 Lindemann's mother died and he became embroiled in an argument with his family. His relations with Olga had for some time been cool.
He had neither forgotten nor forgiven the occasion when he arrived home
for a visit, only to be sent away by his mother because he had not asked her
permission to come and stay. He was further put out when he learnt from
her will that his beloved Sidholme was to pass to his half-brother Gilbert.
A family row blew up when Gilbert asked Lindemann's father to leave
Sidholme, where he had lived contentedly for more than forty years, and
which was soon thereafter sold. The Lindemann family, especially the two
eldest brothers, took great offence at this, although it seems they were not
aware that their mother was only a life tenant of the house, which had
belonged to her first husband. There resulted a rift between the children
of the first marriage and Lindemann who, as was his way, never afterwards
relented.

Despite the slow progress being made at the Clarendon, Lindemann was
now to improve his standing both with the university authorities, who had
become irritated by his dogged attempts to draw funds to the school of
physics, and with his colleagues at Christ Church, who viewed with disdain
his social life away from Oxford. His increased popularity came about when
he persuaded his friend Albert Einstein to come to Oxford and take up
temporary residence there.

Lindemann had been deeply impressed by Einstein when he observed
him at the Solvay Conference in 1911,[54] and he never revised his opinion,

which he was to express in the obituary that he later wrote for the *Daily Telegraph*:

As a theoretical physicist Einstein stands alone in this century and perhaps in any century. His brilliant originality, his fecund adventurous imagination, his uncompromising logic, and his clear exposition have probably never been equalled.[55]

It caused great delight when Einstein accepted the invitation to visit Oxford. After the Great War his fame had spread far beyond the confines of physics, and he himself had become a topic of growing interest:

What brought the attention of the world to special relativity was the verification in 1919 of a prediction of the General Theory, that starlight passing near the sun is bent by the sun's gravity. This verification, which occurred during a solar eclipse expedition, set into being the relativity craze that swept the world and overnight made Einstein a public figure.[56]

Einstein's predictions had been confirmed as a result of photographs taken in the spring of 1919, during an expedition to the volcanic island of Principe, in the Gulf of Guinea, where scientists observed a solar eclipse. Their findings were given the seal of official approval at a celebrated joint meeting of the Royal Society and the Royal Astronomical Society in November 1919, but Einstein's fame spread rapidly to a wider and probably uncomprehending public mainly as a result of coverage in the American press, which came out with typically sensational headlines such as 'Stars Not Where They Seemed Or Were Calculated To Be But Nobody Need Worry'.[57]

That month Adolf Lindemann wrote to Einstein about his new-found fame, saying that the reason for all the fuss was:

that your theory wrecks Newton's theory and that the world is no longer what we are accustomed to regard it as, and the whole Euclidian geometry has, as it were, gone to the devil, that space is bent etc., etc. Naturally this has hurt our national feelings and thrown the world into great turmoil.[58]

It was not Einstein's first visit to England: he had come in 1921, and in 1929 a move was made by the Rhodes Memorial Trust to obtain him as their next lecturer. Lindemann was deputed to invite him to Oxford. On that occasion illness had prevented Einstein from accepting, but in 1930

Lindemann went to Berlin and persuaded him to come the following year, as Rhodes Memorial Lecturer, and to speak on the theory of relativity. 'He was accommodated in Christ Church, the calm cloisters of which he relished as much as Oxford relished him.'[59]

Einstein's reputation outweighed for his Oxford audiences both the difficulty of understanding his concepts and the fact that he spoke in German. His gentle nature was appreciated at college High Tables, and at Christ Church so was the sound of the Stradivarius that he played as he relaxed in his rooms. Whether his lectures were as clear to all his listeners may be doubted, but Lindemann himself had no difficulty, stating with characteristic hauteur that:

> if only scientists had had their wits about them, they ought to have been able to reach the Relativity Theory by pure logic soon after Isaac Newton, and not to have had to wait for the stimulus given to them by certain empirical observations that were inconsistent with the classical theory.[60]

Although no ripples from the upheavals in Germany had yet reached the calm waters of Oxford, Einstein's visit took place against a darkening scene in Europe. During these years Lindemann had not strayed for long from Oxford, although he had spent the first five months of 1929 with a committee examining the Forest Research Institute in India. There he had duly made the acquaintance of the viceroy, Lord Irwin, who took to him greatly. Later Irwin was to become the Earl of Halifax and Foreign Secretary, and a leading exponent of the appeasement policies to which Lindemann became so steadfastly opposed.

Unlike most dons, Lindemann was now beginning to feel considerable unease about the events that were unfolding in Germany, and his disquiet deepened as a result of a journey he made with Churchill in August 1932. This was a tour of the Duke of Marlborough's battlefields, which Churchill had arranged in order to gather background for the 'life' of his illustrious ancestor that he was currently writing.[61]

Journeys such as this consolidated the growing friendship between Lindemann and the Churchill family. Although there was considerable mutual affection and respect, it was also the case that these expeditions were partly made possible by Lindemann's generosity. Churchill was at this time in uncertain financial circumstances, having been badly affected by the turbulence that followed the Wall Street Crash. Lindemann's contributions to the family's travel and holiday costs were therefore particularly welcome, and were typical of his generosity to those he liked and admired.

Their journey in the summer of 1932 took them to Munich. There Putzi Hanfstaengl, a friend and courtier of the Führer, persuaded Churchill to agree to meet Hitler, saying that nothing would be easier to arrange, as Hitler came every day at about five o'clock to the Hotel Regina, where Churchill was staying. Churchill appeared at the appointed hour and place, with members of his family and with Lindemann. However, for various reasons the Führer did not turn up and the meeting never materialised. Churchill was later to record:

> Thus Hitler lost his only chance of meeting me. Later on when he was all-powerful, I was to receive several invitations, but I was busy and excused myself.[62]

Lindemann and Churchill reacted in the same way, and to the same marked degree, to what they saw in Germany. They were filled with foreboding and with a determination to alert their country to the danger. It was a journey that warmed and strengthened their friendship, as they moved together to meet the peril that was clear to them both.

In 1932 and 1933 Einstein came again to Oxford, but by the time of his last visit Germany was in the throes of the upheaval that followed Hitler's election as Chancellor of the Reich in January 1933. This was to lead to Lindemann going to Germany himself, and taking the dramatic steps that were to bring great and enduring benefits to the Clarendon, to Oxford and in due course to England itself.

SIX

Lindemann's List

The cries of '*Ein Volk, Ein Reich, Ein Führer*', which in 1933 echoed from the adoring masses in Berlin, were soon to have an unexpected effect in north Oxford, and to lead in time to the university achieving renown as a centre of scientific learning.

Lindemann quickly forecast the probable consequences of the turmoil caused by the Nazis and, from his base in Oxford, he began to make plans that would in a dramatic way renew his contacts with German scientists. He had always retained a special interest in Germany, but in considering what was happening there he was strongly impressed by a factor quite separate from impulses of patriotism or compassion. He knew, from his position in the scientific world, that Germany contained some of the world's ablest physicists, engaged upon work of great importance; he knew also that they were mostly Jewish, and that they would soon be in grave danger.

To Lindemann the opportunity must have been crystal-clear: with careful planning he might be able to attract some of these scientists to England. At a stroke he could thereby raise the whole status of Oxford science in general, and the Clarendon Laboratory in particular, to international standing, and perhaps snatch the laurel wreath from the foremost physics institution in the country – and possibly in the world – Ernest Rutherford's Cavendish Laboratory in Cambridge.

In order to set in hand this bold plan he had to do two things: first, he had to identify and make contact with those scientists in Germany who would help him achieve his aim; and second, he had to have something to offer them that would be an incentive for them to uproot themselves and make a new life in England.

It perhaps seems obvious now, with the knowledge of all that came to pass under Hitler, that the offer of an escape route would be a godsend to a Jewish scientist working in Germany in 1933. It would not, however, have seemed so clear at the time, and those who contemplated the prospect would have been beset by uncertainty. One reason for such doubt was that in Germany scientists enjoyed all the benefits of popular esteem and of a long tradition of support from the authorities. The Kaiser had encouraged great respect for science and the academic professions, believing that they fostered military and industrial success, and by the 1920s a network of 'Kaiser Wilhelm Institutes' had become well established in several major centres, particularly Berlin, Munich and Göttingen.

To be 'Herr Professor' or 'Herr Ingenieur' was a mark of distinction, as was explained by Kathrin Baxandall, the daughter of one of the most eminent refugee scientists, Franz Simon.[1] Commenting on the reluctance of so many Jewish scientists to leave Germany, she said:

Academics were held in such high regard, you see. They were civil servants, and they were paid about twice what academics got in England; and a professor was almost something with wings, you know. They were incredibly highly regarded.[2]

A second cause of the scientists' reluctance to leave Germany was the risk involved in throwing up a well-paid job in the absence of a cast-iron alternative. Kathrin Baxandall continued:

One was totally dependent on offers, definite offers; there was no question of saying 'I'd like to go to England to see what I can find'. It wasn't like that at all.

The third factor was that many Jewish scientists were unable or unwilling to believe that anything dire would happen to them. This was partly because Jews had become very much assimilated into German society, at least since the end of the eighteenth century, and lived very much like other Germans. It was difficult for them to accept that they would now be treated differently. It was also partly because so many intelligent people thought the Nazis would not retain power for long. It was widely believed that they were in thrall to their supporters, who included the Reichswehr and great industrialists like Krupp and Thyssen, who would, it was thought, sideline Hitler once their own aims had been achieved. Too many scientists could not comprehend, even in 1936 or 1937, Hitler's intentions for the Jews, and so they declined to move. After that it was too late, and their escape route vanished, leaving them to face misery and possible death.

Very early on Lindemann demonstrated an understanding of the emotions that would be involved in suggesting to such Germans that they should abandon their posts, and he supplemented it with a determination to make it possible in practice. He appreciated that an opportunity was emerging from the situation in Germany, and saw that universities and industrial companies would be the obvious beneficiaries of fresh scientific blood. It was to them that he turned.

He believed that, if his view of Hitler was correct, what would start as a trickle of refugees from Germany would develop into a flood. From his struggle at Oxford during the 1920s he was aware how hard it was to raise funds for science. It was, for example, at around this time that a professor of engineering, working on an important project to reduce the noise from motorcycle exhausts, reported that his efforts had been aided by a grant from the British Association – of five pounds! Moreover, Lindemann was conscious of the fact that the cause of displaced German scientists might be hindered if they were to compete with English applicants for existing places. So he set about raising additional grant money over and above what was currently available for English applicants.

The threat to German Jews was soon implemented. In early 1933, very soon after Hitler had gained power, new laws were rushed out in Germany. Jews and part-Jews, who were classified as 'Non-Aryans', were forbidden to hold most offices, and as many doctors and professors, particularly in the fields of physics and maths, were Jewish, there was a sudden and dramatic upheaval in the scientific world.

Meanwhile Lindemann set his sights on industry as a source of new money. Foremost among his targets was Imperial Chemical Industries, by 1932 a major industrial power in the land. Here was an example of how Lindemann did not allow an instinctive anti-Semitism to impede friend-ships that he judged to have compensating merits. ICI had grown out of Mond Chemicals and, although the Monds were Jews, Lindemann was a good friend of Lord Melchett and of several other members of the family, and had often been a guest at their house in Buckinghamshire. He was also a friend of the managing director, Sir Harry McGowan, with whom he now entered into detailed discussions as to the help that the company might give.

Lindemann put forward persuasive reasons for ICI to make grants to selected scientists. He knew that if he were successful in raising funds, he would be all the more able to go to Germany and entice them to Oxford. It was not in keeping with his nature to make an appeal on the grounds of compassion, and he probably realised that in the world of commerce it was not the strongest suit to lead. At this early stage he took the view, which so many of his German friends shared, that before too long the upheaval in Germany would subside, so he advised ICI that the grants he was seeking were for a limited period and would not involve an open-ended commit-ment on their part.

Lindemann suggested to the company that they might achieve several objectives: first, the direct benefits to ICI through advances made in scientific research; second, improvements in the training of university students, who might afterwards become members of the ICI staff or teachers in universities; and third, improvements in British research through new methods and ideas.

His proposals were warmly received by McGowan and his colleagues. After detailed meetings and correspondence, ICI agreed in principle to make some grants, initially for a period of two years. They drew up a scale of remuneration that would reflect the abilities and seniority of the intended recipients. At the top of the scale they placed Nobel Prizewinners, of which Lindemann had one or two in mind as possible candidates. When the plans were finalised in May 1933 he wrote to McGowan confirming, among other things, the following points:

ICI is prepared to finance a certain number of Jewish scientists to come and work in England.

The maximum expenditure over the two years is to be £15,000 . . . probably a considerably smaller sum will suffice to secure as many really first-class men as are available.

I am to go to Germany and interview and negotiate with likely candidates on the lines set forth above and, so far as possible, make arrangements with them . . .

In the circumstances it is unlikely that definite agreement will be reached with more than six or eight men, but it might be possible to secure an option on some of the others.[3]

Meanwhile he had been considering who were the appropriate scientists to persuade to come to Oxford. In this he was greatly helped by the fact that scientists formed then, as now, a fluid and international community: their friendships spread throughout that community, and it was generally known where everybody of any importance was working and what they were doing. So, to discuss likely prospects, Lindemann wrote first to his old friend and mentor Walther Nernst.

Nernst in turn telephoned Franz Simon, who had been a pupil of his before 1914. Simon's wife recalled the conversation, in which Nernst asked Simon whether he intended to come to Berlin for the Easter holidays, and said that he had just had a letter from Lindemann. He had added: 'and I think what he wants to know you can tell him better than I can'.

So it was that Lindemann arrived in Berlin at Easter 1933 and at once went to see Nernst. Lindemann wanted to know who among the younger physicists might have to leave Germany under the new regime, and who might like to work elsewhere for two years or so, by which time, he thought, the situation in Germany ought to have regained some degree of sanity. He therefore put the crucial question to Nernst: 'Have you any scientists for me?' It was immediately clear that Nernst had.

Lindemann turned also to Einstein. Ever since Lindemann had first met him, he had greatly admired Einstein's towering ability as a physicist. It was while Lindemann was planning a third visit by Einstein to Oxford, for the summer of 1933, that on 28 March Einstein raised his profile by resigning from the Prussian Academy of Science and publicly declaring that he would not return to Germany, because of the Nazis' policies. Rather belatedly the Academy had riposted that it had 'no reason to regret Einstein's withdrawal', an announcement that was closely followed by Einstein's expulsion by the Bavarian Academy.

On 4 May Lindemann wrote to Einstein:

I was in Berlin for four or five days at Easter and saw a great many of your colleagues. The general feeling was much against the action taken by the Academy, which was the responsibility of one of the secretaries without consultation with the members . . .

It appears to us that the present circumstances in Germany might provide us with an opportunity to get one or two theoretical physicists to Oxford, at any rate for two or three years. Professor Sommerfeld[4] told me that many of the privatdozenten[5] of Jewish origin would be deprived of their positions and in the circumstances would be ready to come here at a very small salary. I need scarcely say that very little money is available and that it would cause a lot of feeling, even if it were possible to place them in positions normally occupied by Englishmen. The only chance is to get extra supernumerary jobs . . . Sommerfeld suggested Bethe and London as possible men. I wonder whether you think well of them and whether you would be prepared to support their candidature. Perhaps there are others whom you might consider better, but I have the impression that anyone trained by Sommerfeld is the sort of man who can work out a problem and get an answer, which is what we really want at Oxford, rather than the more abstract type who would spend his time disputing with the philosophers.[6]

So began the negotiations that would lead to some of the most brilliant scientists in the world coming to Oxford. Many others would follow their path, with the help of the Academic Assistance Council, a voluntary organisation established in the wake of Lindemann's pioneering rescue work, and funded by donations from British university teachers and the Central British Fund for German Jewry. The arrival of the refugee scientists was to be emphatically Britain's gain and Germany's loss, not least because of the exceptional work that they were soon to do in the development of Britain's atomic power.

Lindemann's particular interest, as we know, was in low-temperature physics, and he remained convinced of the great future importance of this field. It was for this especially that he was to recruit in Germany, and he was to achieve the highest success with his recruitment of Kurt Mendelssohn, Nicholas Kurti, Heinz London and Franz Simon, Lindemann's eventual successor. All these men in time became Fellows of the Royal Society.

Kurt Mendelssohn[7] had in 1931 been in discussions with Lindemann over the installation at the Clarendon of a hydrogen liquefier, which Lindemann knew would be an important step forward for his low-temperature research. After this had been achieved, Mendelssohn returned to Oxford at Christmas 1932 to install a helium liquefier, which had been designed by Franz Simon in his laboratory in Breslau, and of which there were none in England. Within a week of his arrival Mendelssohn had produced at Oxford the first liquid helium in Britain. This was particularly pleasing for Lindemann because it happened before the same success had been achieved at Cambridge, where similar research was taking place at very considerable expense:

> Lindemann was cock-a-hoop: by importing Mendelssohn, whom he thought a first-class man in ability, industry, and power of work, he had at last managed to upstage Cambridge and wipe the eye of the Cavendish.[8]

Before these arrangements had been put in hand, Mendelssohn had declined Lindemann's invitation to spend a year in Oxford, as he had just moved to Breslau to work with Simon, his first cousin. Even so, he had been thinking of coming to England if he were able to get a grant for research – for which he had applied to the Rockefeller Foundation. Rather shortsightedly in this instance, the foundation stuck to its rule that a grant could only be made if the applicant could demonstrate that he would have a post to return to in due course. With Hitler in power, this had become unlikely, to say the least, and although Lindemann put this point to the Rockefeller Foundation while supporting Mendelssohn's application, it would not waive the rule.

Eventually, however, Mendelssohn did agree to come to Oxford, but on the understanding that he could put back his date of arrival so as not to upset the arrangements that he had so recently made.

In the event, the establishment of Hitler's regime changed everything, and its impact on Mendelssohn occurred in a rather dramatic way. At Easter 1933 he and his wife went from Breslau to Berlin to see their respective grandparents. When he reached Berlin and was travelling on the subway, he felt a sharp blow in the back. He turned to find Stormtroopers rounding up at random a dozen or so passengers and cordoning them off, before taking them away to the police station for questioning. As Mendelssohn later told his daughter: had he been a few feet further down the carriage, he too would have been rounded up, and that might have been the end of him.[9]

Immediately on leaving the subway Mendelssohn looked for a telephone and called his wife, to say that he was leaving the country at once and that she must pack up and follow him. So it was that, after the hastiest departure from Germany, Mendelssohn arrived in Oxford in April 1933. He himself described his emotions:

When I woke up the sun was shining in my face. I had slept deeply, soundly and long – for the first time in many weeks. The night before I had arrived in London and gone to bed without fear that at 3 a.m. a car with a couple of SA men would draw up and take me away. Breslau, where I had a post at the university in 1933, was ahead of most German cities in establishing Nazi terror. In Breslau the notorious sadist Heines had been appointed Chief of Police and I had been a member of a militant anti-Nazi organisation. In view of my record I considered it merely a question of time and statistics as to when my own turn for interrogation would come. This state of affairs was injurious to my nervous system.[10]

So Mendelssohn took refuge in England, the first such scientist to do so. His success played a large part in persuading Lindemann to take the lead in helping German physicists whose jobs and lives were threatened in Germany. The fact that some of these scientists were the world's leading experts in the low-temperature work that was so dear to Lindemann's heart clearly made the prospect still more attractive:

The success of Mendelssohn's early research in Oxford presumably suggested to Lindemann the idea of creating in Oxford a worthy continuation of Nernst's cryogenic school, which would develop research in which he had been involved as a young man, using

Mendelssohn's Breslau colleagues. Emotionally this scheme satisfied Lindemann's long-lasting and deep loyalty to Nernst: it would enable him to build a new world of old memories around himself at the Clarendon.[11]

Lindemann now entered into further negotiations. It was known that no letters were safe from prying Nazi eyes, so he sometimes employed a code when writing to German scientists. In the letters to Simon and Kurti, for example, Simon, being the senior of the two, was described as 'the high-pressure compressor' and Kurti as 'the low-pressure compressor' which the Clarendon was purportedly buying; proposed salaries were disguised as working pressures in atmospheres.

Franz Simon, whom Lindemann was also to bring to Oxford, was an outstanding physicist, well known and respected in Germany. In the Great War he had been one of the first German casualties of poison gas, but he had won the Iron Cross, both Second Class and First Class – the latter roughly equivalent to a Military Cross in the British Army – and he had been an officer, which was unusual for a Jew in the German Army and indicated success against the odds. A far-sighted man, he very soon realised what Hitler was likely to mean for him and his family.

He had grown to like England, where he had spent childhood holidays, but there was another reason why Simon was a ready listener when Lindemann arrived in Berlin on his mission. In the words of his daughter:

> One of the reasons why he realised very early on that he wanted to leave Germany was because he had been in charge of one of those big guns in the First World War. When the war broke out my father was studying in Munich so it was a Bavarian regiment that he was drafted into, not a North German one, and most of the people under his command were recruits, peasants and people like that. He found them so disagreeable and cruel and capable of all sorts of appalling things that he decided that a country that breeds people like that was not one in which he wanted to live. That wasn't the only factor, it was just one.[12]

Although he was a *Frontkämpfer*[13] with a distinguished war record, which would, at least at first, have protected him from the discriminatory laws that were to be enforced in the universities, Simon decided to leave while the going was good. But it must have been painful: having accepted an important post at Breslau, he had now been joined by Mendelssohn, who had for the two previous years been his principal assistant, and by Nicholas Kurti, who was just finishing his doctoral thesis. Simon had a happy home in Breslau, with his wife and two daughters, and he had positive memories of his upbringing in Germany, his days in Berlin and his years in the service of the Fatherland. He realised with sadness that the new menace eclipsed all that, so he accepted the invitation to Oxford. Lindemann therefore arranged for him to receive a grant from ICI, and in May 1933 Simon travelled to England to finalise matters. Immediately on his return to Germany he handed in his resignation as director of the Physical-Chemical Institute in Breslau.

Simon's reputation can be gauged by his application, three years later, for a post in Birmingham, when his referees (besides Lindemann) included Rutherford, Einstein, Planck, Blackett and Cockcroft, each of whom was to establish an international reputation and win the Nobel Prize. Simon's later record of holding both the Iron Cross and a knighthood is highly unusual.

The third of the low-temperature trio whom Lindemann brought from Germany was Nicholas Kurti. He was of Jewish descent and originally from Hungary, but had left his native land and, after two years working in Paris, had completed his doctorate in Berlin, before moving to Breslau where he had become Simon's assistant. He also accepted Lindemann's invitation, and on 16 September 1933 arrived in Oxford to rejoin Simon. Many years later he recalled the feeling of joy at his escape from the storm clouds gathering in Germany:

I arrived in Oxford by train at 10 p.m. one Saturday evening; it was dark and raining. I took a taxi to Mendelssohn's flat in Headington. Next morning was bright and sunny, and Mendelssohn took me to the laboratory on his motor bicycle; there was little traffic, and as we crossed Magdalen bridge I thought 'This is fairyland – why should I ever leave it?' And I did not.[14]

These men, by their services to science in their adopted country, both in war and peace, were to repay Oxford handsomely for the sanctuary it gave them.

Lindemann's refugees in Oxford were in due course joined by the brothers Heinz and Fritz London, and by Erwin Schrödinger, for whom Lindemann negotiated a post at Magdalen College. Schrödinger, an Austrian, was not Jewish, but he was nevertheless attracted by what Lindemann had told him about Oxford and decided to take up the invitation. As it happened, Lindemann may in one small respect have come to regret his invitation: Schrödinger was of rather an amatory disposition, and brought not only his wife but his mistress as well. Lindemann was therefore burdened with the necessity of making arrangements for a third member of the ménage, and this he found most uncongenial. However, Schrödinger was a Nobel Prizewinner and Lindemann was confident that he would benefit Oxford science.

Further refugees followed, including Heinrich Kuhn. At twenty-nine he was already a noted spectroscopist, working in Göttingen, a place that prided itself on its scientific reputation: the council there had erected numerous signs announcing the fact that the visitor was in 'Göttingen – City of Five Nobel Prize winners'. In this learned city the physics institute was run by Professor James Franck. He also was a Jew, but he had fought in the First World War and, like Simon, was a *Frontkämpfer* and so exempted from the new race laws. Franck, however, was so disgusted by what was happening that he decided not to avail himself of the exemption. Instead, he not only resigned his position as professor, but published in the national and local press a statement of protest against the new legislation. Despite this courageous act he managed at length to reach safety outside Germany.

Heinrich Kuhn did have some Jewish blood, but his family had long been Christian and he himself looked Aryan, with blond hair and blue eyes. Notwithstanding that generations of his family had lived exactly as other Germans, Kuhn soon received a three-line communication from the Ministry of Culture – ironically named, in the event – informing him that under the new law for reclaiming the Civil Service, which came into effect as early as 7 April 1933, his *venia legendi* had been withdrawn. The removal of this vital qualification for a German scientist who wished to teach and lecture meant that Kuhn's livelihood had disappeared at the stroke of a pen. Unceremoniously he was dismissed from his position as an assistant and was advised not to enter the laboratory.

Kuhn realised that it was the end of his career, for the time being at least, in any German university; and more than that: because he had been categorised as a lower class of citizen, which would exclude him from most forms of employment, he had in effect no choice but to leave Germany.

Kuhn and his young Austrian wife, a cousin of the philosopher Ludwig Wittgenstein, had some money in Germany, but they knew they would be forbidden to take it out if they were to leave the country. They were therefore contemplating the outlook with some dismay when Kuhn received an invitation to go to Franck's house. On reaching the imposing, turreted building discreetly set back in trees, he found Lindemann waiting for him. Kuhn was asked whether he would like to come and work at Oxford; if so, a grant might be arranged, and he could work with Derek Jackson, who was then absorbed in spectroscopy at the Clarendon. The two scientists had not met, but they knew of each other's work through the conferences and colloquia that so effectively disseminated ideas among the scientific community. Kuhn was delighted at Lindemann's suggestion and at once agreed to come.

After an interval Lindemann returned to the Clarendon, where he established that Jackson would be happy to work with Kuhn: he was feeling isolated in his work at Oxford, which he half-jokingly used to say that he had moved to for the hunting – there being no respectable hunting near Cambridge – and he would be pleased to have a colleague. Jackson's good nature and irrepressible sense of humour made him an attractive colleague for the German scientists who, when they arrived at the Clarendon, were sometimes a little uncertain of the customs and traditions of the country. Jackson remembered, for example, coming into the laboratory after a day's hunting, to be politely asked by Simon how many foxes he had shot that day. One of Jackson's first reactions to the idea of working with Kuhn, when Lindemann put it to him, was to exclaim: 'Oh good. He'll be able to teach me how to swear properly in German.'[15]

In fact, as Kuhn himself recounted:

A minor crisis developed quite early on, with lively, plain speaking on both sides, in two languages. This, however, was soon settled and appeared to have cleared the air.[16]

In general, however, strong language was far removed from Kuhn's gentle and amiable personality.

Back in England, Lindemann obtained from ICI a grant of £400 per annum for Kuhn, who was waiting anxiously in Göttingen. His correspondence with Kuhn had to be 'disguised', for fear of interception, and Lindemann wrote from Christ Church on 18 June 1933:

Dear Dr Kuhn,
I dare say you remember our meeting in Göttingen early this month. We have been much interested in your work here and would be very glad if you could come over and help us start similar investigations. Exactly where we should make the experiments would have to be settled later. The figure we find is definitely 4.0.
　　With kind regards believe me,
　　　　[F. A. Lindemann][17]

Many years later Heinrich Kuhn's wife poignantly remarked: 'It was this letter which in the end decided my fate.'[18] Kuhn joyfully received Lindemann's letter, and in August they started out for England. His wife subsequently explained that for them it was both a relief and an exciting adventure: to go to England for two years or so was wonderful. They, like so many others, did not think that Nazism could possibly last, and they shared the view of so many of their friends that it was far too extreme an ideology to have any chance of real acceptance by Germans.

On the way to England the Kuhns stayed with the Warburg family, who were bankers in Hamburg. On arrival, Heinrich Kuhn went to the British Consulate in Hamburg to confirm that his papers were in order. When he got there a young official acidly told him that, on the contrary, they were most certainly not in order, and that it was quite impossible that Kuhn would be allowed into England to earn money. It was a sharp and unexpected blow and his fears came flooding back. It was with desolation and foreboding that he returned to his wife. However, as luck had it, the Warburg father was a friend of the consul and, having heard Kuhn's story, at once telephoned him. After a brief enquiry, Warburg was told that the young official was wrong and that of course Kuhn would be more than welcome in England.

It was an immense relief for the refugees to find a sanctuary from the dangers that had so suddenly beset them, yet they did not all settle in their new environment. Some found the easy-going ways of an English university at odds with the formality and protocol to which they were used; others felt aggrieved that they were not accorded greater deference by their new fellows.

Language, too, was a problem. One story, recalled by Kurt Mendelssohn, circulated rapidly around Oxford: a distinguished professor and his wife, having escaped from Germany and feeling greatly relieved to have found a berth in north Oxford, went on their first day there for a walk around the town. They soon came to a stall selling fruit and vegetables. Seeing a basket of small oranges the professor attempted, in halting English, to buy some. 'Oh, no, love,' replied the girl behind the stall, 'you can't eat them. They're no good: they're only fit for juice.' 'So,' said the professor, turning to his wife, 'it is happening here, too!'[19] On the whole, however, the refugees were rapidly assimilated, and began the excellent work for which they were soon to become renowned.

So it was that, even by the end of 1933, Germany had lost a large number of scientists of the highest ability. As it turned out, they were to become the leaders in the field of nuclear physics, which was then on the threshold of exploration. Their absence was only to make more certain Germany's failure to develop a decisive weapon in the coming war. The refugee scientists would dearly have liked to have been able to stay in their homeland, and would in the years to come have been immensely important for Germany.

Instead the value went to England, thanks originally and very largely to the imagination and determination of Lindemann.

Perhaps Mendelssohn's words aptly describe Lindemann's achievement:

> With great clarity of vision he foresaw what was going to happen and that jobs might be needed for more than one German. Being a strong believer in private initiative and in taking short-cuts by knowing the right people, he created that famous one-man relief organisation which, in due course, enabled many refugee scientists to make their permanent or temporary home in this country.[20]

With the Clarendon Laboratory now host to some of the world's finest scientists, its pulse beating with a new vigour, Lindemann turned his full attention to the deteriorating international picture, made more vivid in his view by the decay in Britain's defences.

SEVEN

Alarm Call

I shall build the largest air fleet in the world.

Adolf Hitler, 1932

His journey through Germany with Churchill in 1932, and his rescue of the Jewish physicists in 1933, had fostered an element of pugnacity in Lindemann's attitude to the political situation. He expressed his feelings in growing concern about two things: the atmosphere of distrust in international relations, and the renascence of German militarism.

Although the Nazis' attentions were for a brief time engaged solely within Germany itself, their leaders soon looked abroad to sustain their momentum. They did this by the simple ploy of blaming others for the plight of the German people. Initially those others consisted of the Jews and of what the Nazis descried as 'international finance', but they soon came to include the leaders of foreign countries, especially France, for which the Germans nursed an instinctive hatred, and England, for which they had developed the antipathy born of fear.

Lindemann began to be increasingly preoccupied by the possible effects of German developments on the defence of England. He continued to maintain links with his wartime associates and to hold positions that enabled him to keep abreast of military affairs, and this supplemented the information that he picked up through his widening social and political connections. He served on the Aeronautical Research Committee, a sub-committee of the Committee of Imperial Defence, on which he was placed because of his scientific experience and particularly his work at Farnborough. He was also on the Committee of Imperial Defence (CID) Meteorology Sub-Committee, and he had been asked to join the Kite-Balloon Sub-Committee, to contribute to ideas on air defence.

As far back as 1925 Sir Maurice Hankey had discussed with Lindemann the contribution that he could make to such committees. Hankey, brusque and diminutive, was the long-standing secretary to the Cabinet. His efficiency was highly respected, but he was not well liked. With typical English euphemism it was observed that his subordinates' admiration for their chief was greater than their affection, and his reputation was not improved by the story that, having received a grant of £25,000 for his services during the Great War, he had presented his faithful secretary with a box of small cigars.

Hankey had become a powerful official, and was part of a select group of civil servants – among whom Sir Warren Fisher and Sir Horace Wilson were prominent – who during the 1920s and 1930s wielded great influence on the composition and terms of reference of the numerous committees charged with advising on the country's defences.

One such committee, on to which Hankey had invited Lindemann, had been directed 'To investigate the scientific aspect of the problem of anti-aircraft defence as it affects the three services, with special reference to new methods'. Lindemann had readily agreed to join. The task of keeping Britain's defences up to date and in good order was close to his heart. Unfortunately, his enthusiasm was not matched by his fellow members, who approached such work with a gentlemanly but rather bored sense of duty and, as with many other such committees, it became sapped by a demoralising drift. It was not long before its chairman was compelled to remind his members: 'If we do not have any papers before the committee the discussion is apt to become rather aimless and lead to no useful results.' On another occasion the members' order of priorities resulted in a notice that a scheduled meeting was 'likely to be postponed as it clashes with Ascot and doesn't suit some of the members'.

Such was the malaise that, as the new decade began, hung like a fog in the committee rooms and conference halls where the nation's affairs were supposedly being managed. To Lindemann it was greatly disheartening, and as the international situation deteriorated he became convinced of the rapidly growing need to apply science to the country's defence.

In Parliament, the leaders of opinion seemed unwilling to pursue a strong line in international affairs, at least towards Germany, or to question closely the practicalities of the anodyne goal of disarmament. It was no wonder that the ordinary Briton gave little thought to the growing turbulence beyond the country's shores, or that the attitude of many people reflected the lines popular at the time:

I was playing golf the day
That the Germans landed,
All our troops had run away,
All our ships were stranded,
And the thought of England's shame
Very nearly spoilt my game.

It was in the course of a debate in Parliament in November 1932 that Stanley Baldwin, soon to become Prime Minister, had sounded a note that was to echo far and wide:

I think it is well for the man in the street to realise that there is no power on earth that can protect him from being bombed. Whatever people may tell him, the bomber will always get through, and it is very easy to understand that if you realise the area of space. I said that any town within reach of an aerodrome could be bombed . . . The only defence is in offence, which means that you have to kill more women and children more quickly than the enemy if you want to save yourselves.[1]

This speech, and in particular the phrase 'the bomber will always get through', aroused widespread dismay and was seized upon by Churchill, Lindemann and a small band of others, who now began to articulate vehement and anxious opposition to the drift in Government policy. However, most politicians, and almost all of the public, accepted without question that it was disarmament alone that could ensure peace and security.

Amid the platitudes that characterised parliamentary debates, Churchill now began to sound a more sombre tone. The Government's view was that all would be well if Germany were accorded equal status with the other major powers. Churchill disagreed: it wasn't 'equal status' that the Germans sought, he said:

That is not what Germany is seeking. All these bands of sturdy Teutonic youths, marching through the streets and roads of Germany, with the light in their eyes of desire to suffer for their Fatherland, are not looking for status. They are looking for weapons . . .[2]

His opinion would have been endorsed in Germany. At the end of 1932, at about the same time as a major debate on international affairs was held in the House of Commons, Hitler – certain now that he was on the final approach to power – held a meeting in Berchtesgaden with his lieutenants Hess, Forster and Rauschning. There he proclaimed his own more trenchant views:

In the air we shall of course be supreme. The air offers many possibilities. We shall surpass all competitors. We have only one serious rival in this field: the English. The Slavs will never learn to fight in the air. It is a manly weapon, a Germanic art of battle. I shall build the largest air fleet in the world.[3]

By now Churchill's admiration for Lindemann's intellect – he was often in later years to refer to his 'beautiful mind' – had led him regularly to seek his advice on scientific matters, and as far back as the summer of 1924 Lindemann had helped with Churchill's article 'Shall We All Commit Suicide', on the nature of future wars. Now, with the German question beginning strongly to engage Churchill's attention, Lindemann's knowledge of the country, his many contacts there and his fluency in the language became extremely useful. When, for example, Churchill spoke in a debate with Sir Arnold Wilson and the economist Professor Bone on the economic situation in Germany, Lindemann was ready with current German statistics, which he had been given by friends in Germany – although he submitted them to Churchill with characteristic cynicism: 'All the facts seem to point inevitably to an immense rearmament programme . . . but the blinding light they throw upon the situation is apparently not strong enough to pierce the dark but optimistic regions of Professor Bone's mind.'[4]

Although, as a professor, he devoted most of his time to his work at Oxford, Lindemann was able to keep abreast of trends in political thought, partly because he was becoming increasingly sought-after as a useful contributor to political debate. For instance, in June 1933 he was asked to speak at the National Peace Congress, debating with Bertrand Russell, H. G. Wells, Rebecca West and several bishops. That year he was also asked twice to take part in discussions at the Royal Institute of International Affairs, first on the Gold Standard, and then on disarmament, on which he was invited to speak as a 'recognised expert'. With the political outlook deteriorating, he did not let his natural reticence prevent him from accepting such invitations.

Meanwhile, impeccably attired and comfortably looked after by his servants, he continued to live a rather spare life in the quiet atmosphere of Oxford. His Christ Church colleague Roy Harrod recalled going to Lindemann's rooms:

> One man showed me in; when I reached his bedroom I found two others. One of these was taking down in shorthand to his dictation, the other was tying up his shoe laces while he himself was putting on his tie. Then he quietly went downstairs and drove round in his large Mercedes to the Clarendon Laboratory, perhaps to be in time for a twelve o'clock lecture.[5]

Lindemann was beginning to fear, however, that this civilised way of life had fallen under serious threat, and he began to increase his criticism of official rearmament policy. The Government, by contrast, seemed to be more interested in electoral opinion, an element of which had been demonstrated in February 1933 in a celebrated debate at the Oxford Union. There, the majority had voted for the motion, supported by Professor C. E. M. Joad,[6] that 'This House will under no circumstances fight for King and Country'. Reports of this debate had been read with keen interest not only at Westminster but also in the dictatorships, where exaggerated importance was attached to the news, as a symptom of Britain's decadence and lack of will.

In the summer of 1933, on his way back to England after a lengthy holiday in Europe, Lindemann tried to arrange a meeting with Hitler. Unfortunately this could not be organised, as Lord Lloyd,[7] the official who submitted the request, explained to Lindemann:

Just a line to say how very sorry I was I could not fix up an interview with Hitler. Hitler had only just come back from a fairly prolonged holiday when he saw me . . .

He bad me to say that he was sincerely sorry not to be able to see you at the time you desired, but that he would be delighted to see you later on in the autumn, some time in November if you cared to come over.[8]

Lindemann had failed to meet Hitler when he was with Churchill in Munich a year earlier, and this second attempt was probably the last time that it might have been possible, as he soon began to express views in public that no doubt extinguished Hitler's willingness to talk to him.

From time to time Lindemann also took part in debates at the Oxford Union, and his notes for a speech that he made at around this time provide a synopsis of his stark view of the world in the early 1930s:

Never has the world situation been more ominous. Japan, in the hands of a military Junta, is overrunning China . . .

The United States are threshing about in an economic muddle enhanced by the entanglement of the executive in the meshes of a rigid constitution . . .

Germany is rearming at a rate unparalleled in the history of the world. Preaching a gospel of force, determined to subjugate Central Europe to her theories . . .

England in its longing for peace is the richest prey for the conqueror, disarmed and defenceless, having tried the Socialist panacea of a bold, generous gesture and pared its defences to the bone, no longer able to control events. Here she lies, the richest prize at the mercy of a conqueror since Rome lay open to Alarich.[9]

Speeches at Oxford were all very well, but Lindemann was beginning to feel the need for a wider audience. He therefore put aside his aversion to publicity and on 8 August 1934 wrote a letter to *The Times*, entitled 'Science and Air Bombing'. In it he challenged the Air Ministry mantra that the bomber will always get through:

That there is at present no means of preventing hostile bombers from depositing their loads of explosives, incendiary materials, gases, or bacteria upon their objectives I believe to be true; that no method can be devised to safeguard great centres of population from such a fate appears to me to be profoundly improbable.

To adopt a defeatist attitude in the face of such a threat is inexcusable until it has definitely been shown that all the resources of science and invention have been exhausted . . .[10]

His letter was prompted by a debate in the Commons that had been held the previous week, in which Baldwin had referred to his contentious remarks in 1932. Baldwin soothed the House of Commons with benign complacency, claiming that his purpose had been principally to encourage people to give thought to the danger:

Mr Keynes told me ten years ago that it is quite impossible to make the English people think, and that I was wasting my time, but I did make a great effort then . . . I had as my object the desire to make people think, not only in this country but abroad. I felt that if I could make them think it might facilitate the work of air disarmament.[11]

It was left to Churchill to challenge these amiable sentiments, which he did by starkly describing the danger into which he believed the country was falling. With four clear warnings he drove the message home:

I first assert that Germany has already in violation of the treaty created a military air force which is now nearly two-thirds as strong as our present home defence air force.

The second [statement] is that Germany is rapidly increasing this air force . . . the third statement is that if Germany continues this expansion and if we continue to carry out our scheme, then, some time in 1936 . . . Germany will be definitely and substantially stronger in the air than Great Britain . . .

Fourthly, and this is the point which is causing anxiety, once they have got that lead we may never be able to overtake them.[12]

By good fortune, the tide now started imperceptibly to turn, and from within the Air Ministry came the first currents of revolt against the Government's policy of benign neglect. The catalyst was a large-scale air exercise held over Britain in July 1934, designed to put the country's air defences to the test. Not only did they emphatically fail the test, but the defences were shown to be so inadequate that even the Air Ministry, long resistant to any hint of deficiency, accepted that the situation could no longer be ignored.

The public, however, appeared to attach little importance to these events, to which the chief reaction seemed to be a large crop of letters to the daily newspapers expressing indignation at the noise of aeroplanes disturbing the peace and quiet. This theme was taken up in the House of Commons by indignant members when the Under-Secretary for Air was petulantly asked if he was aware of the awful fact that 'many inhabitants in Regent's Park and elsewhere were awakened last night, including the hyenas at the Zoo, which in turn awakened several others?'[13]

When the air exercises were over, and London Zoo had quietened down, the Air Ministry began to ponder the results. They were bleak. In addition to operational inadequacy, they revealed widespread technical weakness: none of the aeroplanes used had retractable under-carriages, essential for quick take-off and slow landing; a whole squadron of the most modern bombers had been grounded because minor defects had developed; and overall air speeds were alarmingly slow. It was commented that 'On sheer speed, regardless of power, the air-liners of several other countries could chase our bombers round the sky.'[14] Indeed, it was known that in a strong headwind Heyford heavy bombers, at that time the pride of the RAF, would fly backwards.

As a result of these discoveries, three pressure points now began to build, each of which, from its separate direction, was applied to the same target – the urgent need for measures to meet the German threat, and in particular an improved form of early warning of the approach of enemy aircraft.

One source of pressure came from Churchill and his supporters, including Lindemann; another was from the Defence Requirements Committee under Air Marshal Sir Robert Brooke-Popham; and the third was from the Air Ministry's long-serving director of scientific research, H. E. Wimperis.[15]

One of Wimperis's subordinates was A. P. Rowe,[16] then the one and only research staff member employed wholly on armament problems. Rowe was now, entirely off his own bat, to take action that was to be the starting-point of a series of far-reaching moves which, with almost no time to spare, were to save Britain from disaster in 1940.

Rowe later recalled how in a quiet moment he had decided to examine all the available Air Ministry files on air defence, only to discover that there were just fifty-three, none of which addressed the problem of early warning. Taken together, they disclosed how little effort had been made to enlist the help of scientists.

His initiative was inspired by a typically English incident. Shortly before the air exercise he had been present at a demonstration of the only form of early warning that Britain then possessed: the concrete acoustic screens that had been developed towards the end of the First World War.[17] Rowe later told the story of what happened:

This particular morning I was present when a locator was being prepared for a demonstration to be held in the afternoon before Air Vice-Marshal Dowding, then the Air Member for Research and Development on the Air Council. As the apparatus was being set in order there appeared in the distance an ordinary milkman, driving his horse and cart, with his milk churns jangling away.

The road along which he was coming should have been closed, but for some reason this had been overlooked. The milkman was stopped, reprimanded, and told that under no circumstances would he be allowed to pass along the road that afternoon.

The awful fact became clear that the locators were quite useless except in unattainable conditions of quiet. Of the Romney Marsh locator it was said that if there were any nightingales in Dungeness they might have interfered with it.[18]

Having worked his way through the Air Ministry files, Rowe sent to Wimperis a memorandum with a bleak conclusion: the Secretary of State for Air should at once invite scientists to collaborate in air-defence development, failing which any war that started within ten years would be lost.

Wimperis had independently reached the conclusion that a new committee was needed to address this danger. By chance he had recently been on a holiday in Germany and had stumbled across what had been described as a 'Prohibited Area'. Having asked the local people what it was, he discovered they believed that it related to the development of a system for shooting down aircraft with radio waves. On his return, Wimperis had asked the experts at Farnborough whether such a thing was feasible. The answer was given by Robert Watson-Watt,[19] who replied that it was not, although as an afterthought he added that detecting aircraft with radio waves might be possible. Shortly afterwards Wimperis had lunch with the eminent physiologist Professor A. V. Hill (later to become Independent Conservative

MP for Cambridge), and the two had a thorough discussion on air defence, including the use of radiation for 'death rays'.

A month later, in November 1934, and as a result of this discussion, Wimperis proposed to the Air Minister that a committee be formed to survey ways of applying science to air defence. In particular, he suggested, they should enlist the help of independent scientists, who might have fewer axes to grind than civil servants or servicemen. Significantly Wimperis also expressed confidence that 'one of the coming things will be the transmission by radiation of large amounts of electric energy along clearly directed channels. If this is correct, the use of such transmissions for purposes of war is inevitable, and welcome in that it offers the prospect of defence methods at last overtaking those of attack.'

Meanwhile Lindemann had taken his campaign from the press to the political lobbies, and in October had been to see Baldwin. The result of their meeting was a disappointment for Lindemann: it was clear that the Lord President had not really taken in Lindemann's argument, merely suggesting that he make his case to Brooke-Popham's Defence Requirements Committee. This was far from what Lindemann wanted, as one of his main arguments was that any critical inquiry carried out from within the Air Ministry itself would be hobbled by the department's well-developed weapons of self-preservation. Asked by the Air Minister to state more precisely what he had in mind, he replied:

I thought it useless to have an Air Ministry Committee as one could scarcely expect the very people who had already committed themselves to the statement that there was no defence, to make serious efforts to prove that they had been in error.[20]

Lindemann also had a talk with Henry Tizard at the Royal Society. It was an inauspicious encounter, and was probably the last time for many years that the two would meet on friendly terms. Their discussion was to sour relations between them during a crucial period when the cause of air defence badly needed their co-operation. The gulf that was to develop was to have an importance far beyond the personal animosity between two men, however eminent:

. . . to minimise the failure of two such men to combine their intellectual resources for the common good is to do more than to turn from the clash of right against right: it is also to ignore the impact of the personal scientific argument on the duration, and the casualties, of the Second World War.[21]

Lindemann, no doubt confident of Tizard's support, explained his proposals and received an undertaking to help push them forward, 'if he was consulted'. Tizard made no mention of the formation of any new committee, and it was not until just before Christmas that Lindemann finally learnt of it, from Lord Londonderry, the Secretary of State for Air. The way in which the committee had been formed, and the fact that Lindemann had not only been passed over but kept in the dark, understandably filled him with a resentment that was not to fade: 'a grievance with him cut deep and remained raw'.[22]

Lindemann also carried his message to the higher echelons of the Conservative Party, and in February 1935 addressed its most senior forum, the 1922 Committee. His theme was quite simple: with the development of aeroplanes as a fighting force, England was no longer an island, and had become vulnerable in a way that she had never been before. 'History shows us,' he said, 'that for every weapon there is a shield, but it also shows us that it is very difficult to get the military authorities to realise that such a shield exists.' Finding that shield, he concluded, 'is far more important for the whole future of Western civilisation than anything else, than disarmament, or finding a cure for cancer.'[23]

Meanwhile the new committee, as proposed by Wimperis, had been formed, and had held its first meeting in January. It was officially called the Committee for the Scientific Survey of Air Defence (CSSAD), but under the chairmanship of Henry Tizard it was to become famous as the Tizard Committee. The original members were Tizard, Wimperis, Patrick Blackett,[24] a leading physicist with pronounced left-wing views, Professor A. V. Hill and A. P. Rowe.

When Lindemann heard about the membership of the committee he was not impressed. He wrote to Churchill:

Tizard is of course a good man but both he and Wimperis receive salaries from the Air Ministry.

So far as I know, neither of the other two have ever had anything to do with aeroplanes and one of them holds himself out as a communist, but I do not know whether these points should be stressed.

My main objection is to the intention of the Committee as disclosed in its terms of reference, and to its complete lack of status and power.[25]

The committee's meetings – after Lindemann began attending them – were to be riven by disputes. They stemmed from a fundamental difference in approach between Lindemann and his fellow members – professional divergences that were to be exacerbated by personal antipathy. Both Hill and

Blackett had an imposing presence: they were large men, self-confident and eminent in their fields, and did not take lightly to being contradicted – nor denigrated: Lindemann was heard to say that Hill seemed unable to walk past a mirror without looking in it. Lindemann was also large, very sure of his opinions and unwilling to be criticised. A committee consisting of this volatile mix of personalities, chaired by the red-headed, potentially irascible Tizard and having to grapple with contentious issues, was combustible to say the least. And combustion was soon to occur.

However, almost as soon as it was formed, an immense stroke of good fortune befell the committee. At its first meeting the agenda included a letter from Robert Watson-Watt, then Superintendent of the National Physical Laboratory's Radio Research Station at Ditton Park, near Slough. He was an expert on high-frequency radio and atmospheric research, and his letter was an indirect result of Wimperis' meeting with Professor Hill. Following his talks with Hill and his memorandum to the Secretary of State, Wimperis had decided to consult Watson-Watt, who later recalled that the subject was radiation. He was asked how much of it would be required to heat a certain amount of liquid to a certain temperature. A far lesser scientist would quickly have realised that the amount in question was similar to the amount of blood in the human body, and that he was in fact being asked to advise on a 'death ray'.

The story of the development of radar is famous and need not be repeated in full here. It was known for a long time as R. D. F., or radio direction-finding, in order to confuse an enemy – in that, at the time the name was coined, direction-finding was the principal thing it could not do. Later on, during the war, the Americans were to use the term 'radar', short for 'radio detection and ranging', and that is the name that stuck.

What is attractive, although not the essence of the story, is the very Englishness of the way in which radar came about. In 1931 there had occurred an event that was little noticed at the time, but which was to have far-reaching consequences. Post Office engineers had been experimenting with VHF links between Colney Hatch and the Post Office experimental station at Dollis Hill, to see if it would be possible for wireless programmes to be broadcast between Scotland and the Western Isles. During these trials the engineers had, with some irritation, noticed what they called a 'flutter effect' whenever an aeroplane flew overhead. They accepted it as unavoidable, however, and merely noted it in their report as a 'nuisance'. In due course that report came to the notice of a number of scientists, including A. F. Wilkins, generally known as 'Skip'.

Some time later, in January 1935, Wilkins (by then deputy to Watson-Watt) was in a hut at the Research Station at Slough, discussing with

Watson-Watt the request that he had received from Wimperis. It did not take them long to realise that the amount of energy required for Wimperis' purpose was beyond the scope of current technology, and that 'death rays' would have to remain for the time being on the pages of fiction. Watson-Watt then remarked to Wilkins: 'Well, then, if the death ray is not possible, how can we help them?' It was at this moment that Wilkins recalled the story of the engineers at Dollis Hill, and it struck him immediately that an aircraft meeting a short-wave radio pulse would act as a radiator and reflect a signal back to the transmitter.[26]

So it was that the connection was first made between radiation and the detection of aircraft: over a cup of tea in a hut at Slough, less than four years before the outbreak of the Second World War:

> The result was that within four years we had designed, developed, deployed, and manned a chain of radar stations capable of detecting bombers at a hundred miles range; and a plotting, reporting and control system that would enable defending fighters to be directed to intercept incoming bombers.[27]

Having thought about Wimperis' request, Watson-Watt sent a reply that discounted 'death rays' but suggested that it might nevertheless be possible to locate an aeroplane by the use of radio waves. This letter was circulated at the first meeting of the Tizard Committee, on 28 January 1935, when it was agreed that in view of the appalling state of the current defence systems, the paramount task for the committee was to find a way of receiving early warning of the approach of enemy aircraft. In due course Watson-Watt sent the committee a memorandum setting out further details of his ideas. It was entitled 'Detection and Location of Aircraft by Radio Methods' and has become a historic document.

Events thereafter swiftly gathered pace. Treasury funding for radar development was approved almost without delay, and a few weeks later, on 26 February, an experiment took place that has become celebrated as one of the milestones in scientific advance. It was set up near Daventry, close to a BBC short-wave overseas radio transmitter. A fabric-covered Heyford bomber lumbered off the grass runway at Farnborough, with instructions to fly at 6,000 feet across the path of transmission signals. These signals would in effect illuminate the aeroplane, from which they would be reflected and then received by a screen on the ground, linked to a cathode-ray oscillograph.

The men on the ground were Rowe, Watson-Watt and Wilkins, besides the driver of their white van known as the 'travelling-laboratory'. As the aeroplane made its flight, the three men peered into a small television screen and watched green blobs of light, which began to expand and contract on the cathode-ray tube as the aeroplane drew near. The scattered signal was picked up when the aeroplane was more than seven miles distant. The scientists then realised that what they had witnessed was the clear and definite early warning of an aircraft's approach. It was an historic moment. At the end of the experiment Watson-Watt turned to his colleagues and, perhaps with Blériot[28] in mind, triumphantly exclaimed: 'Britain has become an island once more.'

With the success of this experiment the Tizard Committee had been presented with the basic solution to its greatest problem. It might have been hoped that if radar experiments were then put in hand, the work of the committee would proceed smoothly. The reality was to be very different, largely because of the belligerence directed towards the committee's affairs by Churchill and Lindemann, who strongly believed that not only radar but all other possible channels should be explored in the search for improvements to the nation's defences.

When Lindemann began to suspect that the Tizard Committee was being ineffective, he lost no time reporting the fact to Churchill. Tizard, by contrast, felt, as did the other scientists on his committee, that it was no part of their brief – or Lindemann's – to indulge in such politics. Moreover, being on the CID as well, Tizard could clearly see when Lindemann had been briefing Churchill, and he strongly resented it.

Meanwhile Churchill continued with unflagging energy to expound his fears whenever he saw an opportunity to do so, making use of the valuable information about Germany consistently supplied to him by Lindemann. In November 1935, for example, Churchill published an article entitled 'The Truth About Hitler'. He first discussed its contents with Lindemann, who put forward facts and suggested amendments. After a bleak and damning description of the butchery and excesses that had burst upon the German scene, the article ended:

But the astounding thing is that the great German people, educated, scientific, philosophical, romantic, the people of the Christmas tree, the people of Goethe and Schiller, of Bach and Beethoven, Heine, Leibnitz, Kant and a hundred other great names, have not only not resented this horrible blood-bath, but have endorsed it and acclaimed its author with the honours not only of a sovereign but almost of a God. Here is the frightful fact before which what is left of European civilisation must bow its head in shame, and what is to more practical purpose, in fear.[29]

It was against this background of menace and disorder that Lindemann sat down with the Tizard Committee, and it may in part explain why he behaved with such impatience. He was not concerned with such trifles as his colleagues' feelings: he was drawn by the gravity of England's plight, and by the need for vigour and vitality in the ever more pressing task of rearming the country. His relations with his fellow scientists were also soured by the way in which he was apt to treat people with whom he was not in sympathy. His rather nasal mumbling would assume a harsher edge when he was angry or impatient, and his voice would adopt an offputting sneer. 'What is all this nonsense that you are proposing?' was an expression that he frequently used, and he would often interject with 'You can't mean that seriously, surely not?' Such comments jarred with his colleagues.

From the first committee meeting that Lindemann attended, friction and dispute hovered in the air. His close liaison with Churchill was one difficulty, but there were two other sources of conflict. One was that Lindemann felt that the conduct of the occasional practical experiments that the committee ordered was far too sluggish and half-hearted; that applied, significantly, even to experiments in radar. The other cause of friction was Lindemann's insistence on exploring lines of research that were regarded by his colleagues as both wildly impracticable and complete red herrings – in which respect, it has to be said, they had a point.

One idea that he had was for dispersing clouds of gas or explosive dust, such as nitrogen iodide, in the path of oncoming aircraft: some to enervate or kill the pilots, and some to cause their aircraft to explode. He also called persistently for practical experiments in infra-red detection of aeroplanes; his former pupil, R. V. Jones, was working on infra-red at the Clarendon Laboratory, and Lindemann offered Jones' services to the experts at Farnborough. This work was directed primarily towards developing thermal equipment for night detection of aircraft at a range of about a mile, to fill a possible gap between the minimum radar range and maximum visual range. Jones commented:

> As is well known, relations between Professor Lindemann and Mr Tizard – once most cordial – had already become strained, and it may have gratified the former to have a detection technique being developed in his own laboratory which had been dismissed by the Tizard Committee, particularly since he might reasonably claim to have invented it.[30]

Another idea that Lindemann repeatedly pressed for was the preparation of wire barrages, with which enemy aeroplanes would collide and plummet to earth. This proposal did at least expose one problem that electrified the committee, demonstrating as it did the lack of urgency within the Air Ministry: Tizard was told, first, that for the wire experiments a specially equipped aeroplane would be necessary, but second, that one would not be available for a whole year. The committee's minutes state:

> Professor Lindemann thereupon informed the Secretary that he would be quite ready to undertake the experiment himself as the matter was pressing. Colonel Tizard said that this would be offensive to the Air Force and at a meeting on the 4th December it was stated that the Air Force would make the experiments, using fishing lines instead of wires and small fragile vessels filled with ink to show where they hit the wing.[31]

One can but wonder what the Germans would have made of this.

Paramount among Lindemann's ideas, however, and the chief irritant to the other members, were his proposals for aerial mines. Before his first attendance he had written to Tizard: 'The thing I am keenest on is to get ahead with the small aerial mines.' Ack-ack against night bombers was a forlorn hope, he maintained, and a barrage, 'plastering a certain area of sky' as he described it, was the better way. He produced detailed figures and suppositions, describing the objective as 'rendering certain regions of the air extremely dangerous if not fatal to passing machines'. The possible ways of achieving this, he suggested, included strewing large numbers of small, cheap mines in the path of attacking aeroplanes, supported by parachutes or even balloons; he also proposed non-explosive weights suspended on cables or parachutes, which would wind themselves around an aeroplane wing.

These proposals, repeatedly put forward, were received with growing impatience by the committee, although at length, after long and acrimonious discussion, experiments on the mines were set in hand at Farnborough. The results fully bore out the scepticism of the rest of the committee. It was eventually estimated that the overall efficiency of an aerial minefield as a lethal weapon was about one in twenty, meaning that to have any appreciable effect, a prodigious number of mines would have to be carried up and dropped – or even, as one suggestion had it, fired with parachutes from anti-aircraft guns.

The other scientists were utterly dismayed. The picture of aerial minefields that shimmered before their eyes was one of a sky filled to the horizon with balloons and parachutes, and with enormous and unsustainable numbers of aeroplanes dropping all manner and size of projectile, very few of which would ever hit the enemy, and most of which would land on the population below, no doubt to be picked up by children who would glee-fuly start throwing them at each other.

What, in his colleagues' view, added insult to injury was the manner of Lindemann's delivery. In their youth, Tizard and he had been good friends, but that was no longer the case. Nor did Lindemann hide his lack of personal interest in the other members, and he looked at them with distaste. With Tizard himself he came readily to verbal blows. As Blackett recalls: 'On one occasion Lindemann became so fierce with Tizard that the secretaries had to be sent out of the committee room so as to keep the squabble as private as possible.'[32] This was a side of Lindemann that many people saw and few forgot:

> Lindemann made himself unnecessarily objectionable to a large number of people, although it seems likely that he rarely committed the sin of being rude by accident.[33]

Yet Lindemann seemed unmoved by all such unpleasantness. He was consumed by the thought that German rearmament was becoming a threat to Britain's very existence. To him, the lack of 'push and drive', as he called it, in carrying out the scientific experiments, was a wholly proper matter for strong reactions.

The bubble of resentment among his colleagues became further inflated as a result of a dispute over progress in RDF experiments. Lindemann's critical eye had come to rest on Watson-Watt and his work, by now centred at Orfordness, a suitably remote area about ninety miles north-east of London. Lindemann strongly approved of this research and was more than willing to believe in its potential. He nevertheless took the view that the committee should not put all its eggs in one basket, or exclude examina-tion of other forms of defence.

In a way that was to cause sharp offence to Tizard, Lindemann informed Churchill about Watson-Watt's progress in RDF development. In February 1936 Churchill had written to the Cabinet Secretary, having discussed the draft with Lindemann:

> I am much concerned by the slight and slow progress that we are making in Air Defence, in spite of the fact that we have such a very able and authoritative committee. It is more than eighteen months since Professor Lindemann and I began to press for the experiments upon the proposals set out in various secret papers. I cannot feel that enough progress has been made even in the experiments. The crisis which is approaching may be upon us long before any practical results are delivered. This causes me much anxiety. . .[34]

Lindemann had suggested adding a paragraph:

The only part of the Committee's work which has so far been successful has been the development of methods of detection and location. The reason for this seems to me to be that it has been put in the hands of a man who supported the method and believed in it and that he could and did push ahead with whatever experiments he thought necessary. I consider this work is most important and should be continued with the highest priority. More especially should efforts be made to develop methods to enable our fighter aeroplanes to find and close with the enemy.[35]

However, a short time after Lindemann had made his suggestion Watson-Watt had gone down to Oxford to see him, to sound him out about suitable personnel to help with his radar work. During their discussions Lindemann derived the impression that Watson-Watt felt he was not getting the support that he deserved from Tizard's committee, and that he was dissatisfied with the pace of its activity. He therefore wrote to Churchill suggesting that he had a 'private talk with him [Watson-Watt] and perhaps with A. P. Rowe, the secretary of the Committee. I have reason to know,' Lindemann added, 'they are both most dissatisfied with the slowness and lack of drive which have been exhibited.'

However, on 25 May, and before the proposed meeting took place, Churchill wrote to Sir Thomas Inskip, the newly created Minister for Co-ordination of Defence – an appointment that Lindemann described as the most cynical thing done since Caligula appointed his horse a consul – and in his letter spelt out his dim view of the committee's problems.

You will be shocked to see how slow, timid and insignificant is the progress made. I was astonished that Swinton in the Lords four months ago should have referred to the work of this Committee in such glowing terms. It is a very good Committee; it works most agreeably together; it has many bright ideas; but action and progress, except in the one respect I mentioned, are pitiful.

Accustomed as I was to see how things were done in the war, and how orders can be given for large scale experiment and supply, I have been deeply pained by the dilettante futility which has marked our action.[36]

The 'one respect' that Churchill referred to was of course the work on RDF. However, Lindemann now believed that even that was not being pursued with sufficient vigour, so on 12 June he took Watson-Watt to see Churchill.

When the other committee members heard about this meeting, they were extremely put out, and it soured their relations with Lindemann even further. For it was at this meeting that Watson-Watt suggested that not enough drive was being applied to RDF. He later wrote:

> Winston Churchill expressed anxiety about whether the speed of advance in RDF was as great as could be attained. I replied that it most certainly was not, and I went on to give my diagnosis of the prime cause of avoidable delays. It was that the Air Ministry was stubbornly adhering to a foredoomed policy. It was attempting to force its normal machinery to revolve at an abnormal pace, instead of setting up abnormal machinery to meet a highly abnormal need.[37]

To its opponents it was now beginning to seem that the Air Ministry's whole approach was dilatory. A further example concerned the erection of Chain Home Stations, the line of early-warning radar towers that, it had now been agreed, was to be built along the coast of Britain. These towers were to form the core of the country's defence against the Luftwaffe, yet from the outset they had met with delay.

One proposed site, at Fairlight, near Hastings, had immediately been opposed by the local populace, who objected to the beauty of the place being marred by an iron mast. Another site, in Yorkshire, also met with local protest; in this case, after much wrangling, the matter was referred to an arbitrator, before whom the landowner raising the objection appeared, accompanied by his gamekeeper. It was Skip Wilkins who had been given the task of finding suitable sites for the towers and for negotiating their purchase and preparation. The instructions that were handed down to him from the ministry expressed all too clearly the lack of urgency in official circles, at a time when Germany's rearmament programme was rolling forward; Wilkins' instructions stated that, to avoid argument, the sites should not 'gravely interfere with grouse shooting'.[38]

By June the disputes were coming to a head, and on 15 June Churchill, briefed by Lindemann, produced a memorandum for the CID questioning the lack of progress by Tizard's committee. Poor Tizard must have felt that he himself had flown into an aerial minefield as he was confronted in open forum with this memo, which he was called upon to answer point by point. At the next meeting of the Tizard Committee restraint seems finally to have been abandoned. Tizard was affronted by the grilling that he had received from the CID committee and believed that it was entirely due to special pleading by Lindemann, who in his view had briefed Churchill with erroneous facts.

Lindemann now poured fuel on the flames by dissenting from the committee's Interim Progress Report and submitting his own, prefacing it with a gibe about the lack of time he had been given to do so. This dissenting opinion is of great importance, in view of subsequent allegations that Lindemann had hindered the development of radar.[39] In his report he expressed his regret that the committee had not, as previously agreed, put Watson-Watt in charge of communications as well as detection and location experiments. In fact, Lindemann not only valued and encouraged the RDF developments, but also believed that a unified communications structure should be an integral part of them.

Watson-Watt himself emphatically confirmed Lindemann's support:

> Nowhere, in my memory, in my personal records, or in any official records in my possession, do I find even the merest shadow of evidence that Lindemann ever did anything whatever to obstruct the development of radar in accordance with my proposals.[40]

However, the other scientists had by now had enough of Lindemann. On 15 July Hill and Blackett sent in their resignations to the Air Minister. In his letter Blackett wrote:

> My view as to the best procedure to expedite the study of air defence differs so widely from that of Professor Lindemann that I feel that further work together on the Committee will be too difficult to be fruitful.[41]

Rather like two witnesses giving evidence in court separately, yet apparently reading from the same text, Hill's resignation letter made the same point as Blackett's. The conclusive allegation, however, came from Tizard himself, who highlighted for the Air Minister the ways in which Lindemann had clearly been a difficult colleague. 'I must ask you,' he wrote, 'either to remove Lindemann from the Committee or to accept my resignation', and he continued:

> I cannot have a member of my Committee, who has failed to convince his colleagues, trying to force his views through outside influential people . . . His querulousness when anybody differs from him, his inability to accept the views of the Committee as a whole, and his consequent insistence on talking about matters which we think are

relatively unimportant, and hence preventing us from getting on with more important matters, make him an impossible colleague . . . when at the last meeting he accused a member of your Farnborough staff to his face with slackness and deliberate obstruction, without the smallest justification, I felt that the limit of my patience had been reached.[42]

Faced with this litany of complaint, the Government decided that the only answer would be for the committee to be dissolved and reconstituted without Lindemann.

So now he had to take his fight to a different battleground. He had campaigned through the columns of the press and he had fought in committee, to no avail; there was one further platform that he felt he could mount. Professor Hill's resignation letter referred with some asperity to this new development. It had greatly upset the scientists, feeling as they did that politics were no part of their role:

It is clear, moreover, from paragraphs in this morning's Press, in reference to Professor Lindemann's candidature for Oxford University, that he intends to use any available method of advertising the unique value of his opinions.[43]

A parliamentary by-election had been called for one of the two university seats at Oxford, and Lindemann had thrown his hat into the ring. Rejected by his fellow scientists, he now moved on alone. While peaceful harmony was restored to the meetings of the Tizard Committee, Lindemann made plans to bring to the ears of a wider audience the discord that was mounting beyond the Channel.

EIGHT

Professors for Parliament

> I suppose nothing will be done until the bombs begin to
> fall and then it will be too late.
>
> Lindemann to Harcourt Johnstone, MP,
> March 1937

Montague Rhodes James is generally thought to be one of the most learned men who have ever lived, and when he died it was said that a considerable body of human knowledge died with him. He was celebrated also as the author of ghost stories so sharp and chilling that they retain to this day their place in English literature. In June 1936 he departed this world for those spirit realms with which he seemed so familiar. This created a vacancy in the post of Provost of Eton, of which he was the incumbent, and shortly afterwards the Crown offered to appoint in his place Lord Hugh Cecil, the son of Queen Victoria's last Prime Minister.

In 1936 Cecil was one of Oxford University's two Members of Parliament, or burgesses as they were idiosyncratically called – the other being the celebrated wit and reforming lawyer, A. P. Herbert. The position of Provost of Eton carried a large stipend and an attractive house, in which Lord Hugh was probably not greatly interested, and considerable honour, in which quite reasonably he probably was. At all events he accepted the offer and in July announced his intention of resigning his Oxford parliamentary seat.

To Lindemann this seemed an ideal opportunity. He had campaigned in the press on air defence, but with muted results, and he had striven for urgent action on the Tizard Committee, but had been thrown off it. Yet all the while he believed that the danger to England was rapidly increasing. His ardent patriotism impelled him to keep sounding the alarm: what better platform from which to do so than a by-election that might open the door to the House of Commons.

The expectation of an imminent poll led at once to a flurry of activity in Oxford, largely in the form of the collegiate caballing and intrigue that delighted authors such as Trollope and C. P. Snow. Over their morning Madeira, dons and undergraduates fell to earnest discussion about who should be chosen to stand, while potential candidates began to draw up their manifestos.

As it turned out, they need have been in no hurry. Although the prevailing rules stated that a Member of Parliament could not at one and the same time draw a parliamentary salary and hold another paid position, what no one foresaw was that Cecil, although in July announcing his intention to resign, could not make up his mind as to when to do so. He gave himself time to ponder the matter by waiving any further payment as an MP. The jostling for position among the interested parties was therefore premature, and they found themselves all dressed up with nowhere to go. This caused a certain amount of resentment.

In the event Lord Hugh did not step down for a further six months, with the election at length being called in February 1937, but the aspirants to his place, hardly expecting such a delay, pressed on as the summer unfolded.

The Oxford by-election of 1937 was one of those rare contests that seem at the time to have tremendous national significance. By custom, the campaign was supposed to be conducted above and beyond party lines, but high-mindedness was on this occasion displaced by the question of European peace, which was just beginning to concern – if not yet to alarm – a great many people. The temperature was also raised by the attentions of the press, with most of the national daily and Sunday newspapers deciding to cover the contest in depth.

Although it was in Lindemann's nature to pay scant attention to what the newspapers, or other politicians, might say, and to follow his own course indifferent to the clamour all around him, his reasons for putting himself forward in this case happened exactly to match the interest of the press and the wider public: the deteriorating state of the nation's defences. Standing for Parliament was against his inclinations because his preference was to shun the limelight; yet, although his candidature would project him to the centre of the stage in Oxford and draw to him the attention of a wider audience, he felt that he must proceed, however distasteful the publicity, if not the inevitable scheming, that was involved.

It was a requirement of university elections that a candidate must have a demonstrable affiliation with the university. Lindemann felt that his qualifications were more persuasive than those of any other candidate likely to be chosen to represent the Conservative interest. At the time that interest was controlled by a committee known, usually derogatorily, as the Caucus, and Lindemann (who was a member of the Caucus) felt that his first move should be to make himself independent of this body. In his resignation letter to the secretary, however, he did not trifle with the usual niceties. His manner, which had ruffled the feathers of many of the dons and other authorities in Oxford, was now to prove an obstacle in his path to Parliament. To the committee he wrote:

As you know I have not attended the meetings of the Oxford Conservative Committee for over a year now. I gather from the fact that I recently received a circular that I am still considered a mere member. As I hear that all work in Oxford has been dropped (indeed at one of the meetings it was designated as eyewash) and as it seems that only 9 people turned up at the general meeting of whom 6 were members of the committee, I can scarcely recognise this body as representative of the electorate. For this, and other reasons, I wish formally to resign from the body.[1]

He also wrote to Sir Harry McGowan, at ICI:

At the General Meeting from which it derives its authority only three outsiders appeared so that it can scarcely claim to be representative of the 22,000 constituents. I cannot understand in these circumstances how anyone can accede to their claim that they nominate the Conservative candidate.[2]

By the time that he had freed himself from the committee, the long summer vacation, which effectively suspended all university activity, was well under way and Lindemann set off for the sun. He outlined his journey to his brother Charles, who was in France:

My present plan is to go via Vittel, Switzerland and Austria to Carlsbad, then towards the Villa d'Este . . . I should much like to get some sun and bathing after that, possibly in the neighbourhood of Rapallo if it is warm enough, alternatively going South as far as the Bay of Naples.[3]

However, he felt uneasy about the situation in Europe and wondered if it was even safe to travel. Civil war had broken out in Spain a month earlier, and Lindemann saw it as a symptom of wider revolutionary unrest, which might upset his plans. He asked for his brother's opinion:

I would be much obliged if you could let me know quickly whether motoring in France is quite all right; whether one can get petrol and whether one ought to avoid industrial areas. Many people think France may go the way of Spain.

1. Frederick Lindemann, Viscount Cherwell, PC, CH, FRS.

2. Royal Aircraft Factory BE2e, back broken after crashing.

3. Scientific staff of the Royal Aircraft Factory outside the Chudleigh Mess in 1917. *Left wall:* H. Glauert, G. P. Thompson, Lindemann; *top step:* H. Grinstee W. S. Farren; *lower step:* D. H. Pinsant, R. McKinnon Wood *right wall:* F. W. Aston, H. Renwick.

4. Lady Elizabeth Lindsay.

5. Lindemann lecturing at the Clarendon Laboratory in 1937, drawn by his pupil William Merton.

6. On board the *Sona* in 1936. The yacht belonged to Lord Camrose, proprietor of the *Daily Telegraph*, whose son, the Hon. Seymour Berry, is pictured here with Lindemann.

7. *Tea at Chartwell*, painting by Winston Churchill, 1928.
From left to right: Therese Sickert, Diana Mitford, Edward Marsh, Winston Churchill, Lindemann, Randolph Churchill, Diana Churchill, Mrs Churchill and W. R. Sickert.

8. On board HMS *Prince of Wales*, August 1941, for the historic meeting between Churchill and Roosevelt that led to the 'Atlantic Charter'. *Sitting, from left to right:* Air Marshal Sir Wilfred Freeman, Admiral Sir Dudley Pound, Churchill, General Sir John Dill, Sir Alexander Cadogan; *back row*: Commander Thompson, Lindemann, John Martin.

9. Churchill and Lindemann watching an anti-aircraft demonstration, June 1941.
From left to right: Lindemann, Air Chief Marshal Sir Charles Portal, Admiral Sir Dudley Pound, Churchill, Major-General Lock.

BUCK RYAN

A Military Intelligence officer drives Buck Ryan and Zola from the late Lord Brompton's shooting estate to Ack Ack Headquarters, where Ryan now reports his findings

...THOSE ARE THE SPOTS FROM WHERE THESE NAZIS INTENDED TO WORK. THEIR SCHEME WAS SIMPLE AND BASED ON THE ELEMENT OF SURPRISE. THEY HOPED—

TO DISORGANISE OUR RADIO LOCATION CONTROL AT SUCH TIME WHEN THE ENEMY DECIDE TO INVADE OUR COUNTRY. IT WOULD BE AT NIGHT TIME AND NAZI AGENTS WERE TO TOW BOX-KITES—MADE WITH METAL ALLOY FRAMES—FLYING AT ABOUT 5,000 FT AROUND THAT ZONE OF ACK-ACK GUN SITES. CARS WERE TO HAVE BEEN USED FOR TOWING—HIRED OR STOLEN!

10. 'Window'.
The veil of secrecy surrounding its development was inadvertently threatened by a cartoonist in the *Daily Mirror*.

THIS WAS THEIR THEORY... THE GUN-LAYER PICKS UP AN OBJECT ON HIS RADIO LOCATION SCREEN CALCULATED TO BE MOVING AT 20 TO 40 MILES AN HOUR. TOO SLOW FOR A PLANE! WHAT IS IT? HE KNOWS IT ISN'T A BALLOON ADRIFT! HE REPORTS IT. SO DO NEIGHBOURING GUN-LAYERS. EVERYONE'S BAFFLED! ORDERS ARE: HOLD FIRE UNTIL THE SEARCHLIGHTS SORT IT OUT! NOW—

WORKING TO SCHEDULE, THE LUFTWAFFE TROOP CARRIERS FLY IN OVER THIS ZONE TO LAND THEIR JUNKERS WHILE CONFUSION REIGNS BELOW! GET THE IDEA?

YES. AND IT MIGHT HAVE WORKED TWELVE MONTHS AGO, RYAN, BUT NOT TODAY!

GOOD OLD ACK-ACK!

The End

11. Magdalen Bridge, Oxford, photographed by Lindemann.

12. Drawing of a vase, by Lindemann.

13. Brigadier Lindemann and Franz Simon.

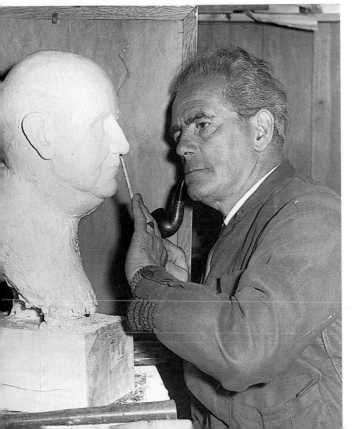

14. Lindemann's servant, Harvey, was almost as artistic as his master. Here he is seen working on a sculpture.

15. Lindemann with the daughter of fellow scientist Franz Simon, who fled the Nazis.

And he ended his letter on a note of gloom: 'The more I see of Europe the more I wish I lived in America.'[4]

He shared the fears of many people that the civil war might threaten the security of capitalist society. Youthful idealists from both sides of the Atlantic had gone to fight in Spain, and it became a popular subject for modernist poets, parodied many years later by Osbert Lancaster in his poem 'crackup in barcelona':

> *. . . and I am left balanced on capricorn*
> *the knife-edge tropic between anxiety and regret*
> *while the racing editions are sold at the gates of football grounds*
> *and maxi lies on a bare catalan hillside*
> *knocked off the tram by a fascist conductor*
> *who misinterpreted a casual glance.*[5]

An invitation that Lindemann had no qualms about accepting that summer came from Lord Camrose, proprietor of the *Daily Telegraph*, who asked him aboard his yacht *Sona*, cruising across the Baltic to Russia. Despite being prone to sea-sickness, Lindemann happily accepted and joined the luxurious boat. He took with him his specially designed Leica camera. This had a false lens in the front and a real lens in the side, and when they reached Moscow he delighted in appearing to photograph permitted views such as the beautiful buildings, while in fact – without the knowledge of their official guides – capturing with the side lens the tramps and drunks and Stalinist squalor that lay all about them. After this trip he wrote that he found Russia 'incredibly drab and discouraging – the most ferocious state capitalism with the most brutal exploitation of the workers. It would do our Socialists all the good in the world to see it.'

Back at Oxford at the end of the summer, Lindemann turned his attention once more to the political fight. He still expected his nomination to be officially endorsed, but soon discovered that the dozen or so dons on the Caucus had long memories and were sufficiently hostile to run a candidate against him.

He realised that it would be a serious matter if the Caucus were to field a candidate of their own: it would probably split the Conservative vote, and thereby hand victory to the independent candidate. This was Sir Arthur Salter, a professor of political theory and a writer on economics. He was also a Fellow of All Souls College, to which at that time belonged many eminent men sympathetic to the Government's policy of appeasing the dictators. Salter's politics, however, also had a liberal element, and he strongly supported the League of Nations, despite its history of utter futility.

Lindemann was popular with undergraduate Conservatives, of whose committee he was a vice-president, but their voice counted for little, and at the selection meeting held by the Caucus, at the House of Commons, it was decided by fourteen to eleven to nominate a different official candidate.

The man they selected was Sir Farquhar Buzzard,[6] a well-known specialist in mental health, although his expertise in this field was not accepted without murmur. In the words of one of Oxford's leading historians:

> Buzzard was Regius Professor of Medicine, but he was widely thought to know nothing whatever about medicine. He had only taken a Fourth Class in his degree, but he had subsequently managed to get himself appointed as nerve specialist to King George V; and as the king had nerves like an ox Buzzard's ignorance didn't matter.

However, the Regius Professor had in his time played football for the university, and was known to take an active interest in the physical welfare of undergraduates. The electorate could also take comfort from his claim that he was 'neither a politician nor an expert in any brand of departmental administration'. Buzzard had a further appeal to the Oxford electors: he was both physician to, and a good friend of, Lord Nuffield, who was believed to be considering large donations to the university – during the later 1930s he was to give to Oxford exceptionally large sums of money (amounting to approximately £120 million today).

The Caucus also objected to Lindemann's electoral platform. It was an unwritten rule in Oxford elections that there should be no campaigning, beyond the publication of rather bland manifestos and statements of intent in the local press. Lindemann ignored this civilised custom: both he and his prominent supporters in Parliament and in the press thought that the times were too serious for the customary delicacies, and that the issues should be sounded more audibly than the graceful chimes of Oxford's bells.

He based his call to the electors on the fact that he was an expert in aeronautical matters and that it was vital that they should return to Parliament a scientist, who could make it difficult for Government ministers to fob off the back benches. As he wrote:

> In scientific matters the ministers themselves are usually at a loss. They call for a report and a committee assures them, often in language so technical as to be incomprehensible, that everything is going well. Here the presence of a scientist in the House of Commons may do some real good. Even the knowledge that he is there will stimulate the

committee or body concerned. And in the matter of air defence this is badly needed.[7]

Lindemann published his manifesto almost as soon as Lord Hugh announced his retirement. He could make a real contribution, he said, 'today when aerial bombardment threatens not only our lives but our very national existence', and he added:

> I have long maintained that it should be possible to defend our coast-line and to prevent, by other means than mere reprisals, enemy planes from bombing our cities. To develop some form of defence on these lines and to see that our air rearmament effort is well directed is one of my main objectives.[8]

In the cut and thrust of the campaign, rumours about Lindemann's ancestry abounded, so he made a rare exception to his reticence on the subject by directly addressing the matter. To an official of the Oxford Union who had confronted Lindemann with the question, he wrote:

> . . . In reply to your question I can state categorically that I am not a Jew and do not number any Jews among my ancestors. I cannot under-stand how such a rumour was started; it may have been because I gave some eminent Jewish scientists, who had been compelled to leave Germany, an opportunity to continue researches in my laboratory.[9]

Lindemann did not help himself in this respect by his occasional taunts at Jews: this aroused suspicion in the same way as Oswald Mosley, whose polit-ical profile at this time was particularly high, and who also suffered from accusations of anti-Semitism. Yet when, many years later, Mosley's wife Diana was asked if her husband was anti-Semitic, she was able to answer: 'Well you know he really wasn't. He didn't know a Jew from a Gentile; but of course some of his supporters *did*, and they made trouble.'[10] As Lindemann stated, there was no evidence of Jewish blood in his family, and whatever others may have thought about the matter, he himself appears to have paid it scant attention.

The Caucus's resentment was further inflamed when Churchill came down to Oxford to support Lindemann. He made a speech at the Oxford Union, where, according to the *Oxford Times*, he drew the largest crowd since Lloyd George's appearance in 1912. Churchill rose to the occasion, pouring amused scorn on Salter as an economist, saying that 'economists as a class have been rather under a cloud since their pathetic failure to give any practical lead in the great financial crisis of 1930'. He continued, describing Salter as 'a great authority on economic subjects':

> Like all of them he has made mistakes; for instance when he eulogised the late Ivar Kreugar as one of the portents of future finance, one of those guides who blazed trails along which mankind would follow. While the book was still in the Press the unfortunate gentleman who was the subject of his praise had to commit suicide through gigantic frauds.[11]

This was a reference to the misplaced admiration that Salter had expressed for the 'Swedish Match King', one of the long and loathsome line of those who have been hailed and fêted by the City and the financial world, only to turn out to be as crooked as sixpence. In the end Kreugar concluded that to hear the heavy tread of creditors, and to be divested of his fraudulent gains, would be a fate worse than death, and he took the only course open to him.

Autumn turned to winter, and still the sitting MP, Lord Hugh, found 'no means of knowing when he expected to go'. However, the forthcoming election had become the topic of widespread discussion. Harold Nicolson recorded in his diary that he attended a lunch party at the House of Commons in honour of Ramsay MacDonald and the celebrated American aviator, Charles Lindbergh:

> Ramsay is inane. We talk of the Oxford bye-election, and he turns to Lindbergh. 'Now mark my words,' he says, 'that Professor Lindbergh is no good at all – I know him – no good at all.' 'Lindemann?' I suggest. 'Of course,' Ramsay asserts, with a cursing gesture, as when one has missed a putt at golf. 'Of course I meant Linderbergh.' He is completely gaga.[12]

As the year drew to a close, all other politics became eclipsed by the dramatic news of the King's affair with Mrs Simpson, and by the abdication that followed it. The nation was stunned, as was the royal family itself: 'Really,' said Queen Mary, 'we might as well be living in Rumania.' Once made public, however, the matter came swiftly to a conclusion, and in the small hours of 12 December the destroyer *Fury* set sail from Portsmouth for France, to speed a most unsuitable king to join, in exile, a wildly improbable queen. It was perhaps as well that at the last minute a sharp-eyed official had noted that the ex-king had been due to leave in the Admiralty yacht *Enchantress*, and a ship with a less inappropriate name had been hurriedly substituted.

Five days later Lindemann was staying at Chartwell, before setting off to spend Christmas in Rome with the Earl and Countess of Berkeley; he did not do so without characteristically going to the top and asking the Italian Ambassador, Count Grandi, to arrange an interview for him with Mussolini. Lindemann would have had few illusions about the Italian dictator, and no doubt recognised the cynicism implicit in Mussolini's comment on his countrymen: 'Every Italian wants to be invested with a little bit of authority, and the permission to misuse it.' It is a pity that a meeting did not occur, if only because Lindemann and Mussolini had one thing in common, which was a keen interest in Napoleon. Lindemann was an avid student of the emperor, and could recite almost every date and fact that was of interest in his life story; for his part, Mussolini had written a play about Napoleon that had been adapted for the London stage by John Drinkwater. Sadly, *Il Duce*'s crowded calendar did not permit a meeting to be held, and Lindemann was back at Chartwell in time to see in the New Year.

In January 1937 the writ for the Oxford by-election was finally moved, with polling arranged for five days at the end of the following month, it being considered at that time unnecessary to finish an election campaign with a single day of polling. Lindemann at once multiplied his submissions to the press, and prominent well-wishers added letters of their own. *The Times* noted that Lindemann had the support of a number of London daily news-papers, two evening papers and three or four Sunday papers. Responding to correspondents, Lindemann re-emphasised his theme, writing that it is 'most encouraging to receive support in my endeavours to make our houses safe against the most vile and dangerous form of attack which has ever menaced any country'.

As the election temperature increased, slogans and sayings were minted and circulated caricaturing each of the candidates. Lindemann's reputation for snobbery was unkindly attacked, with an imagined glance at his diary: 'Why is Professor Lindemann like a channel steamer?' This begged the answer 'Because he runs from peer to peer'. Another saying that gained circulation held that 'If you want to be saved from shell shock, vote for Lindemann, if you want to be treated for shell shock, vote for Buzzard, if you want to *get* shell shock, vote for Salter'.

By now Lindemann had developed an implacable grudge against the dons who had appointed Sir Farquhar Buzzard in his place. As he wrote to his younger brother Sepi, in the South of France:

I expect you have seen about my election business. Unfortunately a set of second-rate duds here have got on the Caucus and are running a Conservative against me, who will split the vote and very likely let the Socialist in. According to the Daily Chronicle the reason they object to me is that I do not go to their wives' tea parties sufficiently assiduously, also that I do not ride a bicycle. The man they are putting up is a well-known luny doctor. It is believed that in his day he must have had most of them under his care, but evidently has failed to effect a complete cure . . .[13]

The *Daily Chronicle* had touched on a point that was wholly accurate: however sociable Lindemann was with the upper classes and with those scientists who engaged his interest, he took little part in the middle-class life of north Oxford. One exception was his habit of visiting Professor Simon's family for tea on Sundays. Simon's daughter remembered him on these occasions:

Difficult, arrogant, which some people say was just a cover for various resentments, especially the way he was received in England – he had a lot of trouble with his German name; and frightfully introspective and unwilling to open up. Very quiet, reclusive almost. He used to come to us every Sunday afternoon when we had open house for tea. He always came but he didn't want to be involved with family life or anything like that. He was a very definite bachelor. He would talk to my father about important issues but he was not sociable at all in any sense of the word. He was always in a dark suit and a bowler hat. He didn't mix with the other people. He would just sit there and try to talk to my father. He was not a mixer at all and he'd obviously arranged beforehand with the chauffeur to pick him up at a certain time. But he wanted to come because underneath it all he rather enjoyed it.[14]

In the place of support from north Oxford, Lindemann had the backing of nearly a hundred MPs, who had circulated a statement expressing his suitability for the seat and saying that his knowledge of the scientific and practical aspects of aeronautical questions would be of real value to the House of Commons.

Yet the voters were not persuaded. When the results were announced it was seen, as Lindemann had feared, that he and the official Conservative had split the vote between them, letting in the independent. At first Lindemann was downhearted, and wrote in tired despair to a friend in Parliament:

As you know, I have been fighting for nearly three years now to get more done on developing a real air defence; in fact it was to focus attention on this that I fought the recent election. But apparently nothing can be done about the inertia or perhaps even hostility of the Departments. Questions in Parliament can always be ridden off by an answer in technical language provided there is no scientist there to cope with it. Direct approaches to the Cabinet are met with sympathy and the assurance that their advisers tell them everything possible is being done. Letters to the Press are ignored. I suppose nothing will be done until the bombs begin to fall and then it will be too late.[15]

In a letter to *The Times* he refuted the suggestion, which had dogged him throughout the election, that as a professor he would do more good in his laboratory:

The suggestion that I should make my contribution to national defence by work in my laboratory can only emanate from persons completely ignorant of scientific and technical matters, people whose ideas of science are apparently derived from the books of Jules Verne and Marie Corelli. They seem to think I have some wonderful ray or other, whose virtues I desire to expound at Westminster. Such things do not happen in real life . . . The defeatist attitude which inspired the saying 'the bomber will always get through' has not been exorcised.[16]

And so the dogs barked and the caravan moved on, and Lindemann wrote a last note on the election to his brother:

It is disappointing to find that an educated electorate (so-called) is so little alive to the air danger but at any rate I have done all I could to make them realise it, and if they get it in the neck now they have no one but themselves to blame.[17]

Sir John Masterman, Provost of Worcester College and Lindemann's former Oxford tennis partner, later observed:

You could trace the beginning of the growth of Lindemann's popularity and the softening of his angularities to the aftermath of that election. When that bone of contention was out of the way he was no longer regarded as a personal enemy. People more and more tried to sit next to him, whereas formerly they had other ideas, and the little puzzles that he produced after dinner became the subject of affectionate attention.[18]

Perhaps it was as well that Lindemann was not returned to the House of Commons. In the words of Lady Townsend, the wife of one of his colleagues at Oxford:

> Lindemann was just about the worst person who could possibly have entered the House of Commons, since he hadn't the slightest rapport with either the lower or the middle classes, was quite unsuited to the hurly-burly and would have been a pitiable figure there.
>
> He had no comprehension of the way of life or the manner of behaviour of the vast majority of the population of the British Isles – nothing whatever about the proletariat, and little more with the retired clergyman type with whom I had so frequently to deal, although he was capable of great kindness, as when he listened with exemplary patience to an old friend of mine who told him the same story six times.
>
> His views on penal conditions were medieval. He truly believed in making prisons as gruesome as possible, setting back the clock and intensifying hanging and the cat o'nine tails.[19]

Certainly it would be hard to imagine Lindemann handling with relish an MP's surgery. Yet, as it turned out, his loss of the election was to be the country's gain: he would now be free to provide invaluable assistance to Churchill in his lonely efforts to warn both Government and people of the growing menace to peace.

NINE

While England Slept

I have no hesitation in saying, after the personal contact I had established
with Herr Hitler, that I believe he means what he says.

Neville Chamberlain, 1938

During his campaign Lindemann had stayed no fewer than eight times with
the Churchill family at Chartwell, and it was there that he went shortly
after the election was over. Lindemann's many invitations to Chartwell,
which continued until war broke out, were not merely social, even though
Churchill and his family loved having him to stay: they were working visits,
during which he helped Churchill develop his unremitting campaign to
regain office. Both men were determined by all means possible to force the
Government to take note of the state of the country's air defence, which
was poor and getting worse with every month that passed.

By now Churchill and Lindemann had formed a happy partnership, and
it was flowering at a most opportune moment in the country's fortunes. As
Jan Bronowski put it:

> He and Churchill were matched socially, in tastes and in temperament;
> but they were also matched in intellect, and from the time of Hitler's
> rise they formed the most powerful combination of minds that dared
> look over the political horizon.[1]

Lindemann had his own reasons for taking to heart the growing threat
to Britain, and they fortified him against the hostility that he aroused. First,
his years in Germany before the Great War had opened his eyes to the
bombastic and aggressive traits in the Prussian character; despite the many
friendships that he had formed with Germans in those years, he had been
left with a deep-seated dislike of the Prussians in general.

A second influence was his predilection for people who were well-
informed, influential or of good family. He much enjoyed the life of the
rich, and took pleasure in the stately homes of England, and in the attractive women and knowledgeable men who occupied them. He also liked the
convivial dinners at The Other Club and similar gatherings, and he relished

the freedom to travel. He cherished these adjuncts to his life as a professor, with its collegiate atmosphere and donnish discussions, and viewed with hostility any threat to their stability.

Third, in Lindemann's character there was a certain ruthlessness that nursed a desire for power; he did not necessarily continue to seek political power, but he wanted his voice to be heard where he believed he could wield same influence.

Lastly, Lindemann's intellect was such that he could perceive only too clearly the stark figures and trends that were emerging, exposing the comparative strengths of Britain and Germany. To him they spelt danger in bolder letters than they did to the majority of politicians, who by their nature tended to consider such questions from many angles.

These attributes made Lindemann a persistent critic of the Government, but there may have been another factor that coloured his outlook. The Lindemann family had for generations inhabited a border area, which had many times been forced to change its nationality. Despite Lindemann's own upbringing in the green hills and lanes of Devonshire, his father had been born and brought up in Germany, and his mother was American – and possibly half Russian. It probably did not escape him that many people thought of him as slightly foreign, and it may be that a sense of not being wholly English increased the strength of his anti-German feelings. Such cases are not unusual. History shows that the most extreme nationalists are sometimes people who do not really belong to – or are on the fringes of – their adopted nation: Cavour could hardly speak Italian, Napoleon was Corsican, Stalin was Georgian, Hitler was Austrian.

In any event, once the Oxford election was over, and despite his disquiet at the political situation, Lindemann turned inwards – to Oxford, to his social life and to building up the Clarendon Laboratory.

He also had a more specific interest. One of his well-wishers during the by-election was a girl for whom he appears to have developed a special affection. She was Lady Elizabeth Lindsay, daughter of the Earl of Crawford and Balcarres and niece of Sir Ronald Lindsay, the British Ambassador in Washington. Lindemann first met her in 1935 and soon they were seeing each other regularly in London and in Oxford, writing to each other and meeting at parties and the theatre. From her letters Elizabeth Lindsay appears to have been an engaging, attractive and intelligent woman – with slight 'blue-stocking' leanings – and her attributes seem to have appealed to Lindemann.

By today's standards the letters seem rather restrained – even Lindemann's name is not at first easily dealt with, as Elizabeth did not like calling him 'Prof', and was not comfortable with 'Lindemann'. Yet her letters show a warmth and tenderness that had clearly penetrated his reserve, despite the considerable difference in their ages: when their friendship began she was twenty-seven and he was forty-nine:

3.viii.35.

Dear Lindemann,

(What else to call you, please? Since you scorn your own names and I scorn 'Prof'.) Thank you so much for sending Winston's book; how kind of you to remember. I haven't read it yet, but I mean to begin it this evening. I have just alternately skipped-and-waded through an interesting but rather too statistical book on the New Deal, & I think it will be a pleasant change!

It is so heavenly here now – how I love being in the country. Do you like it too? Or are you too sociable to make a really good cabbage – like me? How is the ankle – better, I hope. Am I forgiven yet for your early rise on Tuesday morning – I am afraid you must have cursed me, all the way from Oxford to Devonshire. There is no news at all for you, but I hope you are well. Please take abroad a few visiting cards and write me an occasional letter.

A little later she wrote happily again:

Dear Malade Imaginaire,

(Here's the French superscription which your multi-lingual soul demands.) Thank you for writing – I loved hearing all your news, and I am so glad you are enjoying yourself – but oughtn't you to be in Norwich with all the other scientists? They are being very busy there, and will be missing you sadly. I was much amused at you trying in vain to persuade the Vittel physicians to prescribe a cure for your non-existent maladies – but I hope you didn't go there because you were feeling ill? Your route sounds lovely except for the Riviera which I hate the sound of without ever having been there. You make no mention of Hungary, so I suppose you were able to persuade M . . .? (whatever his name is) to give you carte-blanche with his cellarful of radium.[2]

I came down from Balcarres yesterday & shall be here for a few days. I think it is the first time I have ever been in London in September, and I find there is a certain fascination in a semi-deserted city and a house in dust sheets.

Last week I made a brief excursion into Inverness-shire . . . It was a lovely place. I picked gentians, and fished and caught nothing, and – unlike you! – climbed little mountains. But I like the nice peaceful sound of just looking at the big mountains. And anyway it conjures up a pleasing picture in my mind's eye – of you and the psalmist David (complete with sling and harp) sitting side by side in your broken-down car, and lifting up your eyes *only*, unto the hills. I can never remember if the Harp David and the Sling David are one and the same, or not; but anyway, here I have given him the benefit of the doubt.

Please don't invent any more horrible sayings and attribute them to me; I find that most upsetting to my peace of mind. I am sorry if I disturbed your peace of mind. It was unintentional, I assure you. You shall be called almost anything you like, *except* Prof. My objection to that is that it reminds me too forcibly of a certain intellectual disparity which I wish did not exist.

Write again soon, please,
　　Elizabeth.

At the end of that year she went to the British Embassy in Washington, to work for her uncle. Lindemann sent her a New Year telegram, to which she replied:

British Embassy,
Washington.
1. January, 1936

My dear F.,
This is to wish you a very happy New Year and to thank you for the telegram, which I loved getting. I sent one to you, too, but it returned to me after many days, so I presume, Dr Livingstone, that you are travelling incognito. But cognito or incognito, I hope you are enjoying yourself and that the snow had all melted before you arrived. It is deeply snowy here, and I have just been endangering my worthless life tobogganing down a steep and woody hill-side.

Thank you again for the books. They were especially welcome, as there was no-one very nice on board (and the Atlantic is desperately wide) – so the study of science continued apace. But I confess I was ashamed to display my crass ignorance to less kindly eyes than yours, so 'Simple Science' stayed in my cabin, and the others, which at least *look* slightly less elementary went out and faced the world with me most bravely.

Write to me soon please,
　　Your un-hustling Elizabeth.

She soon followed up this letter with another.

My dear F.,
Last week my letter to you was cut off in the flower of its youth by
the FO Bag suddenly deciding to leave by an earlier train . . . I am
therefore enclosing a photograph of myself, in the hope that it may
bring a fleeting smile to the wan countenance of the convalescent . . .
I wish you would not describe yourself as old and crabbed and a grim-
galet. Such wanderings from the truth distress me not a little.
    Thank you again for writing to me.
    Goodbye,
        Yours, Elizabeth.
            (Au contraire – Venus was in heaven.)

Letters in this vein continued throughout the year, presenting a picture
of a young, intellectual girl fascinated by a self-deprecating but kindly
professor, each attracted to the other. With his earlier, hesitant steps towards
marriage, Lindemann had found himself unable to reach the journey's end.
We may never know whether things would have turned out differently in
this case: the friendship was cut short by a poignant blow. Elizabeth Lindsay
was staying with friends in Rome when she caught pneumonia. After a very
short illness, she died. In his diary for 4 February 1937 her father wrote
bleakly: 'The heartbreaking news came through this morning.' She was
buried in Rome two days later.

Lindemann had appeared to have been deeply hurt by the rejection of
his earlier advances, so the effect on him of the death of Elizabeth Lindsay
can be imagined. He seemed from then on to put ideas of married life
out of his mind; certainly he did not welcome discussion of the subject.
Nor did he warm to any frivolity in such matters: at a party at Blenheim
a group of people were discussing sex and one lady, a rather garrulous
socialite known as 'the bedbug', suddenly turned to Lindemann and said:
'Now come on, Prof, tell us when you last slept with a woman.' The poor
professor was completely nonplussed, and there followed a long and awkward
silence.

Although during these years there seemed to be widespread curiosity
about his private life, with suggestions from time to time of discreet meetings with ladies of the world – or even something darker – there is no
evidence of anything untoward. It would seem most likely, and perfectly
understandable, that having been hurt on several occasions in his early years
at Oxford, Lindemann simply squeezed such desires out of his heart.

For a time he did little work beyond overseeing the Clarendon and seeking funds to develop its research. Very soon, however, this void was to be filled by Churchill.

During the remainder of 1937 Lindemann was to be the Churchills' most frequent guest, and one of the reasons he was so often asked to stay at Chartwell was that he was much liked by Churchill's wife, Clemmie. However valuable Lindemann was to become to Churchill, the fact that he was popular with Chartwell's chatelaine must have oiled the wheels. A common bond was tennis, and a rare glimpse of Lindemann on court comes from Lady Mosley, a cousin of Clemmie, who used often to see Lindemann at Chartwell:

He played a lot of tennis with Cousin Clementine and the other guests; he played to win. There was no thought of an exhilarating volley with Prof about; his method was to drop the ball just over the net with a spin on it to stop it bouncing, if his opponent was on the back line; or if the enemy was up at the net, he would scoop up the ball so that it fell dead on the back line before it could be reached. He must have been most tiresome to play tennis against, but it amused me to watch.[3]

She was also struck by his mental agility, and recalled that at Chartwell they used to play 'Earl Grey' patience, introduced by another close companion of Churchill's, Eddie Marsh. Lindemann occasionally looked down from on high:

Prof would look over one's shoulder while one was puzzling what to do, and say: 'That won't come out. There's no point in going on'; or else, 'You can get that out in three moves'. He was a real magician.[4]

Lady Soames, Churchill's daughter, recalled:

I saw Prof as a great friend who was always there working with Papa, and was more than the other sort of people working on the books. They, and 'the invisible men', were not part of the weekend scene, they didn't come as weekend social guests.

It is very interesting, Prof never irritated my mother at all. He was the perfect guest. He always appeared at the proper time and, in the military expression, 'punctual, sober and properly dressed'. My mother took endless trouble: there was always a special, different dish cooked for Prof, endless egg dishes, and he would carefully pick out the yolks and eat the whites. Prof was never a worry; he wasn't any trouble to entertain: he would take himself off to play golf, or he was working, or he was enlightening Papa, or he was playing tennis. He was a totally wonderful guest.[5]

She added, however:

I always rather dreaded sitting next to Prof as he didn't make many jokes, and for a young person he was a little boring. I never felt cosy with Prof. He was absolutely charming but he was a different animal altogether.[6]

Saturnine and rather stooping, he had a somewhat sarcastic way of talking, even in the familiar surroundings of Chartwell, but his charm and good humour with those that he liked, and his dry persuasiveness, led to his peculiarities largely being ignored. His bleak diet and his abstinence might otherwise have been unwelcome at Chartwell's ample table. Lean, sallow and quiet, with what was described as a titter rather than a laugh, he must have seemed a strange contrast to the noisy and colourful ebullience all around him.

Since the visit to Germany by Lindemann and Churchill in 1932, political developments, both in England and in Germany, had served to heighten their anxieties. These circumstances now led Lindemann to draw steadily closer to Churchill, and to put an increasing amount of effort into helping him with his work.

At about this time there also began to appear at Chartwell a number of men who were not social guests of the Churchills, but whose presence had an ulterior purpose. These were the visitors described by Churchill's daughter as 'the invisible men':

Perhaps I can't now put names to them, but serving officers in the forces, who knew things, and who came to my father at risk of their professional life, because they were so aghast at what was going on, and understood how unprepared this country was; and I remember one or two Germans coming too, who came to try to be seen by my father to get the French and British Governments to face up to what was happening in Germany, and to tell him that there were Germans who were against Hitler, but with every month and year that passed the ones who were against Hitler were getting weaker and unable to make their voices heard.[7]

Lindemann shared the unease felt by such people, and wrote to his friend Dr Cahn, Nernst's son-in-law, in Germany:

I am very pessimistic about the political situation. The persecution of the Jews is worse than anything in the Middle Ages and I can scarcely believe that more than a very small fraction of the German people approve. One's only hope now is that the majority, who in my view must be just as shocked as we are, may make their opinion felt.[8]

The activities of 'the invisible men' have since been revealed. They were mainly officers in the Royal Air Force, whose position gave them access to military information. They were so appalled at England's lack of readiness that they were willing to risk their professional careers, and possible court martial, by showing secret documents to Churchill and supplying him with up-to-date figures, particularly on the strength of the air force.

That soldiers and airmen were driven to such lengths is a measure of how blind those in office were to the growing disparity between British and German capability, and of the impenetrable air of complacency that surrounded politicians and service departments alike. 'The invisible men' were also appalled by the discrepancy between Britain's actual military strength, of which they had professional knowledge, and the official figures being given to Parliament and the public. They concluded that they must find a method of exposing the true state of affairs: Churchill, with his connections, his determination and his eloquence, was perhaps the only person who could effectively challenge received opinion.

By contrast, the Government seemed unwilling to address the reality of what was happening in Europe. Moreover, its reluctance to excite potential enemies abroad or to disturb the British public, by highlighting the country's military predicament, made it instinctively hostile to those who threatened its purpose.

As an MP, Churchill was able to stay in close touch with political developments, but what enabled him to be a most effective opponent of the Government was his access to secret information concerning the nation's defence. Those who made this possible included Ralph Wigram, who, before his premature death in 1936, became head of the Central Department of the Foreign Office; Rex Leeper, head of the Foreign Office News Department; and Desmond Morton, head of the CID's Industrial Intelligence Centre, which was charged with monitoring arms manufacture and war stores in foreign countries.

In view of his professional knowledge, Morton had on occasion found the talk at Chartwell greatly embarrassing, and had become uneasy about passing on secret information to Churchill. Curiously, however, he seemed to have obtained permission to do so. He had explained his predicament to the then Prime Minister, Ramsay MacDonald, who had said: 'Tell him whatever he wants to know. Keep him informed.' At Morton's request this permission was put in writing, and had been endorsed by MacDonald's successors, Baldwin and Chamberlain.[9]

One source of information was the director of training at the Air Ministry, Squadron Leader Charles Anderson, whose work gave him a wide knowledge of the state of the Royal Air Force. The information that Anderson passed to Churchill was complemented by that of Group Captain Lachlan MacLean, a senior air staff officer in Bomber Command. These two men in particular helped strengthen Churchill's hand by giving him much of the information that was supplied to Government ministers themselves.

Lindemann's skills were now to prove invaluable. He took on the role of subjecting to clear quantitative analysis the mass of detailed technical information that Churchill received, and pointing up for him its important aspects and implications:

> The material brought to him by Anderson and Morton lent itself to Lindemann's scrutiny. Were the figures being presented in the most scientific and accurate manner? What lay behind them? What could be deduced from them? All this was discussed by the two men weekend after weekend, and with a remarkable sense and unity of purpose.[10]

He also carried out a task that was essential, if seemingly mundane. It was vital for the protection of Churchill's informants that no one should discover that documents were being borrowed: not an easy matter in the days before photocopiers. Churchill's daughter remembers seeing Lindemann on many occasions packing papers into the boot of his Rolls-Royce at Chartwell, from where he would take them to the Clarendon Laboratory, to have them photographed and returned before their absence was detected.

In November 1937 an event occurred that highlighted the alarming state of drift and muddle in the Air Ministry, and proved all too clearly the need for a well-informed voice to query Government policy. Churchill learned from Group Captain MacLean that an invitation to inspect British air preparations had been extended, by the Air Staff, to a mission headed by General Milch, then German Secretary of State for Aviation and shortly to become ADC to Hermann Goering.

The story of this mission's visit to the RAF is a telling example of the frailty of England's response to the growing threat from the dictators, and it encapsulates much of what depressed and infuriated both Lindemann and Churchill.

The near-farce that characterised the whole event was exemplified right at its start, when the air chief marshal in charge of plans for the visit had to announce that 'we shall have to comb the country in order to produce sufficient aircraft to put up any sort of show'.[11] This point had clearly not been lost on MacLean, who had sent a note to Anderson about the imminent visit:

How we have been let in for this visitation at the present moment is beyond imagination.

The attached notes are a pretty incisive commentary on our state of preparedness to receive such a mission. Everyone concerned must realise that the impression created on these people now must inevitably influence German policy with regard to us & foreign policy generally.[12]

It was clear from MacLean's information that the visiting German officers would be shown a whole range of material and equipment of a sensitive nature, and that they would soon notice the prevailing state of air deficiency.

The RAF base that the Air Ministry had selected for the Germans to see was a 'typical Heavy Bomber Station', RAF Mildenhall. The heavy bombers in question were biplanes, paraded before a German mission flushed with success at home, with the Luftwaffe growing from strength to strength and being armed with the most modern equipment. The visitors were invited to examine one of each of the new types of bombers that were scheduled – in the fullness of time – to reach the RAF: Blenheim, Battle, Whitley, Harrow and Wellesley. Behind the parked biplanes was proudly exhibited a range of ground equipment, such as floodlighting, bomb-loading gear, bomb-sights and camera guns. While the Germans were inspecting these, a fly-past of the new bombers took place. Unfortunately variations in the formations indicated only too clearly that the fly-past was made up of almost all the aeroplanes that the RAF could muster. It had in fact been laid on only by scraping together the equipment of numerous different – partially equipped – squadrons and, as Churchill was told, 'amalgamating all the reserves available for the purpose, i.e. borrowing from one squadron machines or trained pilots to make up deficiencies in other squadrons of the same types'.[13]

MacLean's report continued:

The Germans were told that another squadron of Wellesleys and a squadron of Whitleys ought also to have flown past but that they were fog-bound on their aerodromes. This was an unfortunate admission because at Mildenhall the day was clear and the Mission itself was flown to Cranwell after lunch.

Summarised, the Mission saw that the standard equipment of two service squadrons was the Heyford biplane – whose range, performance and capacity was doubtless fully known to them. The Heyfords did actually evoke the question 'are these training aircraft?'

The question which must inevitably form itself in any mind is: 'Why was a station armed with an obsolete type of aircraft selected as the show station in preference to one with modern equipment?' There can only be one explanation, which is that there is no station so equipped.

Wherever the Mission went the standard equipment was the biplane type . . . and the DH86, in which they themselves were transported, must have shown clearly that we are still in the biplane age, with all that that implies.

This in turn is equivalent to saying that after three years of intensive effort we have not succeeded in re-equipping a single squadron for war, and it is obvious that it must be at least two years before the air force as a whole can be re-equipped.[14]

Churchill might naturally have supposed that anyone with influence to wield, and with the interests of the country at heart, would be only too grateful to be leaked this awful tale of muddle and naivety. He therefore sent MacLean's report, rendered duly anonymous, to his old friend and colleague Sir Maurice Hankey, confident that as Cabinet Secretary he would be in a strong position to take remedial action.

Churchill explained his objection to the invitation to the German mission – to whom, he said, 'a desperate effort is now being made to present a sham' – adding that he could 'unfold a most shocking state of affairs in the Air Force'. He left the information with Hankey for him to take appropriate steps.

To Churchill's great surprise, Hankey's reaction was not at all one of gratitude. Instead he replied with shards of ice. As his biographer noted, his response was:

perhaps the worst tactical error he ever made. After promising 'not to probe the origin' of Churchill's information he said he was 'a good deal troubled by the fact of your receiving so many confidences of this kind' . . . And he confessed to being 'shocked not a little that high officers in disciplined forces should be in direct communication with a leading statesman who, though notoriously patriotic beyond criticism, is nevertheless in popular estimation regarded as a critic of the Departments under whom these officers serve' . . . And he went on and on in this vein for eight quarto pages of typescript.[15]

Churchill replied in five abrupt lines: 'I certainly did not expect to receive from you a lengthy lecture when I went out of my way to give you, in strict confidence, information in the public interest . . . you may be sure that I shall not trouble you again in such matters.'[16]

The excuse offered for Hankey's unexpectedly hostile response was frank, to say the least:

Hankey had [during the previous two decades] been subjected to virtually unremitting strain and overwork, and had become a part, if not an integral part, of the machinery of Government. This was surely bound to direct his mental processes along conventional channels, to stultify the powers of imagination and original thought . . . and in general to cause a hardening of both arteries and attitudes.[17]

It was hardened attitudes such as these that caused those in power to view Churchill and Lindemann with increasing distaste and hostility.

The Government was also able to use an economic argument against demands for a change in defence policy. The Exchequer was in the grip of the icy fingers of its Chancellor, Sir John Simon,[18] who kept a tight rein on the public purse even though Germany's rearmament programme was pulling well clear of Britain's. He was able to do this partly because in 1937 it still seemed possible to remain optimistic that there would not be another war, although that year was the last in which that illusion could be sustained – in the words of Lord Jenkins, 'in the sense that people of judgement and foresight could for the last time avoid acknowledging that war was inevitable'.[19] Simon and Chamberlain were therefore able to adhere to their natural inclination to thrift, and to maintain their preferred policy: that the country's normal trade and commerce should not be dislocated by putting the economy on anything approaching a war footing.

Yet those who knew the real situation were becoming increasingly anxious. Air Chief Marshal Slessor expressed such feelings poignantly:

The sense of urgency crowded upon one and I was soon to know for the first time the meaning of fear . . . the gnawing dread of national shame and disaster that curdles the tummy and wakes one up at three in the morning to lie tossing and wondering what can be done and what will happen if nothing is done.[20]

At that time Slessor was the RAF director of planning. He was well able to sense the atmosphere in the Air Ministry, which of all the departments of state most exuded the dank air of defeatism, instead of the vigour that was so sorely needed. With the exception of Lord Swinton, a man of vision and determination who was devoted to the Royal Air Force, the roll-call of Air Ministers in those years – Hoare, Londonderry, Wood – throbbed like a dirge at a funeral for those who longed for a robust response to Germany's renascence. Appeasers to their fingertips, it has been aptly said of them that 'if the spiritual home of the appeasers was at Cliveden, their happiest working hours were spent in the Air Ministry'.[21]

However, despite Lindemann's increasing political agitation, his calendar remained that of an Oxford don, and in the summer of 1937 he went on a long holiday, travelling via the Riviera to Venice, which he loved more than Florence or Rome or any other Italian city – even if he was more interested in natural than architectural beauty, and would go into an art gallery only if there was nothing else to do. On this, as on many of his journeys, he was accompanied by Edward Bolton King, one of his protégés at Oxford and the manager of the Oxford Instrument Company, which he and Lindemann had set up in order to produce photo-electric cells.

They had formed the business, which achieved considerable financial success, partly because of resentment at the university about Lindemann spending time on 'commercial interests'. The ideas behind the venture went back to 1928, when Lindemann foresaw that photo-electric cells would be essential for the 'talking pictures' that were beginning to be made.

Lindemann's anxiety at the lack of response to the growing disparity between German and British air power was briefly alleviated when, in the winter of 1937, the Government decided that it could no longer ignore criticism of the Air Ministry.[22] The unrest was crystallised by a very public complaint from the industrialist Lord Nuffield, who accused the Air Ministry of ignoring his offer to make his factories available for the rearmament programme. This led to calls for an Air Minister in the Commons rather than the Lords, and Chamberlain therefore looked for a scapegoat. He lighted upon Lord Swinton.

The unfortunate Air Minister now fell from grace, and in due course found himself appointed Minister Resident in West Africa. His removal provided an opportunity – spurned or at any rate missed by the Government – to bring to the helm a man of stature and vision, able to take the rearmament programme firmly in hand, and to infuse officials and servicemen alike with enthusiasm for redeeming the Government's pledges. It would have been reasonable to hope that in the whole of Britain and its widespread Empire there were men well qualified to fill the post. In the event Chamberlain selected Sir Kingsley Wood, the Minister of Health.

Wood had been a City solicitor, and had made a fine name in pensions and insurance work, but he wholly lacked the martial aspect and drive that were needed to impress the Germans. His attitude towards Germany was made evident two years later, when war had broken out and when the Germans had violated vast acres of sovereign territory and begun massacring the Poles. Although Poland was crying in anguish for military support in accordance with her treaty with Britain, Wood would not allow the RAF to bomb the Black Forest, Essen or even Krupp's armament works. Leopold Amery recorded in his diary that he had mentioned the plan of setting the Black Forest alight with incendiary bombs. 'Oh you can't do that,' said the Secretary of State for Air, 'that's private property. You'll be asking me to bomb the Ruhr next.'[23]

Dismayed by the chronic lack of urgency at the Air Ministry, Lindemann had initially been encouraged by Swinton's dismissal. On the announcement of the new appointment he wrote to Churchill urging him to raise the question of air defence at once, as a new Air Minister

> might consider it one of the scandals which ought to be removed, whereas once he gets into the saddle Tizard & Co. will explain to him that all is for the best in this particular world and it will be impossible to get him to stir things up.[24]

Lindemann also postponed his plan to go to the United States, where he was due to make some investigations on behalf of the TV pioneers Baird Television, for whom he had become a consultant.[25] He did not, however, interrupt his plans for less distant travel that summer, and soon set off for Deauville, having sent ahead his chauffeur, Topp, to meet him there with the Rolls-Royce. He then went on to Broglie, to stay with the Duc and Duchesse de Broglie, and from there to Mimizan to stay with the Duke of Westminster. He rounded off his travels by meeting his brother Charles at Vittel, before returning via Paris to Oxford.

Back at home, there was little he could do in practice except continue to offer support to Churchill, and his dismay at the growing threat from the dictators was greatly increased by his lack of official defence work. He expressed his frustration in April 1938, when he wrote to Lord Astor's son, who had invited him to stay at Cliveden: 'I have had nothing to do with the actual carrying out of the work since I was thrown out of the committee nearly two years ago because I endeavoured to instil some enthusiasm and drive into its extremely deliberate activities.'[26]

A week later Lindemann wrote to him again:

> It is infuriating to think that all our difficulties might have been avoided if only certain people had not been so anxious to prove that they had

been right all along when they said there was no defence and that the bomber would always get through.[27]

Meanwhile, the new Air Minister settled in his office, and Churchill began to fire a battery of memoranda and letters at him to try and get him to inject some drive into the air-defence research programme. In this he greatly relied on Lindemann's technical support, as a result of which a spate of notes, files and suggestions beset the hapless minister – floating mines, unrotated projectiles, tactical and technical aspects of air defence, counter-attack ideas, three-inch rockets, side-firing aeroplanes – all were eloquently presented to Sir Kingsley Wood. However, whether the ideas were good or bad, they were met not with a vigorous response, but with the 'bright suavity', as *The Times* put it, with which the new minister peered at the world from behind his spectacles.

Churchill referred in particular to the work of the various committees on air defence, including the one from which Lindemann had been so acrimoniously ejected:

In all my experience in public offices, I have never seen anything like the slow-motion picture which the work of this Committee has presented; and I fear it is typical of a whole group of committees which have been in existence during these vital years . . . Professor Lindemann, who has a far greater insight in this sphere than anyone I know, was very soon turned out of the Technical Committee for pressing more vigorous action.

So far as the ADR Committee is concerned, there seems to be a complete lack of driving power. The final result is that we have nothing that will be of any effective use in the next two years, when much either in war or humiliation may be in store for us all.[28]

Kingsley Wood replied to Churchill's exhortations with every indication of enthusiasm, yet ignoring the picture of delays and lethargy that Churchill had described:

I have been a good deal impressed by the particulars of the comprehensive programme of research with which I have been furnished, and with the manner in which very different lines of research are being followed up, so far as I can judge, with considerable energy . . . I am a little tempted to take up your statement that you have never in the past known anything so slow as the work of this committee, but I hope very much that it will not be necessary for us to go into past history.[29]

As the months slipped by, the minister's replies to Churchill, although couched in friendly and willing terms, became progressively more bland. His answers were exemplified by his letter to Churchill of 23 July 1938, commenting on the progress on trials of proposed three-inch rockets:

. . . though the trials are progressing satisfactorily it will take some little time yet to enable the War Office to draw a true average picture of the results from which to deduce final data. In consequence the War Office feel that they would not be able to give us a full report by the end of July.[30]

Churchill did not hide his frustration at the pace the new Air Minister was setting, and he wrote again to Kingsley Wood:

I am still despondent about the Committee, which has been little more than a damping-down apparatus. Do you realise that a whole three years have passed since it was sought to make it a real pioneer of discovery? When I think of what might have been done in this period to make us all safe, I find it difficult to express my grief.[31]

The bumbling delay was typified by a startling report on rocket trials, outlining the technical difficulties that had arisen:

For this reason consideration is now being given to the possibility of carrying out trials . . . overseas . . .
    The present suggestion is that this should be done in the West Indies, and if arrangements can be made, after reconnaissance shall have shown that conditions are likely to be satisfactory, it is hoped that trials may take place in January and the following months . . .[32]

The reaction of Lindemann and Churchill to this note can be imagined: instead of blueprints, trials, amendments, retrials, adjustments, orders for production, training, retraining and all the associated energy and work that were needed, there was offered only the damp and muffled 'hope of trials . . . if arrangements can be made . . . after reconnaissance . . . should conditions be satisfactory . . . in the West Indies' – with the proposed calendar now stretching into 1939.
    Dismayed, but undeterred, Lindemann returned to his proposal for a mine-curtain to protect the English coast, urging the development of a 35,000-foot balloon barrage on the 'necklace' principle, with armed cables strung out as a curtain-rail. The balloons could, he suggested, be deployed

from the Isle of Wight to the Tyne, and around particular cities. Despite widespread initial scepticism, the principle was eventually adopted and was later to become known as the 'Lindemann Necklace'. As Lindemann was to say, in a letter to Churchill on 30 January 1939:

If the Air Ministry had started working on it earlier, so that it could be put into operation at once, it would appear on their own showing that we should be safe until the Germans had either developed a machine to shoot it down in daytime or introduced some method of countering it, especially the latter plan which would mean redesigning the whole German bombing fleet.[33]

He then referred to the defeatism in the Air Ministry:

Of course, if one takes the line that it is not worth doing anything because the enemy can invent a counter, there is not much to be said. On that principle we might as well not put armour on ships as the enemy can use a bigger gun etc.[34]

The other members of the Air Defence Research Committee poured scorn on Lindemann's 'necklace'. They dismissed the idea as impracticable, and said that the mine-curtain would be blown away by the wind. Lindemann, however, feared that precious time was being wasted. Churchill took up the theme of lost time, writing to Kingsley Wood:

We go buzzing along with a host of ideas and experiments which may produce results in '41, '42 or '43. Where will you find anything that can operate in June, July and August of 1939?[35]

As it was to turn out, Lindemann's fears were well grounded:

Even in the Air Ministry the gaps were enormous, for Munich had come before the radar and communication chains were complete; when of the twenty-nine fighter squadrons reckoned mobilisable, only five had modern aircraft; when of the 450 balloons in the London Establishment only 142 could be deployed; and when only about one-third of the country's required number of anti-aircraft guns and search-lights were available – most guns being obsolete or obsolescent and some not in working order.[36]

At last, however, as a result of continual pressure from Churchill,

Lindemann was once again given an official role. This unexpected development came about after Churchill, exasperated by news of yet another postponed committee meeting, had written to Kingsley Wood:

I learn that the meeting of the ADR Committee has again been postponed, until November 14. This leads me to draw your attention to what I wrote to you on June 9, when you first took office as Air Minister. The importance of this subject to our safety has now become paramount but the Committee, in my opinion, is failing in its task, and is in danger of becoming an actual barrier upon swift progress.

I therefore venture to ask you to consider reinforcing it by adding Professor Lindemann to its numbers. This would enable me, with his assistance, to put before you a continuous stream of valuable ideas and also to criticise with technical knowledge, which I do not possess myself, the progress or non-progress on existing lines of enquiry. I make this suggestion to you with full knowledge of what has happened in the past and after maturely considering it in all its bearings. I am sure that this step would be in the public interest and is essential to a genuine effort being made to overtake the time that has been lost.[37]

Churchill added the threat that unless Wood gave a new impulse, he would free himself from his silence and try to achieve action through Parliament.

The idea of Lindemann's reinstatement was anathema to many in the scientific establishment, but Rutherford, who had been one of Tizard's strongest supporters, was now dead and a powerful voice of opposition to Lindemann was therefore lost. For Lindemann, the Government's response was welcome, if surprising: Kingsley Wood accepted Churchill's suggestion, and on 30 November 1938 Lindemann was invited to join the Air Defence Research (ADR) Sub-Committee of the Committee of Imperial Defence.

So, after eighteen months without an official platform, he returned to the fray. Professor A. V. Hill was also appointed to the committee, as a sop to Henry Tizard, who was another member, but this bounced lightly from Lindemann's armour. In the event, Lindemann's new appointment proved to be the moment when the tide of influence on the scientific approach to air defence began to ebb from Tizard and flow towards Lindemann. The clash of personalities that brought to an end the former committee was renewed, but now the balance of power had shifted. Tizard and Hill once more faced Lindemann across the table, no doubt with gritted teeth, but this time he was there to stay.

At last a sense of urgency had begun to weigh upon the committee, and the first ADR meeting that Lindemann attended resulted in firm recommendations. The consequences of the new determination were soon evident and included more money from the Treasury, an enlarged rocket-development establishment, more committee meetings, the advancement of aerial mine proposals and the acceptance of Lindemann's offer of the Clarendon Laboratory for research into short-wave detection methods.

No doubt international events had played their part in quickening the committee's deliberations. In the spring of 1938 Austria had been annexed by Germany; that had been followed by a crisis over Czechoslovakia and fears of imminent war. Immediately after the Austrian *Anschluss*, Lindemann had written to his brother Charles:

I think the Austrian business is appalling. We are back where we were in April 1918 with the Germans winning all along the line. The main difference seems to be that we are now on the run whereas twenty years ago people were prepared to fight. The Nazis could have been stopped at each and every stage; but every time we postpone making a stand they get stronger and we get weaker. All the small Balkan nations will now try and make terms with them and when the show finally comes there will be nobody but France and England to stand against them. All because Mr Baldwin wanted peace in his time and thought it easiest to win the election by talking sentimental nonsense and refusing to arm.[38]

Yet hardly was the blood dry in the streets of Vienna when Hitler menaced Prague, and a crisis arose that was resolved, but only for a time, by the Munich Settlement. Lindemann deplored Chamberlain's efforts at the expense of Czechoslovakia, and was quite unmoved by the reaction of the majority of the country, exemplified by the trembling voice of the *Gaumont British News* presenter saying, 'Posterity will thank God, as we do now, that in a time of desperate need our safety was guarded by such a man as Neville Chamberlain.'

In January 1939 Lindemann wrote to a colleague, the mathematician Professor E. M. Wright, and poured scorn on the Munich Settlement:

As you may guess, I am convinced that we were bluffed at Berchtesgaden and Munich and that, far from having achieved peace in our time, we shall simply be exposed to another crisis which we shall have to face in much more unfavourable circumstances in a very short time. Still, so many clever people seem delighted with Mr

Chamberlain's policy of appeasement that I try hard to think I am wrong. I pray it may be so, but with even less certainty than I attach to most of my prayers.[39]

Nor did he let up in his campaign for deeds rather than words from the Government. Writing in the *Daily Telegraph* in October 1938, he said:

In fifteen or twenty years, even at our present rate of progress, no doubt the danger of aerial bombing will become a thing of the past. The pity is that the matter has been allowed to slide so that we are neither safe today nor likely to be, unless drastic steps are taken, for many years to come.[40]

As the months passed he continued to devote as much time as he could to air-defence committee work, and in July 1939 inspected the radar-development establishment at Bawdsey. Radar was by now the one bright star in the dim constellation of the country's defence programme. Great advances were being made, and from the time that the Germans overran Czechoslovakia, on 15 March 1939, there began a twenty-four-hour radar watch from Scapa Flow to Portsmouth – the 300-foot towers of the Chain Home Stations being popularly described as 'Death-Ray Stations'.

Furthermore, radar development was complemented by outstanding progress, instigated and directed by Henry Tizard, in teaching the air force to make use of the boon that radar offered them, so that a highly efficient RAF fighter interception plan became linked to the early-warning signals from the radar stations. This was to prove invaluable in the Battle of Britain the following year, and its achievement is rightly considered one of the high points of Tizard's career. It was later said:

this intimate cooperation of scientific and military minds will remain as the real secret weapon in the British armoury, as something which grew to full vigour with radiolocation . . . The Air Marshal took advice from the junior scientific officer on how to make war, and the laboratory assistant was told by the Admiral why physics has sometimes to give way to psychology in the planning and conduct of operations.[41]

R. V. Jones endorsed this view, and emphasised Lindemann's contribution:

Throughout the secret war the greatest advantage that we had was a sense of purpose, starting with the need to defend ourselves against the Luftwaffe. It was that threat that drew scientists and serving officers together in the years before 1939 in a way that had never happened before; and the close relationship that first sprang up between Fighter Command and scientists ultimately spread throughout the services. In this, Lindemann was as enthusiastic as Tizard. And as a result, while we scientists would rarely give the services exactly what they wanted, we could persuade them to modify their demands in the light of what we knew we could do. So, new weapons appeared quickly, and yet the services had already thought out how to use them.

The Germans had no such driving force resulting from an obvious danger to their homeland until late in the war. And then it was too late.[42]

However, despite the rapidly increasing contribution from scientists, the links in the chain of defence remained incomplete, as Churchill pointed out in a letter to the Air Minister in June 1939:

A weak point in the wonderful development is of course that when the raid crosses the coast it leaves the RDF, and we become dependent on the Observer Corps. This would seem a transition from the middle of the twentieth century to the Early Stone Age.[43]

Lindemann visited Bawdsey to see a demonstration of an experimental air-interception set. He asked for a flight in a Battle aeroplane and this was arranged for 10 July. E. G. Bowen, one of the scientists at Bawdsey, explained what happened:

It was late in the day when he arrived and he was quite worried about a dinner appointment in London that evening which he did not want to miss. So we rearranged the demonstration flight to take place along a line from Martlesham to London, so that we could drop him off at North Weald at the conclusion of the test. This was an RAF station on the outskirts of London; his Rolls Royce was sent ahead to meet him there.

Hetty Hyde was the pilot and his two passengers, a very portly Lindemann and myself, were squeezed onto the wooden plank across the back seat – the same plank which we had used for Stuffy Dowding, and for Winston Churchill only a few weeks before. We made a normal take-off but were hardly off the ground before it became obvious that something was badly wrong. Masses of black smoke started to pour out of the engine and boiling oil came streaming back over the cockpit. Hetty Hyde said: 'Christ' and snapped back his cockpit cover. The thought shot through my mind: could we ride it out or would we have to jump for it? In the rear cockpit were two seat-type parachutes, but they were on the floor and it would have taken Houdini himself to get into them.

Hetty made reassuring noises from the front 'I think we can make it'. He throttled back and as he did so the smoke subsided but the oil kept coming. With his head out of the cockpit he did a very sedate circuit and, after what seemed an eternity, we made a smooth landing . . . I have to say that Lindemann – an old Farnborough pilot from World War I – took all this in his stride. There was simply no panic and no visible reaction to speak about.

Lesser souls would have quit right there, but both Lindemann and Hetty Hyde were prepared to have another go . . . We finished by giving Lindemann a very effective demonstration of radar interception and at the end of a long and rather eventful afternoon we headed for North Weald as planned. As we were on the final approach, Lindemann's Rolls Royce came through the Station gates to meet him. The timing could not have been better.

We expected that Lindemann would be impressed, at least with the technical part of the demonstration, but it was not so. He seemed to be in his usual mood of finding fault with everything and did not have a single positive suggestion to make. I wrote later '. . . he seemed rather peeved about the whole thing, and generally gave the impression it was a bit of a fraud'. When he got back to London he gave us a poor report. Of all the distinguished people to whom we demonstrated airborne radar, Lindemann was the only one who was unimpressed. For reasons best known to himself, he continued to deprecate British radar, at least in its defensive role, for most of the war. Strangely enough, only when it was realised that radar might play an important role in the bombing of Germany did he become enthusiastic about its potential.[44]

That Lindemann should be described as portly is surprising, considering his acreophagous diet of salad and egg whites, but, by now in his early fifties, he had given up tennis and squash and had assumed a more sedentary life. However, Bowen's assessment of Lindemann's view on radar was not accurate: he continued to be a strong advocate of radar development, while conscious that the Germans might also be working on it. Yet Bowen's account gives a good example of how effortlessly Lindemann was able to arouse resentment. As Tizard's biographer put it: 'Lindemann could charm birds out of trees when he wanted, but he also had an incomparable facility for doing the reverse.'[45]

By 2 September 1939 Britain had, despite all her attempts at appeasing the dictators, arrived at the threshold of war. Germany had invaded Poland, whose towns were being bombed and whose armies were being decimated. Poland called on Britain to honour her treaty obligations, and the delay in the Government's response led to one of the most dramatic moments in the history of the House of Commons. The Prime Minister was due to speak at 7.30 that Saturday evening, nearly forty-eight hours after the German armies had rolled across their eastern frontier. At a Cabinet meeting earlier in the day Chamberlain had agreed to issue to Germany an ultimatum that would expire at midnight.

The chamber was full, expectant that at long last the country would be at war and once more able to lift its head in honour. Yet when Chamberlain rose, it was to speak of a possible conference; there was no word of an ultimatum. Sir Edward Spears recorded the scene:

The benches were packed. The unbearable suspense was about to be relieved. One and all were keyed up for the announcement that war had been declared. Most were ready to show their intense relief that suspense was ended by cheering wildly. But as we listened, amazement turned into stupefaction, and stupefaction into exasperation.[46]

Leo Amery took up the tale:

The House was aghast. For two whole days the wretched Poles had been bombed and massacred, and we were still considering within what time-limit Hitler should be invited to tell us whether he felt like relinquishing his prey.[47]

It was when Arthur Greenwood, the acting Labour leader, rose to reply that Amery made the historic intervention: 'Speak for England, Arthur.'[48] The poignancy was expressed by Major-General Ismay:[49]

Before Munich I had hoped against hope up to the very last moment that peace might be preserved. Now I prayed that we should spring to arms the moment that Hitler laid hands on Poland. If we did so, we might or might not be destroyed. But if we failed to do so, we would be dishonoured for ever. I was not frightened or even excited, but I was furious – furious with ourselves as well as with the Nazis. Less than twenty-one years had passed since the Germans had lain prostrate at our feet. Now they were at our throats. How had we been so craven or so careless as to allow this to happen? The Cenotaph was almost on the doorstep of our office, and every time I passed it I felt a sense of guilt that we who had survived the First World War had broken faith with those who had died.

> *To you from failing hands we throw*
> *The torch; be yours to hold it high.*
> *If ye break faith with us who die*
> *We shall not sleep, though poppies grow*
> *In Flanders fields.*

But the die was finally cast: war was declared on 3 September, and the same day Churchill was invited to join the Government, in his former post as First Lord of the Admiralty. A week later he appointed Lindemann to be his personal and scientific adviser.

TEN

To the Admiralty

The scenes in the House of Commons on the evening of 2 September 1939 had demonstrated beyond any remaining doubt that the time for talking had passed. That night, anxious and brooding, Churchill waited at his London flat. Shortly after midnight he sent a note to Chamberlain expressing his dismay at the momentous scenes that had been witnessed in the House of Commons: 'There was a feeling to-night in the House,' he wrote, 'that injury had been done to the spirit of national unity by the apparent weakening of our resolve.'

In the event there was to be no further delay or prevarication, and at 5.00 on the morning of Sunday, 3 September, the Foreign Office telegraphed the British Ambassador in Berlin, instructing him to deliver a final note to the German Government. It was an ultimatum stating that unless the German Government had given satisfactory assurances, by 11 a.m., that they had suspended all aggressive action against Poland and were prepared promptly to withdraw their forces from Polish territory, Britain would be at war with Germany.

In Whitehall the minutes ticked silently by as the deadline approached, until at 11.15 the mournful tones of Neville Chamberlain were broadcast from Downing Street, telling the British people that, finally, an ultimatum had been delivered, that the required undertakings had not been received 'and that consequently, this country is at war with Germany'.

Within a mere three hours of Britain's declaration of war the opening shots were fired, and the passenger liner *Athenia* was sunk by a German torpedo off the coast of Ireland; more than a hundred people drowned. In the afternoon the War Cabinet held its first meeting. As if torn between the old ways of appeasement and the hard demands of war, it was agreed both that a bomber force should immediately attack the German fleet, which was reportedly setting sail from Wilhelmshaven, and that propaganda leaflets should be dropped over Germany, in the belief that they would have 'an important effect on German public opinion'.

That morning Winston Churchill had been to the Prime Minister's room at the Commons, where he had been offered the Admiralty and a place in the War Cabinet. His acceptance was the first major news of the war, and on hearing it the Board of Admiralty had signalled to the Fleet: 'Winston is Back'. Early that evening Churchill entered the Admiralty building and set foot once more in the First Lord's Room, which he had vacated after the Dardanelles crisis in 1915. The next day he told his predecessor, Lord Stanhope: 'Fortune of War which chased me a quarter of a century ago from the Admiralty, has now reversed its action.'[1]

It was with a storm-force wind that Churchill returned to the Admiralty, and at once the dust of the inter-war years began to scatter. From the moment of his arrival he galvanised his colleagues with his infectious enthusiasm and unceasing urge to wage war. Very soon his vital energy was felt in every naval base on shore, and in the warships and merchant vessels on the oceans, as the First Lord's ardent gaze illuminated the machinery that was to drive forward the war at sea.

Without delay Churchill set out for his colleagues the way in which he would work. His preferred tool was the 'minute', a dictated note sent to advisers or colleagues, short and to the point, and bearing questions, comments or commands. At once the hectic pace was set, and the minutes began to speed from Churchill's desk. Some were heavy, others light; some stern and some with engaging humour; but from each he 'expected to learn what was happening over the full range of his responsibilities, and to probe every area of potential war policy and action'.[2]

During the next few days Churchill introduced himself to his staff and discussed their duties, swiftly weighing up each person's worth and capability. The country had been brought to war after years of neglect of its defences, but the Royal Navy had remained supreme, and in 1939 it was the paramount weapon with which to resist the enemy. Churchill was sure that science would be a dominant factor in the war – at sea as much as in the air – and he was determined to harness it to the fight. As if to herald this, air-raid sirens had been audible during Chamberlain's very announcement of war, set off by an Oxford physicist whose radar screen had picked up an unidentified object. The First World War had been described as a chemist's war, but in one of their earliest scientific discussions Lindemann had told Churchill that the next war would be fought using electricity; now it was to be the turn of the physicists.

In this context the new First Lord did not have to look far for support, or to find the ideal companion, and, six days after his return to office, a notice was posted in the Admiralty:

The First Lord has made the following appointment:–
Professor F. A. Lindemann, FRS, to be personal adviser to the First
Lord on scientific development. The appointment will be temporary
and unpaid. It will take effect from September 9th.[3]

Lindemann was given leave from his Oxford duties for as long as
Churchill required his services, and at the outbreak of war all current work
at the Clarendon was stopped, with the Admiralty taking over direction of
the laboratory. The ground for this had been laid before the war. When
Lindemann first attended the Air Defence Research Sub-Committee
meeting in December 1938, following his return to the fray, it had been
agreed that the committee 'would avail itself of Professor Lindemann's offer
to conduct research at the Clarendon Laboratory, Oxford, into valves for
use with very short waves'. This must have pleased him, especially with
Tizard present at the meeting, and it was the start of what was to become
a vital contribution to Britain's defence in the war.

The offer had been taken up the following year at a meeting between
Lindemann and Keeley, from the Clarendon Laboratory, and the director
of scientific research and Vice-Admiral Somerville, from the Admiralty. For
Keeley, that meeting had been memorable not only because of its importance in respect of the war, but for a story that he was told by Admiral
Somerville, which illustrated the lighter moments that could occur even
amid the burdens of war. The admiral had explained how a short time earlier
he had been called before the First Sea Lord and told of problems that the
navy was having with carrier pigeons released from submarines to take
messages back to base. Many failed to make the journey, apparently being
overcome by diesel fumes from the vessels. The admiral was happily able
to tell the First Sea Lord that he had recently read, in *Scientific American*,
that the American Navy had experienced exactly the same problems, which
they had solved by designing gas masks for the pigeons. He was at once
instructed to read up on the problem, talk to his US counterpart to see
what could be done, and report his findings the following week.

The admiral duly looked through *Scientific American*, but was puzzled to
be unable to find the article he was thinking of. Suddenly, to his horror, he
remembered that he had actually read the story in *Punch*. The celebrated
cartoonist H. M. Bateman, who enjoyed drawing irate admirals, would have
relished witnessing the meeting that subsequently took place.[4]

Easter 1939 had seen the start of the continuous radar watch that was to
be maintained from the east- and south-coast stations for the next six years,
and during that spring and summer a nationwide scheme was implemented
whereby some ninety university physicists had spent many weeks at radar

stations around the coast, as part of the precautions against war. At the Chain Home Stations newly enrolled scientists devoted their efforts to scrutinising radar at work. Several of Lindemann's team at the Clarendon were sent to Pevensey, where their great value – and that of the radar station – was such that the Air Ministry considered they should be placed under the command of a flight-sergeant.

In September 1939 the Clarendon staff moved into their newly completed building, where Lindemann arranged for them to be set up as a research team working under the Admiralty. From the beginning of 1940 the British-born members of the team concentrated on infra-red and on receivers for centimetre waves. Those who had come from abroad, however (mainly those on 'Lindemann's List'), were not considered by the Admiralty to be sufficiently trustworthy for such work. Yet it was apparently quite all right for them to be set to work on the atomic-bomb project that was to commence a few months later.

In the Admiralty itself, Churchill now set to work. The days were to be long and hard, and the peacetime routine was banished at once. It was a new and exhilarating atmosphere; no doubt it was uncomfortable for many, but there was no escape. Churchill was quick to root out vestiges of the previous regime. He asked about oil-storage, for example, and did not like the answer he received. He minuted: 'We are not now building a good and satisfactory installation of oil fuel storage to make the Navy comfortable after the war. We have to meet the immediate danger.'[5] Nor was he happy with the state of contracts for ship deliveries. He drove home an obvious point:

I cannot feel that the table of deliveries for 1940 and 1941 are in harmony with war conditions. Too much emphasis must not be placed upon the maintenance of the Navy after the war. If we lose the war we shall not be allowed to have a Navy at all.[6]

Even as the German fleet was putting to sea, Churchill found an appalling catalogue of delays in the construction of the most important new British ships, including the battleships *King George V* and the *Prince of Wales*. The aircraft carrier *Illustrious* was five months behind schedule, and so was the *Indomitable*; *Formidable* was six months overdue, and *Victorious* nine months. The cruiser *Dido*, due by June 1939, was now offered by the builders, Cammell Laird, for August 1940.

He summoned the contractors to the Admiralty. 'All these ships,' he said, 'will be wanted to take part in the war, and not merely to sail the seas – perhaps under the German flag – after it is over.'[7]

Even in the early days of the war and before battle had been joined in earnest, it became clear that the pace set by Churchill demanded an exceptional system for the collection of vital data, and for presenting it in the correct order of priority. Without such a system, decisions could not be properly taken or plans correctly set in hand; without it, the First Lord – dynamic and able as he was – would run the risk of being swamped by a mass of information that he would not have the time to assess, imperilling the ships at sea.

When Churchill arrived at the Admiralty there were many disparate sub-departments responsible for gathering and preparing the details of naval work. Among them were a Naval Store Department, covering the oil fuel position; a Personnel Department; a Civil Engineer-in-Chief's Department; a Dockyard Expense Accounts Department; and an Estimates Department. Although, when the war started, the work of collecting statistics was widened (for instance, to include figures for submarine attacks and the losses caused), and although there were many statisticians already employed at the Admiralty, the existing organisation did not meet Churchill's exacting demands. What he wanted was a clear overall view of naval readiness, and of the present and prospective strengths and weaknesses of his command. Within a short time of his arrival he called for a report on the existing facilities, to see if they would meet his needs.

The fact that the new First Lord had held exactly the same office, twenty-five years earlier during the Great War, was remarkable, and it gave him the invaluable benefit of first-hand experience as he addressed the needs of the hour. He saw that so many different departments in the Admiralty, all working separately in the production of figures, would be entirely inadequate and might even be a source of grave danger.

Yet straight away Churchill was met with resistance to his requirements, and change was resented. His staff also harked back to the Great War: then, they protested, the Admiralty had set up a department designed to supply information to all who required statistical returns. It was a better way, they thought, than the current proposal:

It will be noted that already many experts are employed. It may well be that experience will show that more are required. If so, it will still be desirable that they should be employed in the various departments which require statistics. A single statistical department would, according to Admiralty experience, be undesirable as well as extravagant. Statistics are not an end in themselves. They are the servant of the department which deals with the wares they are concerned with.[8]

Churchill was having none of such patronising special pleading. 'Surely the account you give,' he responded, 'constitutes the case for a central body which should grip together all Admiralty statistics, and present them to me in a form increasingly simplified and graphic.'[9] He was clear as to what he required:

> I want to know at the end of each week everything we have got, all the people we are employing, the progress of all vessels, works of construction, the progress of all munitions affecting us, the state of our merchant tonnage, together with losses and numbers, of every branch of the RN and RM . . .[10]

The facts and figures about Britain's ability to fight the war at sea were enormous in number and widely spread. Unless they could be harnessed, and presented clearly and in good time, the First Lord would be unable to use them, and his power and vision would be lessened. How was he to tap this rich resource? As he put it to his officials: 'How do you propose this want of mine should be met?'[11]

Churchill himself had the answer. He had at hand a man entirely suited to the task, with an unrivalled ability to bear down rigorously on the myriad statistics to be analysed, to present them swiftly and simply and to provide Churchill with the essential information with which to make his plans. He therefore called for Lindemann, his newly appointed scientific adviser, and set him up with his own department. On 12 October he issued the following minute: 'The First Lord's Statistical Branch [as it was christened] should consist of Professor Lindemann who would do this besides his scientific duties.' After it had been operational for some months, the branch's functions were summarised as follows:

> To analyse statistics relating to the Navy and cognate matters and present the results in diagrammatic form both for the information of the First Lord and for his use in discussions.
>
> To compile and keep up to date the album of charts which the First Lord has circulated to the Cabinet. This album presents a variety of statistical information on matters of national importance.
>
> To answer at short notice questions by the First Lord on any matter involving statistics with which he may have to deal as a member of the War Cabinet and other Committees.
>
> To read all Cabinet papers on economic matters and draw the attention of the First Lord to points which he might wish to take up.[12]

The summary added: 'The extremely responsible position of advisers in direct touch with the First Lord and the lamentable results which would flow from mistaken or ill-judged advice require that the members of this Branch should be of first-class calibre.'

Lindemann was perhaps the only man who could provide this service. He had, more than anyone, the skill to capture the vital facts, translate them so that they could be understood, and present them so that they could be swiftly acted upon. As the war gathered pace an invaluable partnership began to develop. Lindemann's collection and analysis of data that was vital for the war at sea, and its presentation in simple form, enabled Churchill to see quickly how each day was unfolding. Very soon the First Lord was fully prepared for his meetings, and able to discuss policy and plans with Cabinet colleagues and with military experts from a position of strength and understanding.

However, as the weeks passed, Churchill's demands mounted. He considered that, as a member of the War Cabinet, he should be well informed about the whole range of the war effort, and not just the Admiralty brief. His instinct, reinforced by what he had long regarded as the supine attitude of pre-war ministers and civil servants, was to submit to searching questions the papers and propositions that were discussed in Cabinet meetings. To do this he had to educate himself on topics beyond the bounds of the Admiralty. Lindemann, who had the same critical turn of mind, was the obvious man to help. So he was given the task of commenting on an increasing number of the papers put before the Cabinet.

Many of these papers were on economic topics, concerning production and supply of goods in the war economy, and Lindemann quickly realised the need to engage some economists to help him. The instructions establishing the First Lord's Statistical Branch called for 'a secretary who knows the Admiralty, a statistician, and a confidential typist who is also preferably an accountant'. As the work grew, Churchill urged Lindemann to furnish himself with a larger staff quickly. However, Lindemann disliked the Civil Service in all its forms, and thought that if he asked them to provide people for his branch they would send him 'duffers'. He therefore turned to his Christ Church colleague, Roy Harrod,[13] and asked him to look for a clever economist to help with the work. As Harrod said, the matter required very careful thought:

I knew so well Lindemann's habit of laying down the law to ripe scholars on matters on which he himself had no special qualifications. An economist might easily take offence if he found that his own expertise was totally scorned, and, if offence was given too often, the partnership would not be a happy one. When the Prof said 'not stupid', this meant that the victim must be one of quite first-rate intellectual calibre . . .

what I had in mind more than anything else, however, was Lindemann's insistence on putting everything into quantitative terms . . .[14]

Harrod introduced Lindemann to Donald MacDougall, a young economist at Leeds University, and within a short time he became Lindemann's chief-of-staff in his statistical department. In the early days, however, MacDougall's territory was uncharted. He was told that his first task was to discover whether sugar rationing was essential, as claimed by the Ministry of Food. He recorded:

Contingency plans for food rationing had been drawn up before the war and the Ministry were naturally itching to use their new toys. But Winston feared that this would boost German morale, by suggesting that their attempted blockade of Britain through U-boats was already, so soon after the outbreak of war, starting to bring us to our knees. So I picked up my phone, rang up the Ministry and said: 'This is MacDougall, First Lord of the Admiralty's Statistical Branch, and I wonder if you would be so good as to give me some information about sugar stocks, consumption, production and imports.' The response was immediate: 'What the hell has it got to do with you?' I politely explained that my minister, as well as being in the War Cabinet, was in charge of the Royal Navy which was responsible for convoying ships carrying to this country, among other things, sugar.

This was my first essay, as a youngster of 26 with no civil service experience, in the gentle art of wheedling out of officials – usually of quite long standing and much older – information which as often as not was going to be used against them.[15]

Harrod also set about finding other staff, and telegrams were sent to economists in various universities summoning them to the Admiralty to take up duties as 'economist/statisticians'. Herbert Robinson, an economics don at Oxford, was one such recruit. Arriving at the Admiralty, he was introduced to MacDougall, Helen Makower from the Institute of Statistics at Oxford, and G. L. S. Shackle from the London School of Economics. They told Robinson that they would all be working for Professor Lindemann, on Admiralty administration, shipping, foreign trade, the economy and all the various matters that would be brought before the War Cabinet. Robinson recalled:

I was soon introduced to Professor Lindemann and found him to be distantly friendly but somewhat uncommunicative. He gave me no indication of how he intended to organize the branch, what my position would be in it or how he intended to use my services. I gathered that we would all be at his service either individually or as members of small teams to undertake particular projects.[16]

Robinson was allocated the task of responding to all Churchill's statistical requirements in respect of the army, anti-aircraft defence and the Ministry of Supply. Alone among S Branch (as it came to be known) he was given an assistant, an economics graduate from Manchester University, Dr Cyril Martin, who described his own arrival for duty:

One morning I received a telephone call from my professor informing me that I should attend at the Admiralty at 2.30 the following Monday and ask for Roy Harrod. He stated that he could tell me no more. I duly arrived at the large hall and was escorted around the Admiralty for nearly an hour while the messenger tried to find Mr Roy Harrod. Finally we arrived back at the main hall where all hell had broken loose. The messenger was told to take me to the First Lord's private office immediately. I remember the messenger saying: 'What him? To the First Lord's office?'

I had met Roy Harrod before, and after apologies we started talking but I had no real idea of what was involved. Suddenly and most quietly a tall man, pale faced and dressed entirely in black except for a perfect white shirt, entered the room. Harrod informed me that it was Professor Lindemann. He started talking and asking questions and then asked how much I could live on each week. He then stated that I was to start the following Monday. I objected, saying that I needed to get my work at the University organised. This I did – and stayed until the Branch was disbanded.[17]

Lindemann also sought a scientific assistant of his own, in October 1939 engaging J. L. Tuck, who was later to lead the British contingent working in America on the atom bomb. Although Lindemann usually gave the impression of caring little for people's opinions, hiring Tuck was a shrewd move on his part and demonstrates his instinct for selecting clever and independent-minded subordinates whom he could use as a sounding-board. R. V. Jones recorded:

Surprisingly, Lindemann had brought Tuck with him when he had come to the Admiralty from Oxford. Up to the outbreak of war Lindemann had tended to choose to talk more to 'yes men' than to those who would honestly differ from him, and I had expected that he would select one of the former. Instead Lindemann chose Tuck, who was certainly no 'yes man' . . . it was a very hopeful sign, for Tuck was both clever and honest, and just the man for straight action in a tight corner.[18]

Lindemann was to prove ready, when the moment demanded it, to bring forward the best experts to advise Churchill, even though such experts might not agree with Lindemann's own opinions. This he was to do on important occasions in the case of Jones himself, who was to achieve a position of great significance in the world of Intelligence.

Churchill was now placed in a position of much greater strength than his predecessors. As Sir Charles Goodeve said, in his account of the war against the U-boats, the combination of Churchill and Lindemann was 'immeasurably important':

Up to the outbreak of the war scientific and technological 'facts' in the defence Services were what authorised experts said they were, and anyone who challenged these did so at his peril. Within weeks of Churchill's arrival at the Admiralty this entrenched position was undermined, and the expert was forced to back up his position by observational evidence, or else change it.[19]

Soon S Branch began to supply Churchill with a steady stream of papers covering many fields. As Herbert Robinson recalled:

These, he insisted, had to be no more than a one page, double space, typescript summary, and if he thought more action was needed we would be requested, in red ink, to amplify our points in a formal report. These reports would be sent to the head of the Government agency concerned, or became Cabinet papers from the First Lord to the Prime Minister or the Cabinet. On one occasion we had made an important analysis critical of the way the merchant fleet was being used and Churchill asked us to put it in the form of a Cabinet paper. In so doing we elaborated and made some additional points. Our paper came back with his red ink message: 'You have mauled your own child. Please comfort it!' We speedily went back to our original draft.[20]

In December 1939 Lindemann drew up a memorandum describing the work of his branch. Charts were a prominent feature and were to cover a wide spectrum of military and economic statistics, their bright pictures transforming a mass of complicated detail into simple and compelling images that instantly told their story. Churchill found charts especially clear and helpful, and S Branch began to use this medium to portray in vivid terms the cogs that were driving the wheels of war. Chart production soon fell to a team of specialists, under the Balliol graduate Alan Kitching.

In Donald MacDougall's words:

> Churchill loved charts, so did the Prof and so did I. So we produced many hundreds during the war, all painted in beautiful colours and collected together in innumerable loose-leaf albums or, if they were to be shown to important personages like the King or President Roosevelt, bound in cloth covers. At Churchill's request while still at the Admiralty, Prof personally presented the King's first album of charts, and explained them to him, at Buckingham Palace. Figures to bring the President's album up to date were cabled regularly to Washington . . .[21]

Yet Lindemann's primary role remained that of Churchill's scientific adviser. His appointment had naturally caused great interest in the scientific world. It had also aroused indignation, particularly among those who remembered the difficulties of the Tizard Committee. When the war began Tizard had been given charge of the Committee for the Scientific Survey of Air Warfare, but with Lindemann's ascendancy, Tizard's position soon became invidious. At first he had hoped that old enmities might be forgotten, and he had written to Lindemann on 10 September:

> Dear Lindemann,
> I hear that you are at the Admiralty.
>   I'm sure that you will agree with me that any remnant of a private hatchet should be buried, and that we should remember old friendship & cooperate as much as we can.
>   There is indeed an urgent matter affecting navy and air force that I should like to talk over with you soon . . . if there is a possibility of meeting.[22]

It appeared from Lindemann's reply that he had uncharacteristically allowed himself to abandon a grudge. He wrote to Tizard:

> Many thanks for your note. Hatchets are made to be buried, above all when so many trenches are available. All I want is to cooperate as much as we can in the common cause . . .[23]

For the country, it was a matter of some urgency that two such remark-able scientists should not waste energy on antagonising each other at a time of such gravity. Charles Lindemann certainly thought so, and he therefore invited the two adversaries to lunch, managing at least to force a handshake at its conclusion. Unfortunately, it seems that Lindemann's words belied his thoughts. 'Now that I'm in a position of power,' he told R. V. Jones, 'a lot of my old friends have come sniffing round'; and when a friend told Lindemann he had heard that the hatchet had been buried, he was met with a thin smile: 'Not very deep'.

Meanwhile, although the Germans continued to wreak havoc in Poland, there was little action from the Allied armies in the west. It was the Admiralty alone that was able to embark on aggressive action against Germany. The general sense of frustration increased Churchill's eagerness to look for ways to attack, and he was immediately enthused when Lindemann came up with the suggestion that the River Rhine was an obvious target. His own expe-riences, and his family's European origins, had given Lindemann an instinc-tive feel for French and German attitudes and he had a greater knowledge of those countries than most of Churchill's close advisers.

Aware that a long stretch of one bank of the Rhine above Strasburg was French, he conceived the idea of floating mines downstream from French territory. With the thoroughness and speed that Churchill valued so highly, Lindemann set about collecting statistics, partly from the Intelligence Division of the naval staff, on the use that the Germans were making of the Rhine, and on the cargoes, types of barges and other relevant details. He then formed a plan, and produced a short and clear summary, presenting it to Churchill on 16 October:

The advantage of being upstream might enable the French to cause a good deal of disturbance to German shipping on the Rhine. It would seem possible to float numbers of comparatively small contact mines down the river, which would be large enough to sink the barges which carry so much traffic between the Ruhr and other districts. A 20 kg (45lbs) contact mine would almost certainly suffice. Even if some got stuck on the banks the majority would probably stay in the main channel. They could be arranged to float a metre (3 feet) or so below the surface and would probably cause a great deal of destruction on their way down.

Alternatively, one could float larger mines downstream of the non-contact type. These could be arranged to sink after a certain period and lie on the bottom of the stream until something passed over them.

Any action of this type should take place suddenly on a considerable scale. Otherwise the enemy will net the stream to prevent it. Indeed, this may have already been done. If so, the nets would collect a considerable amount of waste matter, weeds etc., which would impede the flow of the river and be easily observable from the air. Mines could be made to detonate on contact with the nets so as to destroy them if necessary, but it may be hoped that in the first instance such complications could be avoided.[24]

Here was an idea that had strong appeal to Churchill. Above all it involved attack, in contrast to the distressing inaction on the Western Front. He presented the idea to the Admiralty chiefs: 'Professor Lindemann has pressed these ideas upon me,' he said, 'and is ready with plans.'[25] Shortly afterwards the project was given greater urgency by the sinking, with a magnetic mine, of a Dutch merchant vessel in the mouth of the Thames. The Germans had begun laying such mines in large numbers around the British coast. They were indeed a new 'secret weapon' as Hitler had boasted; their advent caused the gravest concern and Churchill was impatient to respond.

Meanwhile, between the work of his infant Statistical Branch and his roving brief as the First Lord's scientific adviser, Lindemann was tirelessly counselling Churchill on a wide range of subjects, either at his own instigation (as with the Rhine mines) or in response to requests from Churchill, whose inquisitive mind would light upon an enormous variety of questions. In each case Lindemann would root out all the relevant detail and simplify it for Churchill. In response to a query from the First Lord on gas defences, for example, Lindemann minuted on 19 October 1939:

There are so many organic compounds that it is possible that the Germans have found one which enables an adequate concentration to be reached. It is unlikely that any of them are very much more poisonous than mustard gas. Our respirators provide reasonable protection for a short time at low concentrations . . .

Any respirator with a better general absorbent than ours would of course also absorb the arsines better. The fact that the new German issue absorbs better in itself does not prove that they propose to use arsines. But the fact that the Germans bought up all the arsenic supplies just before the war justifies the suspicion that they intend to use one of the gases at the front . . .[26]

As it turned out, Hitler's own experience of being gassed in the trenches in the First World War was partly to ensure that the Germans refrained from using gas in any of their military operations during the Second.

At the same time Lindemann sent Churchill a series of minutes on trade statistics, and notes on figures produced by the Ministry of Shipping. Lindemann's role now required him to be able to prise statistics from Government departments in order to be able to brief Churchill, or to comment on departmental papers. It was the independent approach that Lindemann was able to bring to this work that Churchill appreciated. Yet it was a situation that could easily have led to rancour and jealousy and to the consequent diminution of Lindemann's value to Churchill. His anomalous position and the influence that he was thought to wield were to prove a potential cause of irritation both to officials and to ministers:

It will at once become obvious in what an invidious position the Prof was placed. It was, in fact, so delicate that, had he not behaved with unusual restraint, bloody mutiny might have broken out in the Departments. In spite of the immense usefulness of its work, his Section had no definite status. He was not a Minister with a Department behind him, yet he had the task of requiring statistics from them, often with the object of hostile scrutiny . . .[27]

The staff at S Branch had quickly to become experts on merchant shipping, and well versed in the complexity of its correct measurement – gross tons, net tons, superficial cargo, and so on – and they soon learned to do their calculations in 'deadweight-ton-days'. Here was an area in which the new-found expert might well fall into a trap, no doubt to the delight of the seasoned professional, but with possible grave consequences for war arrangements and for men's lives. An example of such potential disharmony and consequent hindrance to war business occurred in January 1940, when a sharp exchange of views took place between the Ministry of Shipping and Lindemann, who had alleged a wasteful under-loading of ships. As he told Churchill: 'To under-estimate our shipping capacity is nearly as bad as to over-estimate it. It may lead us, in order to save shipping, to buy in dollar countries what we could purchase in more remote sterling areas.'

On this occasion Roy Harrod, who had just joined S Branch himself, had gone astray in the maze of definition and had provided erroneous statistics for Lindemann, who had in turn briefed Churchill. This had stirred up a hornet's nest of animosity. At the subsequent ministerial meeting to discuss the figures, the minister had stood his ground. As Harrod described:

He rebutted the criticisms, and went further; with his eye on the Prof he said it was wasting the time of all the Ministers present to bring up all these ill-informed allegations, implying that they were mere rubbish.[28]

When the error was discovered, Lindemann sent Harrod round to talk to the minister, Sir Cyril Hurcomb. As Harrod recalled:

Hurcomb gave me a thorough 'dressing-down'. He had a good command of rough and strong rebuke, available for his service, when he required it. Members of Professor Lindemann's staff kept ringing up the Ministry of Shipping, asking to be supplied with irrelevant figures; then the First Lord was briefed to make ridiculous criticisms. His, Hurcomb's people were busy, trying to contribute to the war effort, and their work was interrupted and their time wasted by these idiotic questions. Unless a stop was put to this he would feel it his duty to report the matter to the Prime Minister . . .[29]

Unless care was taken, Lindemann's scorn for civil servants – both as a general rule and in particular cases – might exacerbate unrest. He expressed himself freely to his staff, and was sometimes in danger of allowing a sharp tongue to prevent him from acquiring, at least without difficulty, information that he needed for his work. That would be a high price to pay for the pleasure of expressing venomous sentiments. It was vital for the country that Churchill should be able to carry out his task successfully, and it was important for Churchill that Lindemann should be able to unearth the necessary facts without delay or hindrance.

In this Lindemann was greatly aided by his staff, especially the young economist Donald MacDougall, whose tact in dealing with ministries and officials was to prove invaluable. Lindemann's support for his staff was constant, and they in return were loyal to him, despite the many occasions when they found him difficult. As with his selection of researchers for the Clarendon, he displayed great skill in his choice of wartime staff. MacDougall recalled S Branch's relations with officials:

To begin with, we antagonised some people. Shortly after Roy Harrod joined the Branch at the beginning of 1940 he kept on pressing an argument that we were under-loading ships bringing in imports, long after I had discovered that it was based on a misunderstanding of the statistics. This lost us some credibility, which it took us time to regain. But we did regain it . . . partly because we were proved right on an increasing number of occasions, but also by being tactful, making friends with the officials concerned, showing them how we were doing our sums, trying wherever possible to get their agreement in advance, and by becoming as expert as they were – or preferably more so – on their subject . . .[30]

Early in 1940 the Government's Adviser on Economic Co-ordination, the economist Lord Stamp,[31] for whom Lindemann had formed a healthy contempt, produced a pessimistic paper on the cost of the war. Lindemann analysed the paper, which was based partly on comparisons with the First World War, and sent Churchill his conclusions, describing it as 'a postponement of the maximum war effort'. He added his opinion that it was a deplorable beginning for economic co-ordination, and continued:

> . . . what with fears of a Blitzkrieg and the general knowledge that Germany is waging a totalitarian war, there is far greater willingness by people to do what they are told and make the necessary sacrifice more quickly than in 1914, when it took some time for the war to be taken seriously by all classes.[32]

In the Cabinet, Churchill circulated both Lord Stamp's paper and Lindemann's comments. He himself endorsed the condemnation of the report's pessimism, and related it to the broader war picture, which he saw so clearly.

Two months later Lord Stamp produced another paper, presented to the Cabinet by the Chancellor of the Exchequer, Sir John Simon, and the Lord Privy Seal, Sir Kingsley Wood, on the results that would flow from a German occupation of Scandinavia. Churchill asked Lindemann to comment on it. Lindemann was scornful, in keeping with his opinion of its author. 'This paper,' he told Churchill, 'gives a quite unduly pessimistic picture of the results of the German invasion of Scandinavia.' He made his own analysis of how imports might be affected, giving a comprehensive description of alternative sources of the various commodities that would be threatened if the Germans advanced into Scandinavia: iron-ore, paper, timber, ferro-alloys, butter and bacon.

Churchill, perhaps more alive than Lindemann to the benefits of harmony in discussion, replied with a 'First Lord's Personal Minute':

> I promised to show the Chancellor of the Exchequer the paper I intend to circulate to counter the effects of the Stamp pessimism beforehand. Will you prepare a paper incorporating all the points, but in less controversial form, and I will circulate to the Cabinet.

Scandinavia was about to become an area of strategic importance in the developing conflict, and was to have a profound effect on the fortunes of both Churchill and Lindemann himself.[33] Since the first week of the war Churchill had been agitating for action in northern waters, partly to give vent to his compelling desire to go on the offensive, and partly because there was an obvious and vital target in the form of the iron-ore being shipped in large quantities from Sweden and Norway to Germany. Iron-ore was vital for producing the steel that fuelled the entire German munitions industry, and the Swedish mines at Gallivare were the Germans' paramount source. The mines were being worked around the clock, and eighteen trains were leaving the ore fields each day, to be unloaded at Narvik on the Norwegian coast. This traffic, Churchill told the War Cabinet, 'would become a means of sending hundreds of thousands of British and French troops to their deaths'.[34]

The tempo of war was about to quicken, and Lindemann was often asked at short notice to discover and present comprehensive details on a plethora of subjects, as, for example, in Churchill's request of 31 December 1939:

> Let me have at earliest a full report upon tonnage and ships which entered the British Isles during the month of December, and how this compares with December 1932 as well as with December 1938. I should like to have a good statistical survey of this month.[35]

S branch would get to work, and Lindemann would distil the results to a clear précis so that the First Lord could easily grasp the essentials and quickly give the appropriate instructions. It was as if, long before the days of computers, Churchill was able to press a button and have, more or less instantly displayed, a vast array of information clearly ordered and analysed, with conclusions attached. In sharp contrast to the usual leisurely pace of Government business, Churchill was able to act on the results of his enquiries with the minimum delay. To Lindemann he would often give full authority to prompt ministers to instant action, with such instructions as: 'Please take this up at once in my name with the Minister of Shipping.'

The breadth of Lindemann's work in the first months of war can be seen from a random sample of the subjects on which he sent minutes to Churchill. They included such disparate matters as deliveries of aircraft to the RAF, shipping losses, trade returns, Sticky Bombs, recognition of shipping channels by pilots, RDF developments and street lighting.

In his minutes, Churchill also demonstrated his interest in the development of scientific ideas, and his belief in their importance to the war effort. He told Lindemann:

If we could have large supplies of multiple projectors and rockets directed by the RDF irrespective of cloud or darkness, and also could have the proximity fuse working effectively by day and to a lesser extent in moonlight or starlight, the defence against air attack would become decisive. This combination is therefore the supreme immediate aim. We are not far from it in every respect, yet it seems to baffle us. Assemble your ideas and facts so that I may give extreme priority and impulse to this business.

The proximity fuse was to be developed, at the instigation of Major Millis Jefferis,[36] from a rather unorthodox experimental department called MD1. The fuse was to be one of the most important inventions of the war, proving to be especially useful for shooting down the V1 flying bombs that would rain upon London in 1944. Lindemann had talked to Jefferis' team and had perceived the fuse's value. His success in bringing such matters quickly to Churchill's attention was on many occasions during the war to ensure that good but unorthodox ideas, many from MD1, were not held up by committees or by the cumbersome machinery of departments such as the Ministry of Supply.

During the first months of the war Lindemann moved into rooms at the Carlton Hotel, within walking distance of the Admiralty, so that he had not far to go to get some sleep after the long hours that Churchill's regime demanded. In these exhilarating, hard and dangerous months he became Churchill's close companion, and would go to the Admiralty and talk to him after the long day's business was over – often well into the small hours of the morning – and would stay and talk until the First Lord retired to bed.

It has often been asked how a prickly, eccentric, arrogant, opinionated, sarcastic and uncooperative man – to use some of the adjectives from time to time levelled against Lindemann – could have developed and sustained such a warm friendship with Churchill. The answer is of course that he did not display those characteristics to Churchill, and in the dark months early in the war, when Churchill feared that the full might of Germany would soon be unleashed in the west, and before he had the great confidence that came with overall command, it must have been easy and consoling for him to talk to Lindemann in his moments of reflection.

Lindemann was an old and trusted friend, who shared Churchill's determination to get at the Germans in every way possible, and whose powerful intellect meant that he retained and understood much of the detailed information of war with which the First Lord grappled each day. Although Lindemann did not enjoy the champagne, cigars and brandy that gave pleasure to Churchill, his clarity of mind and his humorous cynicism exactly met Churchill's requirements of a companion.

His beneficial effect on Churchill became widely acknowledged: 'On one occasion a conference with a number of generals had run late into the night. Eventually they spilled out, roaring: "The Old Man's being impossible. For God's sake send the Prof in." Lindemann was found and sent in. When the conference resumed, all was smiles and accord. Somehow or other Lindemann had the secret of relaxing Churchill.'[37]

If he had spare time at the weekend, he would return to Christ Church. There he would find respite in the serene and graceful quadrangles and in the ancient, panelled Common Room, where even in wartime there remained a sense of ease. Even so, when don met don sparks would sometimes fly, and Lindemann's often contemptuous remarks would roll discordantly among the decanters. A typical encounter is portrayed in a letter he wrote to an eccentric colleague at Christ Church, who had within Lindemann's hearing rashly questioned the value of science:

Dear Dundas,
. . . Whilst I do not set up as an arbiter of Common Room conventions I think most people would agree that it is improper to decry a foreign guest's subject and to endeavour to create dissension by pretending that another member of the Common Room habitually disparaged the said subject.

As to the original point of disagreement I consider it most untimely, when your whole future and even survival may depend upon their efforts, to sneer at the scientists and to claim that historians are the real repositories of culture and civilisation. I do not think a teacher of Sumerian in Athens would have selected the moment when the Persian army was advancing on Attica to ingeminate his view that reading Sargon of Akkad was the only hallmark of culture and far better than learning how to make effective weapons.

Still, I hope we both have more important things to do than to argue about such trivial matters.[38]

More important things were indeed waiting to be done. The advance of the Wehrmacht seemed to be irresistible, and its spears were turning to point even at the pale-gold walls of Christ Church, with its port and panelled rooms, its lawns and its leisure, its silence, its silver and its snuff-horns. The British campaign in Norway, committing troops and ships to a hazardous operation, had begun too late, and with too light a punch, and it was beginning to disintegrate. The account of some French officers in Sweden exposed the chilling truth:

The British have planned this campaign on the lines of a punitive expedition against the Zulus, but unhappily we and the British are in the position of the Zulus, armed with bows and arrows against the onslaught of scientific warfare.[39]

In April 1940 Hitler turned north, and with almost no warning Denmark and Norway were invaded by German troops. This was followed by developments of the greatest consequence, first in the House of Commons, and second on the Western Front.

On 7 May 1940 the House of Commons began to debate the conduct of the Norwegian campaign. Almost at once Chamberlain's Government came under fierce attack, not just on account of the failures in Scandinavia, but because of a deeper, wider sense of unease – a feeling that the war was being conducted half-heartedly and by peacetime methods.

The debate soon took on the nature of a Vote of Censure on the Government, yet Chamberlain, confident and determined as ever, rose to this challenge to his leadership. Doubtless without intending it, at this vital moment he appeared to personalise the issue, and that further inflamed the House: 'I accept the challenge,' he cried, 'I welcome it indeed. At least we shall see who is with us and who is against us, and I call on my friends to support us in the Lobby to-night.'[40]

It was an unwise choice of words, and the temperature of the debate rose steeply. Before it had ended, Lloyd George – a legend in his lifetime and the country's Prime Minister during the Great War – had delivered a fatal blow:

It is not a question of who are the Prime Minister's friends. It is a far bigger issue. The Prime Minister must remember that he has met this formidable foe of ours in peace and in war. He has always been worsted. He is not in a position to put it on the ground of friendship. He has appealed for sacrifice . . . I say solemnly that the Prime Minister should give an example of sacrifice, because there is nothing that can contribute more to victory in this war than that he should sacrifice the seals of office.[41]

Chamberlain's days as Prime Minister were numbered from that moment, but memorable as this scene was, it was overtaken by matters of even greater moment a little over twenty-four hours later. In the early hours of 10 May, German divisions crossed the borders of Belgium and Holland, as Hitler turned his blitzkrieg on the west. A few hours later Churchill told his son of these grave events: 'The German hordes are pouring into the Low

Countries, but the British and French armies are advancing to meet them, and in a day or two there will be a head-on collision.'

At seven o'clock that morning the Military Co-ordination Committee met at the Admiralty. Among its many orders was one that set in hand Lindemann's proposal for the use of river mines: Operation Royal Marine. At half-past eleven the War Cabinet met, for the second time that morning. Even at this hour of crisis Churchill found time for the excitement of science, and called Lindemann into the room to demonstrate an anti-aircraft homing fuse. The Chief of the Imperial General Staff, Field Marshal Ironside, was impatient at this diversion, as Sir John Reith noted:

> Ironside very snotty about a homing rocket which Churchill's tame scientist, Lindemann, was demonstrating on a side table. 'Do you think this is the time for showing off toys?' he asked me.[42]

By early evening, as the Nazi tide engulfed Belgium and Holland, Churchill had been summoned to Buckingham Palace and the King had appointed him Prime Minister.

For Lindemann these events were to be momentous. He was now being drawn to the heart of Government. For the next five years he would be among the Prime Minister's closest and staunchest companions. He would remain in Churchill's inner circle, and his advice would have a marked effect on the whole conduct of the war.

ELEVEN

At the Centre

As the maelstrom tore into Europe, with armoured columns and motorised infantry punching through the defences of Belgium and Holland, and dive-bombers pouring deadly hail on to a fleeing populace, a whirlwind of a different type bore down on the British Government. At its centre was the new Prime Minister, who began work at 10 Downing Street on the afternoon of 13 May 1940.

Churchill's ways in office were redolent of government in an earlier age. They were something of a reversion 'to the time when personal capriciousness was not yet stifled by regulations and administrative specialisation'.[1] He readily assumed the role of sole decision-maker, leaving subordinates and colleagues frequently to act as creatures of his will – his 'instruments', in Pepys' phrase.[2] He was deeply conscious of the British constitution, and would in the end always act on advice when it was his duty to so, but he chose that his contact with those who turned the wheels of government should be largely through people whom he knew and trusted, or for whom he felt affection, such as friends or family.

Churchill was clear about how he would play his part: he had been chosen as master, and he knew from recent experience that 'the machinery he inherited for the central direction of the war was totally inadequate to the task. In May 1940 he was bent on its transformation. In effect, the machinery had to be customised for Churchill's personal use.'[3]

For the new Prime Minister, there were obvious attractions in fashioning his administration to his own preferences. As he himself described it:

> At the top there are great simplifications. An accepted leader has only to be sure of what it is best to do, or at least to have made up his mind about it. The loyalties which centre upon number one are enormous. If he trips up he must be sustained. If he makes mistakes they must be covered. If he sleeps he must not be wantonly disturbed. If he is

no good he must be pole-axed. But this last extreme process cannot be carried out every day; and certainly not in the days just after he has been chosen.[4]

The official organisation that was to be closest to Churchill, as Prime Minister, was his Private Office. It was administrative rather than advisory, but it played a vital liaison role throughout Whitehall. Besides becoming Premier, Churchill had also, of his own volition, been appointed Minister of Defence (a previously unknown office), and he therefore became not only head of the Government but also the overlord of defence policy, with a direct link to the Chiefs of Staff.

To serve him as Minister of Defence a Secretariat was set up under Major-General Ismay,[5] who became the point of contact between Churchill, as political chief of Great Britain at war, and the professional heads of the armed services who were responsible for waging the war in all its details.

Into this personalised form of administration, the hub at the centre of the formal structure of the Government, Churchill was able, in a way that had not been customary for many years, to introduce an intimate group of personal advisers. He wasted no time in doing so, and accordingly there soon arrived on the scene three men who would fulfil that role: Brendan Bracken, Churchill's Parliamentary Private Secretary and later to be Minister of Information; Desmond Morton, who had spent the previous ten years as head of the CID's Industrial Intelligence Centre; and Lindemann. Each of them satisfied Churchill's criterion of having been his staunch supporter in the 'Wilderness', and of having in their respective ways won the great man's trust and affection; each was given considerable responsibility, in Lindemann's case that of personal adviser on scientific and economic matters.

His brief was to cast a critical eye over the whole course of the war effort, with the notable exception of military strategy and tactics. He was wholly in Churchill's confidence, and was placed on the very restricted list – of approximately eighteen people – of those who were supplied with the secret Enigma decrypts, known as Ultra. This fact, together with the efficiency of his Statistical Department, meant that Lindemann's advice to Churchill was made cogent by his possession of a great deal of information. It may seem surprising that he was placed on such a restricted list, but as Lord Briggs later noted:

Prof was undoubtedly interested in young people who had anything to do with intelligence. It provided a contrast to dealing with Churchill. I was a cryptographer rather than an intelligence analyst but I did know pretty well what happened to the information that was passed on from Bletchley during the war.

It came about that Churchill desperately needed people who understood the intelligence significance of what the Ultra messages said, and at Bletchley itself there was not an iron curtain but a silken curtain between intelligence and cryptography. The people who were doing the intelligence analysis were not sufficiently well known to be able to make a mark on Churchill, indeed I don't think there was anybody on the straight intelligence side of Ultra at Bletchley who was particularly well known to Churchill.

Churchill decided to bring Prof into the news. There was more intelligence available to Prof than was derived from Ultra and Bletchley. He was in a position to put bits and pieces of intelligence together which nobody else knew how to co-ordinate. I think he got some of his intelligence from Bletchley, some came from the Statistical Section, and some from agents and people who were employed in different bits of intelligence from MI8. The Prof would be given as much access to a variety of intelligence sources as anybody. He wanted to be fully informed and in order to be so you had to get your intelligence from different sources.[6]

It was to be a role of immense importance, but although Lindemann's influence was to become very strong, and his advice frequently accepted, it was to remain at all times an advisory role. Churchill's own breadth of vision and his strength of character ensured that it was he who was the driving force in all that he did. In the words of one of Churchill's long-standing private secretaries:

He always retained unswerving independence of thought. He approached a problem as he himself saw it, and of all the men I have ever known he was the least liable to be swayed by the views of even his most intimate counsellors. Many people made the mistake of thinking that somebody – it might be General Ismay or Professor Lindemann – for whom the Prime Minister had the utmost respect and affection, would be able to 'get something through'. Unless the Prime Minister was himself impressed by the argument, pressure by others seldom had any effect.[7]

As it happened, this independence was often obscured by the fact that Lindemann's arguments were so persuasive, so intellectually robust and so lucidly expressed that Churchill often accepted them in the form in which they were presented: 'Many of Lindemann's ideas were put up by Churchill as his own. Many of Lindemann's draft letters were circulated unaltered over Churchill's signature.'[8] However, it was Lindemann's own independence of mind that was so useful: he would never descend to giving Churchill an answer that he thought was the one required. He always said what he thought was right, oblivious to anyone else's preferences. Churchill valued this highly.

It was of course likely that such influence would give rise to jealousy and resentment, and this was made more certain by the breadth of the area in which Lindemann was permitted to roam:

Just as Lindemann had been the single most frequent guest at Chartwell in the 1930s, so, during the war itself he was the most regular attendant at Chequers. Neither a Member of Parliament nor, until 1942, a Cabinet Minister, Lindemann was Churchill's watchdog and guide over a whole range of scientific and technical matters, from poison gas to manpower; he saw the most confidential documents, and was privy from the outset to the most secret source of British Intelligence.[9]

As the German armies drove inexorably forward, and as May gave way to June, the defenders of France and the Low Countries began to disintegrate, but in contrast to the flux and uncertainty spreading through those countries, in London the new Government, revolving around Churchill, was securely in place. Sir Edward Bridges, the Cabinet Secretary, and General Ismay, Churchill's chief-of-staff, began to link the powerhouse at the centre to the wheels of Government. The Chiefs-of-Staff Committee, meeting daily, was in direct contact with the executive head of Government, in his role as Minister of Defence, and together they took full control of the conduct of the war. At its moment of peril the defence of the island was therefore carried out smoothly, albeit at a hectic pace.

Lindemann was to be an integral part of this new establishment, seeing Churchill every day, as well as late each evening, and at weekends travelling with him to Chequers, or to Ditchley Park in Oxfordshire when bright moonlight exposed Chequers, which was easily recognisable to the German bombers. It was to Chequers that he went on Saturday, 15 June, the day after the Germans had entered Paris, and a moment at which it seemed as though the heavens were about to fall. The events of that evening were recorded by Jock Colville, whom Churchill had taken on as private secretary – even though Colville had worked for Chamberlain, of whom he remained a firm admirer:

We arrived at Chequers in time to dine at 9.30. The party consisted of Winston, Duncan and Diana Sandys, Lindemann and myself. It was at once the most dramatic and the most fantastic evening I have ever spent . . . telegrams had been received from Bordeaux to the effect that the position was deteriorating fast and the request to be allowed to make a separate peace was being put in a more brutal form. I imparted this to Winston who was immediately very depressed. Dinner began lugubriously, W. eating fast and greedily, his face almost in his plate, and every now and then firing some technical question at Lindemann, who was quietly consuming his vegetarian diet . . . Winston, in order to cheer himself and us up, read aloud the messages he had received from the Dominions and the replies he had sent to them and to Roosevelt. 'The war is bound to become a bloody one for us now,' he said, 'but I hope our people will stand up to bombing and the Huns aren't liking what we are giving them. But what a tragedy that our victory in the last war should have been snatched from us by a lot of softies.'[10]

In those early days Colville was one of those who greatly lamented the fall of Chamberlain, and who shared widespread doubts about Churchill. As he was later to say, 'Seldom can a Prime Minister have taken office with "the Establishment", as it would now be called, so dubious of the choice and so prepared to find its doubts justified.' Yet, as he continued: 'Within a fortnight all that was changed. I doubt if there has ever been such a rapid transformation of opinion in Whitehall and of the tempo at which business was conducted.'[11]

Nor did Colville at first take readily to Lindemann, describing him on early acquaintance as 'supremely unattractive'. He amplified this opinion in a note written on the Prime Minister's writing paper: 'He thinks he is a mixture of John the Baptist, Maynard Keynes & Lord Leverhulme: he is really an ingenious but slightly inflated frog with an unpleasant croak . . . (His foreign connections are fishy.)'[12]

Such was the impression Lindemann was capable of making on people before they – at least those whom he allowed to do so – got to know him. Colville, however, was soon won over and was to become a firm friend. His barb may have been prompted by the breadth of Lindemann's commission, which was to act, as Churchill put it, as the Prime Minister's eyes and ears: assembling, checking, comparing and criticising departmental figures and arguments.[13]

Meanwhile, the possibility of invasion had become a stark reality. Lindemann gave Churchill a detailed aide-memoire of matters that he believed needed urgent attention in order to meet the threatened invasion. His paper ranged over landing grounds, pill-boxes, the transporting across the Channel of enemy tank divisions, radar equipment, vulnerable beaches, local police equipment, petrol bombs, mines, the placing of field-guns, enemy wireless jamming, the control of refugees and other salient points. He introduced his proposals by saying: 'No doubt most of the points in this note, many of which are obvious, are covered by the existing plan of Home Defence. Proposals to adopt scientific methods for coping with special diffi-culties can only be useful if the general picture is reasonably accurate. It is to make sure that I am on the right lines that I have gone into so many details.'[14]

In supplying such details he was greatly helped by S Branch, which, with the formation of the new Government, had been renamed 'The Prime Minister's Statistical Department' (or S Department). It had moved from the Admiralty to Richmond Terrace, from where in due course it moved again, to the Cabinet Offices in Great George Street, which were to remain its home for the rest of the war. There Lindemann was to become a familiar figure, not least to the charwomen who cleaned the corridors. When he passed them on arriving in the morning he would always raise his bowler hat and greet them: they thought him 'lovely'.[15] At the beginning of the war he lived in the Criterion Hotel, whose famous bar had been a cele-brated rendezvous. The hotel was comfortable and near his office, and the maître d'hôtel understood what he liked to eat. However, it was destroyed by a bomb, after which Lindemann moved to a flat in Westminster, at 77 Marsham Court.

Not surprisingly, work at S Department suffered during the Blitz, and the staff became tired by fire-watching duties at night and by travel delays in getting to and from work. Lindemann therefore looked for a way in which the department could continue its work undisturbed by air-raid warnings and falling bombs. He arranged that, for as long as the Blitz continued, at around six in the evening the department would escape to a house called 'Sentry Hill', at Marlow, which Harrod had requisitioned. Some of the married staff complained when they heard of this plan, but Lindemann merely replied: 'Your views are interesting but irrelevant. Perhaps you would rather serve in the Army!'

Having arrived at Marlow they would discuss their work over dinner, after which Lindemann usually retired to his room, only occasionally taking part in subsequent discussions. The others would stay at their desks until the early hours. Even then they were not assured of rest: C. J. Martin recalls going to bed at 1 a.m. but being called down at 3 a.m. to state what a ton of 25-lb shells cost. During these long hours S Department would discuss the information that it had collated and would argue about the lessons it contained. At eight o'clock the next morning its members would depart again for London.[16]

During their discussions Lindemann would fortify himself with cups of very milky tea laced with four or five spoonfuls of sugar, which perhaps gave him the energy he needed. He could be as stubborn as a mule, and it sometimes took hours of arguing and coaxing to persuade him of the merits of a case. Often, after patient exposition and apparent agreement, he would revert to his position at the start, with all the fallacies that his staff thought they had exposed. In argument he had what they called a 'Common Room Technique' – he would press his interlocutor to set out his case, which he would then demolish. Yet he was quite ready to be persuaded once he saw the force of an argument. Then he would get to work on the drafts and papers put before him and prepare his fabled précis:

> First of all, it seemed astonishing that he could even read them, as he crouched forward in his chair with the paper held a few inches away from his one good eye, and with the other bad eye screwed up (for his vanity would not permit him to descend to spectacles). Then his hand would go out for a pen, and the cuts and alterations would begin.[17]

Moving down to Marlow in the evening had another advantage: it relieved Lindemann, who must from time to time have become extremely tired, of the onerous duty of having to wait around in smoky rooms or cellars, with others in Churchill's circle in whose talk he was not particularly interested, until the Prime Minister was ready for the late-night discussions with Lindemann that he seemed to enjoy and value.

The Statistical Department was staffed by about twenty. Lindemann's initial deputy was Roy Harrod, who had originally recruited the economists. Harrod had the important jobs of reading War Cabinet papers, representing Lindemann at Ministerial Committees and negotiating with departments where points of difficulty or delicacy might arise. However, after a time he left, apparently somewhat disgruntled and feeling that he had no longer very much to do. Lindemann did, however, recommend him warmly to the Foreign Office, suggesting that Harrod would be an excellent choice for developing economic plans with the Americans. Harrod was later to say that Lindemann had interfered with his career. He was left with the feeling that, as he put it, one of the dangerous results of being closely associated with Lindemann was that one made large numbers of unnecessary enemies oneself.

Harrod's relationship with Lindemann veered between warm friendship and the reverse. He was often discomfited by Lindemann. When, for instance, in order to find a way of improving the use of shipping space for importing livestock, Harrod came up with a calculation of the cubic volume of the hold of a particular ship, and divided it by the cubic volume of pigs, Lindemann dismissed the idea out of hand, with a terse 'Pigs are not cubical'. Word spread, and for some time thereafter, in the Christ Church Common Room, there was jovial reference to 'cubical pigs' whenever Harrod appeared.

Harrod was also put out when, with his professional skill as an economist, he put up a set of economic proposals accompanied by advice on the lines that he thought Lindemann should take and Lindemann's response was terse, recommending that Harrod try and make a little money of his own before he started advising others on how to do so. The logic of this did not appeal to Harrod. Yet, in spite of such setbacks, he retained a certain veneration for Lindemann and would remark that three people had told him, quite independently, that Lindemann and Keynes were the two most brilliant people they knew. That counted for something with Harrod, who was later to write the standard life of Lord Keynes, whose pupil he had been.

For the rest of the war the guiding light of the Statistical Department was Donald MacDougall, who commented:

On the average there were perhaps half a dozen economists; one scientific officer; one established civil servant (with economic training) to help keep the amateurs on the rails, some half a dozen computers, who were girls who worked on rather primitive calculating machines, two or three typists and clerks, and last, but not least, a number of what were called 'chartists' – about four were fully employed in the early period when there was much drawing of new charts and diagrams.[18]

The department, with a brief much enlarged and widened since its days at the Admiralty, began to establish a network of contacts and sources of information with which to prepare data and advice for Lindemann to give to the Prime Minister, or with which he could take up the cudgels with other departments, often on Churchill's instructions. His method of communication with the Prime Minister remained the minute, of which during the course of the war Lindemann sent about 2,000, an average of roughly one a day. Often many weeks' work would result in a minute of one page or less, in keeping with Churchill's insistence on brevity:

The Section was thus much more than a purely statistical one. It was concerned not merely with the collection and presentation of statistics but with the conclusions to be drawn from them, and it also made frequent recommendations on general economic policy. Except at the Prime Minister's request minutes were seldom submitted unless they recommended action.[19]

In short, it was an organisation personal to the Prime Minister. Its value lay partly in its independent approach to its work, free from departmental bias or compromise. Its function was to discover, digest, present and advise on a mass of military and economic statistics and papers, which the Prime Minister had not the time to examine in detail.

One of its most important tasks was to warn Churchill of shortfalls or difficulties in the supply or use of men or materials. There were therefore crucial distinctions between S Department and the superficially similar offices of the Economic Section of the War Cabinet Secretariat and the newly formed Central Statistical Office, which had the job of informing ministers and departments generally, without offering advice.

As the plans to resist invasion were being completed, organisation of the 'Home Front' took on a vital importance. Lindemann regarded the correct use of manpower as another arm of war, and he believed that action must be taken to rectify the fact that, as he saw it, there were in England probably over a million men unemployed, or employed unnecessarily, who could instead be put to defence work. He therefore instructed his department to gather evidence to support his belief. The sequence of what happened next provides a good practical example of how the Statistical Department operated. Lindemann's ability to evaluate priorities clearly was translated first into skilful detective work, then into marshalling the relevant statistics, until finally, after long hours of preparation, he would draft a minute to the Prime Minister. In many cases the result was the issue of orders for the action that Lindemann had recommended.

The need to analyse the efficiency, or otherwise, of the Home Front arose from industry's paramount objective of arming and equipping a total of fifty-five divisions. The Statistical Department soon discovered that the plans for this great endeavour were being frustrated. Munitions factories were lying idle for want of skilled workers, who were instead engaged in work that was a hangover from peacetime, and which was unproductive for the war effort. The Government departments in charge – in this case the Board of Trade and the Ministry of Labour – seemed to be failing to address the matter with any success or, worse, in Lindemann's view, with any sense of urgency.

Donald MacDougall set the ball rolling when he informed Lindemann bleakly that: 'It is possible that the war may be lost this year unless there can be a very rapid increase in the output of munitions.' The answer that he suggested was at once to transfer machine tools and skilled labour from export industries to armaments. 'It is no good,' he said, 'preserving our foreign exchange resources so that we can win the war in 1942, if it means losing it in 1940.'

S Branch then held discussions with relevant officials, including the economist Maynard Keynes, and made calculations showing that the number of skilled men who could be drafted into munitions production could be doubled over the following two months, if exports of engineering products were stopped. Lindemann set to work on distilling all the statistics into a minute for the Prime Minister – neither he nor Churchill regarded such minutes as respectable without reference to orders of magnitude – and with a recommended course of action. The problem, he said, was that the civil servants at the Ministry of Labour were maintaining that few workers were required, and that the supply programmes had been drawn up under the apprehension that there was a labour shortage: it was in fact a 'chicken and egg' situation.

Lindemann proposed increasing the shifts in factories, transfering labour from export industries to armaments, ordering the Ministry of Aircraft Production to step up its orders so as to soak up labour released for armaments work, and placing large-scale orders in the US:

It is most important to buy from America at once a very large quantity of steel. Once they begin arming seriously they may have none to sell. If we had difficulty in extracting ore from Algeria or Spain we should be in a very grave situation . . .

The cost of finished steel is not vastly greater than the cost of buying iron ore, producing steel and working it up here. While it is obviously unfavourable to have to pay in dollars instead of francs or pounds, this should be faced rather than risk a steel famine.[20]

He added that the Ministry of Supply should increase fivefold its current plans for steel imports. The Prime Minister sent Lindemann's minutes, more or less unchanged, straight on to Sir Andrew Duncan at the Board of Trade and to the Minister of Supply. In the event the measures were firmly pushed through, but only after many and varied objections from what Lindemann dismissed as vested interests. MacDougall recalls: 'Of course we had a great deal of opposition from the steel masters, saying that it's far more expensive buying steel than iron ore, and that they had always done it that way, etc.'[21]

This was an early shot in Lindemann's campaign to ensure that the best possible use was made of scarce shipping, by now under attack from U-boats, and it was driven by the fact that the bottleneck in imports had become one of the gravest threats to the country. Lindemann's concern about the shipping situation was borne out by a request from the Prime Minister on 22 June 1940, when Lindemann had been asked to assess for him a Cabinet paper presented by Arthur Greenwood on the 'Economic Consequences to Germany and Britain of the occupation of Norway, Denmark, the Low Countries and France'. 'Pray give me,' Churchill had written to Lindemann, 'a short appreciation of how bad this all is, and how it affects our means of resistance next year.'

In reply, Lindemann submitted a review of all the commodities that might be affected, assessing priorities and orders of magnitude and enabling Churchill, whose natural interests lay more in the large-scale military picture, to see clearly that the danger might equally lie on the home and economic fronts. In this context the use to which shipping was put was a vital aspect of the war, and the Statistical Department developed invaluable expertise in the matter. As Roy Harrod said: 'I believe that S branch was the governing influence in the disposal of our available shipping during the war . . .'[22]

For all his breadth of vision, Churchill shared with Lindemann a thirst for essential detail, and he was far from being above examining the small print. In this respect the combination of the minute detective work of the Statistical Department fully complemented Churchill's wider outlook. This was exemplified when, in the autumn of 1940, it appeared to S Department that mobilisation had been maximised and that no net increase of manpower for the army would be achieved. Lindemann's scepticism was fired by this suggestion. He arranged to collect all the relevant figures from the army and his office produced a summary of the manpower situation in about six coloured charts, using the official figures. This was sent to Churchill, headed 'Use of Manpower in the British Army'. Churchill himself then dictated, over a weekend at Chequers, a directive to the Secretary of State for War. Adding his own deep knowledge and experience to the dry bones of S Department's facts, he prepared a complete and accurate summary with a step-by-step breakdown of army strength, from front-line troops through all the echelons of supporting units, concluding with the words: 'The Army is guilty of lush disorganisation. It must comb its tail to feed its teeth.' He continued:

Before I can ask the Cabinet to assent to any further call-up from the public, it is necessary that this whole subject shall be thrashed out, and that at least a million are combed out of the fluff and flummery behind the fighting troops, and made to serve effective military purposes. We are not doing our duty in letting these great numbers be taken from our civil life and kept at the public expense to make such inconceivably small results in the fighting line.[23]

The staff at the Statistical Department had to be on their toes, as Herbert Robinson related:

I believe the numbers helped him to paint a mental picture of relative magnitudes and capabilities. This is why he took our S Branch with him into his 'Private Office' when he became Prime Minister in 1940. One example of this side of Churchill came when I wrote him a short memo on some shortfall in munitions production. I used several percentages. He returned the memo with a red ink statement 'I want only fractions, not percentages.' Being a young 'smart aleck' I returned it, retyped, with the percentages transformed into fractions, but all expressed in one hundredths, e.g. 15% became 15/100. I immediately received the memo back with another red ink statement 'I will not deal in fractions less than one-ninth.'[24]

One of the imports that S Department reviewed for Churchill was timber, which was in time to become something of an obsession with Lindemann. As Donald MacDougall explained:

Shipping space soon became a major bottleneck and it was essential to cut out all unnecessary imports. Timber imports accounted for a very important part of the total, and Prof waged a relentless battle to get them reduced: by substituting materials that could be produced at home or needed less shipping space if imported, by felling our forests and in other ways. There was much opposition – from those who argued that the changes proposed were inconvenient or more expensive and from many others. Such opposition made Prof even more persistent.[25]

Roy Harrod also played a part in this campaign:

Timber imports seemed to have an especially obdurate tendency to remain above the level of the previous directives. Nothing raised the ire of the Prof so much. There were excuses, of course. They had expedited imports because the St Lawrence would soon be frozen, or they had used timber as a balancing cargo, etc. But the Prof was not one whit appeased. I think that he suspected that there were some bearers of a degree in the Arts – 'classics', he always called them – who had too sentimental an eye for the preservation of the British woodlands and were working away to frustrate him.[26]

However, the consequent felling of home timber was to become so relentless that at one point even Churchill asked plaintively: 'Can't we keep at least some of our fine ancient trees standing?'[27] Eventually Lindemann's campaign was remarkably successful, and timber imports were reduced to less than one-fifth of their pre-war level.

In this world of inconvenient but necessary controls and directives, Lindemann bore constantly in mind relative magnitudes and the effects of the various Government measures. On one occasion he was walking with MacDougall along a London street and, as MacDougall recalled:

He noticed people sticking up posters, which said 'Stop that dripping tap'. The idea was to save water, which would save coal for the generators, and for the water works. Prof immediately got out his pocket slide rule, and worked out, even as we were walking along, how much paper was involved in the posters, because it had to be imported, or the wood pulp had to be imported, and how much power was involved in making the paper out of the wood pulp, and so on; and of course Prof was right in his initial suspicion that it all added up to enormously more than was going to be saved by the posters' advice being followed.[28]

His concern that people should suffer no greater inconvenience or discomfort than was essential for the war effort chimed with Churchill's, and it is something that runs contrary to the image of Lindemann having no interest in the masses. In this context the question of food rationing is a good example. Rationing became a live question very early on, and only a month after the war had started Lindemann sent a minute to Churchill opposing the Food Ministry's rationing proposals, saying: 'Rationing, especially on a scale scarcely better than the Germans,[29] will have a doubly harmful result. It will depress the morale here and will really enhance it in Germany . . . Great difficulties are worth facing to postpone until the Spring such a public acknowledgement of our difficulties so encouraging to the Nazis.'

Churchill responded to Lindemann's minute by writing to the Minister of Food: 'In view of the depressing effect of general rationing on the Home

Front, and the corresponding encouragement it would give to Germany, I think it should be postponed to the latest possible moment . . . After all, the seas are open at the present time. New dangers may require new developments. But not now.'

In June 1940 the Food Ministry returned to the fray, and proposed reducing the tea ration to two ounces a week, 'as a precaution'. Lindemann was eloquent in his hostility to this proposal, and in his championing of the people. He wrote to Churchill:

> The wisdom of a 2 ounce tea ration is open to serious doubt.
>
> A large proportion of the population consisting of the working class women who do all their own housework, and charwomen, rely exclusively on tea for stimulant. It would be an understatement to call tea their principal luxury; it is their sole luxury. They spend their whole time out of bed dusting, scrubbing and washing. It is their custom to have a kettle always at hand and to prepare a cup once every two hours. Frequent air-raid warnings are likely to strengthen this appetite.
>
> It is this class which suffers most from the war. They meet the direct impact of high prices and scarcities. The blackout and, in certain cases, evacuation impose further hardships. And they lack the compensation of new interests and adventure.
>
> This class is also the least educated and least responsible in the country. They have little stake in the good things of a free democratic community. They can say with some truth, and often do say, that it would make no difference to them if Hitler were in charge.
>
> If the whole of this class lost heart completely they might infect their menfolk and undermine morale, especially if intense air bombardment added to their present troubles.
>
> The consumption of alcohol is likely to rise . . .
>
> The annual saving of cargo if this measure is maintained will be about 65,000 tons. Foreign exchange should not be a difficulty, since the tea comes from India and Ceylon.[30]

Perhaps this insight into the habits of the working classes was provided for his master by Harvey. Lindemann's own touch, by contrast, was not always so sure. Cyril Martin, who worked in the department, mainly on military statistics, recalled:

> On one occasion Prof told me that every working class man drank ten pints of beer a night, and his wife five. When I stated that during my stay in my father's churches I found no such consumption Prof told

me that they would conceal it from me! On another occasion I had to take him somewhere by London bus as his car had broken down en route. When he saw me reach for the fares he said: 'Don't be silly, Martin, public transport is free.'[31]

There are many such stories about Lindemann, but at least some of them should be taken with a pinch of salt: it is unlikely that a man of such intelligence who, despite being a professor, had never confined himself to an ivory tower, was unaware of how others lived. And it often amused him to parody his supposed remoteness; on another occasion he was asked how long it had been since he had travelled on a London bus:

His reply was that it must be over 20 years and, as he had then been bitten by fleas in several places, he had not repeated the experiment. It was his way of caricaturing himself as a snob. Of course, we knew that the story about the fleas had been invented on the spot and, of course, we also knew that he had been stoutly defending the travelling public against unduly severe austerity cuts in the bus services.[32]

After Churchill became Prime Minister, Lindemann was given a room in the annexe to 10 Downing Street. The paramount part of his duties remained advising Churchill on scientific matters and on the technical development of instruments of war. Yet the military situation could not be compartmentalised and his advice also reflected his wider anxiety about the country's ability to import enough for its survival.

The protection of shipping, and the consequent level of imports to the island, had very early in the war become a matter of extreme gravity. The greatest danger came from the activities of German U-boats, which had lost no time in going on the offensive, and which soon began to lie like serpents across the British shipping routes. People remembered 1917, when the war had nearly been lost to German submarines: by 1942 the outlook seemed equally bleak.

Lindemann's department had soon become acutely aware of the submarine threat, and it had collected and examined the statistics in great detail. However, at this crucial moment Churchill's mind was focused elsewhere, on the proposed operations in North Africa. These were to include an attack by General Montgomery from the east, and amphibious landings in Morocco and Algeria in the west, codenamed Operation Torch. It was clear to the Statistical Department that the demands on shipping for these operations were squeezing imports for the Home Front to danger level. Lindemann understood the importance of the African operations, but he also came to the conclusion that the amount of shipping to be used for them was unnecessarily large.

A practical way to save vital shipping, he believed, was to make efficient use of the cargo space available. One answer was to substitute light for heavy imports. Beside the replacement of iron-ore with finished steel, Lindemann had already suggested reducing imports of animal feedstuffs, and instead substituting imports of items such as meat and egg powder. His belief was that this would save as much as nine-tenths of the current shipping requirement, much of which was being wastefully used for supplies to keep animals alive in England, before eventual slaughter.

The overall shipping situation was made worse by the fact that the Mediterranean had been closed by Axis operations: in consequence ships had to make the long journey around the Cape of Good Hope, which meant that they were unavailable for carrying imports for eight weeks.

With their customary lateral-thought processes, the staff of S Department now worked out that equipment for the army – lorries, jeeps, artillery, and so on – would use up much less space in transit if it were first dismantled (at least partially) and then crated for the journey, before being rebuilt on arrival at its destination. Their calculations showed that if the vehicles were completely knocked down – known as 'CKD' – six to ten times as many could be stowed in ships, if stacked on top of each other in crates. Impressed by these ideas, Churchill instructed the Minister of War Transport and the War Minister to hold a meeting with Lindemann, and to discuss his ideas for the shipping of equipment. As Bryan Hopkin,[33] then working under MacDougall, explained:

> The Service Departments, especially the War Office, hated this idea of 'boxing the lorries', and obstructed it, and would have preferred to go on wasting the shipping. Various arguments were put up for not dismantling the equipment for the voyage, including, at one stage, the improbable one that it might be needed to meet a riot in East Africa, which was on the Cape route, in which case it would need to be landed intact.[34]

Rioting in East Africa was a rather implausible excuse; the only possibility, in the department's view, was that the army was referring to Italian prisoners, but they were thought to be too happy to be out of the war to want to riot or escape.

MacDougall recalled S Department's role at this time:

> The most hair-raising moment came in 1942 when we really were in danger of losing the war on the Home Front. Towards the end of

1942 imports were incredibly low and we were running down stocks like mad, to the danger level, and our forecasts of imports, already cut to the bone, were alarming; and I kept warning Prof, and Prof kept on warning the Prime Minister, but the PM was far too preoccupied in military matters to pay any attention. At length Prof asked me to calculate by how much we must cut shipping to the Middle East. I worked out that we had been running at 120 ships a month, although later in the summer it was cut to about 100, and that we had to cut it to 60. Prof said he'd put in 40 to 50 as it would be moved up by the military.[35]

It became a matter of urgency to get the Prime Minister to address this issue. Lindemann had written to him on 9 March 1942, in one of his very rare 'red ink minutes': 'I must press once more for the dismantling of lorries sent abroad from this country. Even a comparatively small measure of this would save millions of tons of imports.'[36] He finally caught Churchill's attention by pointing out the stark detail of the losses in tonnage since the beginning of the war, which were more than double the tonnage built in replacement.

At length the warnings were heeded and, having talked to Lindemann, the Prime Minister sent to the Minister of War Transport a minute that left little room for doubt:

26th December, 1942

Prospective imports into the UK in the first half of next year are so low that we must take immediate definite steps to increase them. In view of the improved strategic situation in the Middle East it would seem possible to fix a definite ceiling to the number of ships made available monthly to the War Office and the Ministry for servicing the Eastern Theatres.

Pray let me know how much imports to this country could be increased if the Service Departments were rationed to the use of (a) 50 ships a month, (b) 40 ships a month, for Eastern Theatres.[37]

Copying this minute to the War Minister, Churchill added: 'Pray let me know the effect this will have upon our fighting efficiency'; and to the Minister of Production he wrote: 'Pray examine what reductions can be made with least damage to our war effort. We should aim at reducing consumption of imported materials to the extent of 300,000 to 500,000 tons a month.' The fact that these instructions were issued is a clear example of how, as a result of Lindemann's intervention, drastic changes were made that would not have occurred, had matters been left to civil servants and generals.[38]

By the end of 1942 the situation was looking so grim, with imports crippled by Operation Torch, bad weather and heavy losses of cargo, that Lindemann drafted a warning paper to the War Cabinet. 'To avoid a crisis in the early summer,' he wrote, 'we have decided to halve shipments of military stores to the East and to reduce consumption of imported raw materials by one quarter.' Stocks were only three million tons above 'the minimum working level absolutely required' and he starkly warned the Cabinet: 'If we let our stocks run down to danger level we must forgo all hope of further military expeditions, however favourable the strategic opportunity.'[39]

The vital need to conserve shipping space led the Statistical Department to peer into all sorts of nooks and crannies to discover the arrangements made for the armed services. Another case concerned Middle East Command's supposed need for huge stocks of ammunition. The demand for a large increase in ammunition production followed the Eighth Army's advances against Rommel. C. J. Martin, who assisted Herbert Robinson as the Statistical Department's army specialist – and whose pass had been removed by the War Office because of his persistent questioning – had opposed this and had placed the facts before Lindemann. With the help of the Ordnance General, Martin had also examined the various stages in the journey of a shell from factory to gun. It transpired that a large amount of ammunition had in fact been collected, but had been lost in the records and was therefore deemed to have been expended,[40] whether it had in fact been used or not. Lindemann's staff reckoned that there was enough ammunition lying around 'to fight the Hundred Years War'. Martin recalled:

Montgomery demanded a large increase in production, which I opposed in minutes to Prof. The essence of the case was that the army considered ammunition to be consumed once it had left field depots. Dumps were then prepared in forward positions and used as required. With the quick success of the Eighth Army the dumps were left behind but the records stated that the ammunition had been used. In fact, more than half was still there. Monty knew strategy but, as I told Prof, he did not know the supply chain. Prof relayed this remark to Monty, which earned me the name 'Whippersnapper'. He demanded a change in the allocation of resources which would have curtailed other production. I disagreed, and was threatened with all kinds of disgrace if I were wrong.

I calculated that we would end the Middle East campaign with a surplus of over ten million rounds of 25-pounder shell ammunition. In fact, after the war millions of rounds of unused ammunition was dumped outside Alexandria harbour. The army will not admit this mistake.[41]

Lindemann gave his staff permission to call any department of Government for information, at any level and at any time, on the basis that if they needed it, Mr Churchill needed it. Inevitably, as S Department began to act as the grit in the oyster, there were contretemps with other departments. There were several brisk exchanges with Lord Beaverbrook, to whom Lindemann was 'an uneasy and far from popular figure without any settled office or portfolio, whose entry into other Ministers' offices was seldom solicited and whose departure was invariably welcomed' – a description that, it has been aptly said, 'others might have often given of Beaverbrook himself'.[42]

Part of the reason for the abrasive manner in which Lindemann so often dealt with others was his curious mix of innate shyness and strong convictions – amounting at times to a belief in the infallibility of his opinion – and the fact that his strict logic often produced answers that others found strange at best, and often provocative or unacceptable.[43] Relations with the War Office were for a time distinctly frosty, and its civil servants were ordered not to give any information to Lindemann's staff without the War Minister's express permission. S Department managed to find other sources until relations were restored, but feathers were ruffled, and Sir Edward Bridges had to intervene to smooth things over – something at which he was fortunately a past master.

Lindemann's open contempt for fools – a department of mankind which, in his view, was full to the brim – led him to unhesitating, uninhibited criticism of many of the papers sent up to Churchill. At times he appeared rather to enjoy the fruits of his biting, sometimes snarling sarcasm, and he admitted that he occasionally made aggressive remarks more for the effect on their listeners than for a strong belief in their content. On one such occasion early in the war he was at the War Office for a meeting to discuss the future make-up of the British Army. His advocacy of more armoured and mechanised divisions was interrupted when a cavalry general, who did not want his units to be converted, protested at the idea. 'My dear General,' Prof replied, 'I think your weapon is the bow and arrow.'[44]

The long hours and intense work must have begun to take their toll on Lindemann's health, particularly as he lived on such a bizarre and meagre diet. His belligerent mentality must also have been a drain on his energy. MacDougall and Thomas Wilson, of the Statistical Department, believed that Lindemann became depressed in 1942, around the time when Beaverbrook became Minister of War Production; both testified to Lindemann saying that he thought his usefulness was over and that he would resign and go back to Oxford.

Yet he kept going, perhaps in a curious way fortified by his growing reputation across Whitehall of being 'very difficult'. On the other side of this coin was stamped the quality of leadership that he displayed to his own staff, and the loyalty that it engendered. One of his recruits remembered this with affection:

> What we, his assistants, appreciated was his loyalty to us in our encounters, sometimes difficult, with the Whitehall departments. MacDougall has observed: 'It would hardly be an exaggeration to say that "My Branch Right or Wrong" was his motto; and he liked to talk contemptuously about "they" meaning, it almost seemed, everyone not in the Branch – except, of course, Churchill.'[45]

The War Minister, P. J. Grigg, was an inveterate opponent of Lindemann and was on several occasions upset by the activities of S Department – not least when it discovered that the army had been putting the wrong fuses in three-inch mortars, which resulted in them blowing up early and killing the troops. Grigg was also driven to submit a catechism of rather querulous points to the Cabinet Secretary, seemingly exasperated by Lindemann's department asking for figures and using them in an inappropriate manner. This, it was alleged, caused extra work and sometimes embarrassment for the War Office. Grigg wrote:

> . . . We are aware that figures have in the past been used by Professor Lindemann's department in such a way as possibly to convey a wrong impression to the Prime Minister. For instance, we found that the Prime Minister was receiving a series of charts called 'Readiness for War' which showed only the degree to which the unit of equipment of divisions in respect of a few important items was complete. The necessity for Reserves, and the equipment elsewhere than in the hands of the Divisions (and independent brigades) was neglected.[46]

The consequences of a 'wrong impression', such as the one in Grigg's complaint, were evident one evening at Chequers in July 1940, when General Sir James Marshall-Cornwall, commander of III Corps, confounded Churchill's belief (which he had based on S Department figures) that the general was ready for war. He later wrote:

The PM looked at me incredulously and drew a sheaf of papers from the pocket of his dinner-jacket. 'Which are your two divisions?' he demanded. 'The 53rd (Welsh) and the 2nd London,' I replied. He pushed a podgy finger on the graph tables and said: 'There you are; one hundred percent complete in personnel, rifles and mortars; fifty percent complete in field artillery, anti-tank rifles and machine-guns.' 'I beg your pardon, Sir,' I rejoined; 'that state may refer to the weapons which the ordnance depots are preparing to issue to my units, but they have not yet reached the troops in anything like those quantities.' The PM's brow contracted; almost speechless with rage he hurled the graphs across the dinner-table to Dill, saying: 'CIGS! [Chief of the Imperial General Staff] Have those papers checked and returned to me tomorrow.'[47]

In July 1940 the Prime Minister had asked Lindemann to design and keep up to date a set of charts showing the state of readiness of each division. S Department then arranged with the army chief of staff's office for the appointment of a liaison officer who would provide, when asked, all the information that it required to supply Churchill with detailed weekly reports concerning the army's state of readiness: personnel, rifles, tanks, field artillery, anti-tank guns, machine guns, mortars, load-carrying vehicles and other such items.

A similar arrangement was established with the Ministry of Supply, for production schedules of army munitions, together with details of production achieved and problems encountered in meeting targets. All this was set out and clearly depicted in chart form, so that in good time the Minister of Defence had comprehensive and up-to-date information. Armed with this he could understand the war situation and keep his military and civilian colleagues on their mettle. Any lack or failing was swiftly exposed, and a remedy demanded by a minute from the top, such as the following:

Prime Minister to Minister of Supply

Recent Air raids have shown that the production of certain vital munitions, and particularly De Wilde ammunition, has been concentrated in one factory, with the result that output has been seriously curtailed by one successful raid. Pray let me have a report on the distribution of the production of every important key munition. It will then be possible to assess the danger of serious reductions in output and to consider what can be done to distribute the risk more widely.

Prime Minister to Minister of Supply

Rifles, New. Since August the production of rifles has fallen off as follows: August 9586; September 8320; October 7545; November 4363; December 4743 (mainly from existing stocks of component parts).

I understand that this fall is due to raids on Small Heath, Birmingham, which completely stopped production. Pray inform me what progress has been made towards resuming production.[48]

Churchill was in the habit of taking a box of Lindemann's charts to Chequers at the weekend and spending hours poring over them. Marshall-Cornwall's account of his contradiction of Churchill over the supply of weapons to his divisions continued with a glimpse of how Lindemann sometimes fulfilled his role as scientific adviser in other ways:

An awkward silence ensued; a diversion seemed called for. The PM leant across me and addressed my neighbour on the other side: 'Prof! What have *you* got to tell me today?' The other civilians present were wearing dinner-jackets, but Professor Lindemann was attired in a morning-coat and striped trousers. He now slowly pushed his right hand into his tail pocket and, like a conjuror, drew forth a Mills hand-grenade. An uneasy look appeared on the faces of his fellow-guests and the PM shouted: 'What's that you've got, Prof, what's that?' 'This, Prime Minister, is the inefficient Mills bomb, issued to the British infantry. It is made of twelve different components which have to be machined in separate processes. Now *I* have designed an improved grenade, which has fewer machined parts and contains a fifty per cent greater bursting charge.' 'Splendid, Prof, splendid! That's what I like to hear. CIGS! Have the Mills bomb scrapped at once and the Lindemann grenade introduced.' The unfortunate Dill was completely taken aback; he tried to explain that contracts had been placed in England and America for millions of the Mills bombs, and that it would be impracticable to alter the design now, but the Prime Minister would not listen . . .'[49]

The guests at that dinner were typical of the mix to be found on such occasions at Chequers, and included, besides Lindemann, Dill and Marshall-Cornwall, Vice-Admiral Fraser and Air Vice-Marshal Portal, as well as one of Churchill's private secretaries and the Prime Minister's wife, daughter and brother.

The description of Lindemann having a grenade in his pocket is true to life. Not only did Prof's role encompass the technical details of instruments of war, their development, production and use, but he was particularly interested in scientific artefacts, especially if they involved an element of 'gadgetry'. So it was that he befriended Jefferis' MD1 department, so called because it was the first Ministry of Defence department to be created.

MD1 was established at a house called 'The Firs', at Whitchurch in Buckinghamshire, and was equipped with testing ranges. Throughout the war Lindemann would call in there, on his journeys from London to Oxford, and he kept in constant touch with its work in progress. MD1 was soon given the Prime Minister's blessing:

> Needless to say the supervision of the experimental section under Jefferis was only one of the many responsibilities which the Prof undertook on behalf of the Prime Minister, but it was certainly one that he found very attractive. Churchill used to say that the Prof's brain was a beautiful piece of mechanism, and the Prof did not dissent from that judgment. He seemed to have a poor opinion of the intellect of everyone with the exception of Lord Birkenhead, Mr Churchill and Professor Lindemann, and he had a special contempt for the bureaucrat and all his ways. In his appointment as Personal Assistant to the Prime Minister no field of activity was closed to him. He was as obstinate as a mule, and unwilling to admit that there was any problem under the sun which he was not qualified to solve. He would write a memorandum on high strategy on one day, and a thesis on egg production on the next. He seemed to try to give the impression of wanting to quarrel with everybody, and of preferring everyone's room to their company; but once he had accepted a man as a friend, he never failed him, and there are many of his war-time colleagues who will ever remember him with deep personal affection. He hated Hitler and all his works, and his contribution to Hitler's downfall in all sorts of odd ways was considerable.[50]

Jefferis himself had hoped to come completely under Lindemann's umbrella, seeking both freedom from control by the General Staff, and access to the Chiefs of Staff. To Lindemann he wrote: 'We are very nearly, with your help, in possession of these facilities.' Lindemann, for his part, pressed MD1's case on Ismay and on Sir Andrew Duncan, the Minister of Supply, with a view to avoiding the red tape that was, he believed, so readily tied by Government departments.

In this context he ruffled particularly the bright plumage of the irrepressible Lord Beaverbrook, who replied uncompromisingly to Lindemann's claims for MD1: 'They must take their directions from me, and not from you. That is the constitutional principle, and no one will persuade me to depart from it.'[51] Nevertheless, throughout the war Jefferis and his deputy, Colonel Stuart Macrae, were able to turn to Lindemann for help when administrative difficulties arose, and always found in him a strong supporter of their cause.

Churchill had in fact already instructed Lindemann, and Desmond Morton, to 'scrutinise and push forward small inventions'.[52] He was enthusiastic about the unorthodox dash shown by MD1, which had been responsible for the 'W' mine used in Operation Royal Marine, and he enjoyed being given demonstrations of their work, sometimes on the firing ranges at Princes Risborough.

Very early in the war MD1 had also developed the 'Sticky Bomb'. This device, designed to stick to a tank before exploding, was being prepared with the help of the Colloid Science Department at Cambridge, and the initial stages involved filling lengths of bicycle tubing with plasticine to represent high explosive. Stuart Macrae described an early experiment:

It appeared that all had not gone well at a recent demonstration of these sticky appliances in one of the quadrangles at Cambridge. Unfortunately this had been held before my time, and it seems that I had missed a most entertaining party. Like the performers in any Harlequinade, the demonstrators had hurled their sausages in all directions and found them to be quite uncontrollable in flight. Only by luck did anyone make contact with one of the metal bins used to represent tanks and if a missile did hit one of these affairs it would not stick. Neither would it poultice. In fact the experiment had been a complete and literal flop.[53]

Churchill, though on high, was well aware of what might go on lower down, and accordingly issued an edict that 'any chortling by officials who have been slothful in pushing this bomb over the fact that it has not succeeded will be viewed with strong disfavour by me'.[54]

Notwithstanding the setback, the bomb did later prove a great success and Lindemann managed to get its production accelerated. On 1 June 1940 Churchill issued one of his shortest minutes on record: under the heading 'Sticky Bomb' he wrote: 'Make one million. WSC.' This was one of many examples of Lindemann expediting matters that would have taken the 'usual channels', or the Civil Service, months to achieve.

W. R. Merton, successor to Tuck as Lindemann's own scientific adviser, recalls an occasion when he was despatched to witness a demonstration of MD1's ingenuity:

I was instructed to board a train for South Wales to see one of Prof's weapons which was a device for blowing up railway engines. It was a string of bombs all tied close together, the idea being that it was very much easier to hit a target if you had a long string of bombs. All sorts of generals were on the train, and we arrived in a valley in Wales where a train was under steam, ready to be blown up. Some Group-Captain whom Prof had enlisted to head the development of the weapon flew over at a low level and dropped a string over the engine, which blew up in a suitably theatrical way. Then we got on the train and all went back again. A week later the poor Group-Captain was himself blown up because the first bomb hit whatever target it was, but then set off the next one, and so on all the way up the string as far as the last one, which was still in the aeroplane.

We didn't hear any more about that weapon.[55]

In all, thirty-three of MD1's weapons were accepted for service use, including the very successful proximity fuse, later to be vital in countering V1 flying bombs; the PIAT anti-tank gun; and others with enlightening names such as Hedgehog, Puff Ball, Limpet, Static Flame Trap, and Jumping Mortar Ammunition. A significant amount of MD1's output was generated by Lindemann himself.

His interest in such weapons meant that he was sometimes accused of being obsessed with gadgetry, but it was an aspect of his desire to see Britain fighting back and taking the offensive to the Axis, wherever she could. This strongly held feeling was to have a more dramatic outlet: it was to be at the root of his persistent support for Bomber Command, something that was to lead Lindemann into a controversy that has not died down to this day.

TWELVE

Out of House and Home

After twelve months of war Hitler's vision of invading England was beginning to fade beyond recall. Yet only a short time earlier, in the summer of 1940, the country's fate had hung in the balance and it had seemed as though the war might soon be over:

> The *Wehrmacht*, fresh from its victories in Poland and Scandinavia, swept into France like an avalanche, and this time there was no miracle of the Marne. The British Expeditionary force was driven into the sea at Dunkirk, Paris fell, and on 17th June 1940 France capitulated.[1]

Yet as the Battle of Britain unfolded in the skies over southern England, there had been a remarkable development. At the beginning of September, just as the Luftwaffe had victory in its grasp, the German High Command made an unexpected and radical change to their plan of battle. Suddenly they pulled their bombers back from attacking the RAF's airfields and bases and switched them to a new task.

The catalyst for this reprieve was an error in navigation made by a handful of Luftwaffe pilots late in August, as a result of which some bombs had landed on central London. There flowed from that miscalculation consequences that led, against all the odds, to Germany losing the desperate fight for mastery of the skies. For at once, on hearing that the capital had been attacked, Churchill ordered a raid on Berlin:

> On the night of the 25th eighty-one British aircraft set out, twenty-nine of which reached their objective. Other night raids followed and, though the damage was small, their effect on Hitler's temper was extensive. On September 4th he announced his intention of wiping out London.[2]

In retaliation came the Blitz: for night after night the inhabitants of British cities were to hear with foreboding the drone of German bombers entering the skies above their homes.

Yet in those fateful months, as Churchill later wrote, 'there was a white glow, overpowering, sublime, which ran through our island from end to end'. As each passing day sustained the peril facing the country, there grew among its people an unaccustomed feeling for England's long history as an independent land. Even those who had wished to come to terms with the Germans understood at last the nature of their enemy. Lord Halifax left a telling account of a summer's evening just after the fall of France, when he walked with his wife in the hills near his home, and of how they rested in the sun for half an hour and looked across the plain of York:

> Here in Yorkshire was a true fragment of the undying England, like the white cliffs of Dover, or any other part of our land that Englishmen have loved. Then the question came, is it possible that the Prussian jackboot will force its way into this countryside to tread and trample over it at will? The very thought seemed an insult and an outrage; much as if anyone were to be condemned to watch his mother, wife or daughter being raped.[3]

So the will of the nation to resist the attackers and their lethal cargo, and Churchill's determination to find a way of hitting back at the foe, were to prove successful in repelling the would-be invader. They would also drive Britain to unleash a bombing campaign herself.

Churchill knew that some form of offensive was needed, to meet the desire of the people to avenge the torments of the Blitz that so many were suffering. It was now that he called on Bomber Command to take an onslaught into the German homeland itself. Quite apart from any other considerations, there was one overwhelming reason for this. Europe had been closed off by the Wehrmacht, and the Royal Navy was engaged to the full in the battle to keep open the shipping lanes to Britain's shores. Therefore a bombing offensive was now, and for a long time, the only way open to enable Britain to retaliate against her enemies. As the Prime Minister wrote at the time:

> But when I look round to see how we can win the war I see that there is only one sure path . . . and that is an absolutely devastating, exterminating attack by very heavy bombers from this country upon the Nazi homeland. We must be able to overwhelm them by this means, without which I do not see a way through.[4]

Since the war many voices have been raised in protest at the campaign that was now unrolled by Bomber Command. However, at the time nobody who had heard the descriptions of the bombing of Warsaw or Rotterdam, or who had suffered from the Blitz, had any qualms about wanting to reply to the Germans in kind. The public sought retribution, as did the Prime Minister. The whole country, he believed, looked to Bomber Command for success.

Yet the RAF was faced with a grave problem. From the earliest weeks of the war German fighter and anti-aircraft defences had been able to inflict heavy losses on the RAF when it attacked by day, and it soon became clear that such raids would have to be suspended for the foreseeable future. The alternative of bombing by night was an altogether more formidable task: then, the enemy was unseen; retaliation was difficult; bomb-aiming was inaccurate; and the chance of collisions was high. Furthermore, Bomber Command's pilots had been trained to rely on astro-navigation, or 'dead reckoning', to take them to their targets, and this difficult process was made all the harder by the distance to Germany and the hazards of flying over enemy territory.

Despite this harsh reality, which had led to Bomber Command being described as quite literally lost in the dark, the crews were habitually reporting considerable success with their missions, and it had become generally accepted – by navigators and pilots, and all the way up to the Air Staff – that, by and large, the bombers were hitting their targets.

Lindemann did not share this belief, and his suspicions were instinctively aroused by the apparent confidence of the experts. He knew from personal experience how difficult the art of bomb-aiming was; indeed, he had long campaigned for stabilised bomb-sights to be fitted to bombing aircraft, which had not been done. It was therefore no surprise to him to hear reports that the accuracy of the RAF might not be what was generally believed. He had already heard some disturbing intelligence reports from R. V. Jones, who later wrote:

> I remember particularly a raid on the Skoda Works at Pilsen, duly announced by the BBC. A friendly Czech indignantly told us that everyone in Pilsen knew that there had been no raid, and that the nearest bomb that had fallen was fifty miles away. Such incidents stimulated Lindemann to institute an investigation.[5]

Lindemann's ability to set such enquiries in hand, and to call for the evidence and explanations that such work required, was strengthened by the fact that in June 1941 he had been raised to the peerage. This was not only in recognition of his services to the war effort – already considerable – but also for the practical purposes of giving him additional status and a voice in Parliament, and as a support both for him and for the Statistical Department in their often complex dealings with ministers, staff officers and officials. Churchill was a firm upholder of constitutional niceties, and these were served by Lindemann's promotion. His position was also to be considerably reinforced when he joined the Cabinet as Paymaster-General in 1942 and became a Privy Counsellor in 1943.

These honours are likely to have pleased at least some of his colleagues at Oxford, although as a result of the nature of his work and of his natural reticence, they had little idea of what Lindemann was actually up to. Inevitably there were mixed reactions, and after his ennoblement some verses began to circulate among the dons:

> *Lord Cherwell, when the war began,*
> *Was plain Professor Lindemann;*
> *But risen now to higher spheres*
> *He takes his seat among the peers,*
> *And from that elevated perch*
> *Cries 'Silence for Lord Christ of Church'.*
> *The Church of Christ, that patient Ass,*
> *Beholds these wonders come to pass,*
> *And rising up with one accord,*
> *Salutes its newly risen Lord.*[6]

It was also said with amusement that when in due course a colleague at Christ Church was asked what difference his elevation had made to Lindemann, the reply was given: 'only that formerly when one went to his rooms, one saw a notice by the door saying "Professor Lindemann. In." Afterwards it usually said "Lord Cherwell. Out."' Another small complication – swiftly dealt with – arose when the newly ennobled professor started signing his notes and minutes to the Prime Minister with a 'C', being short for 'Cherwell'. This gave birth to a minute from Churchill: 'You had better sign yourself "Cherwell" as there is a "C" already in my circle.' ('C' being the acronym traditionally used by the head of the Secret Services.)

There were other less charitable comments, perhaps not surprisingly, as Lindemann had so thoroughly mastered the gentle art of making enemies, something which was later referred to in Sir Alec Cadogan's remark that 'Lord Cherwell's main achievement was to unite against him any body of men with whom he came in contact.'[7] John Colville, Churchill's private secretary, noted in his diary for 12 June 1941: 'The Honours List:

Lindemann gets a barony, which will cause anger in many quarters and especially in Oxford, but not so much as when it is learned that he proposes to call himself Lord Cherwell of Oxford.'[8] The ubiquitous socialite MP, 'Chips' Channon, also dipped his pen in a little light venom, when he wrote: '. . . to Shoeburyness in a special train with the PM, Beaverbrook, Archie Sinclair and others, to inspect tanks and the new anti-aircraft guns and devices. How luxuriously the PM lives, a most lavish lunch and grand train. "Baron Berlin", as Lindemann is called, was of course there too.'[9]

However, Lindemann was not in the least concerned by what such people thought, even at the university. He loved Oxford, and at this stage of the war he returned there whenever he could, to get some respite from the fray in London and to examine work at the Clarendon. Although the administration of the laboratory was in Keeley's hands, Lindemann remained closely in touch with the research that he had set in motion. Teams in one part of the Clarendon were working on infra-red and on the microwave devices that would prove so valuable, both in the war in the air and against the U-boat menace. In another part of the laboratory the project to develop an atom bomb was secretly beginning to unfold.

Lindemann was now working at a hard pace and for long hours, as indeed was everyone in Churchill's 'Secret Circle', and in the peaceful atmosphere of Oxford he could find a little rest from his efforts. On Saturday mornings he would be conveyed from Christ Church to the Clarendon in his black Packard Tourer, a limousine of great length, which had replaced the Rolls-Royce. While there, he would collect eggs laid by the chickens kept for him by George Topp, his chauffeur. Lindemann kept a distant watch on all his staff at the laboratory, and on the whole they developed for him an abiding loyalty. One of the lowliest workers there, a young woman, bicycled into a hole while coming down Cumnor Hill in the blackout and had to be taken off to hospital with a fractured skull. When Lindemann heard about it, he arranged for her to be moved at once to a private ward. Yet he was far from a Pharisee in such matters, and arranged for the bill to be sent to him, while insisting that no word of the arrangement should reach the girl's ears.

While regaining his strength at Oxford, he was able to mitigate a little the exigencies of wartime. His rooms had been transformed from their earlier sparseness, and now contained a Bechstein piano, expensive curtains, sofas and good carpets, and exuded overall a discreetly comfortable atmosphere. To look after him he had Harvey, and there were others in support. One of these was Gordon Rosborough, Harvey's assistant until he was called up, and he in turn was helped by his brother Dennis, a laboratory technician at the Clarendon, who recalled that time with affection:

The Meadow Buildings had spacious rooms and also a small kitchen with a cubby hole for Harvey to conduct his paper work. Prof's telephone was equipped with a scrambler for talking to Churchill at Chartwell or Chequers. The scrambler was under the bed, from where Prof conducted most of his work and kept up to date with the daily newspapers. His books were mainly scientific, but for light reading there were such as P. G. Wodehouse and Dornford Yates, and he also had *Isis*,[10] and *Men Only*.

Prof had a small dog, called Dinah, which needed very careful looking after, and was exercised by Mrs Harvey. Prof was a stickler for organising his personal affairs – his bath water had to be no deeper than six inches, the wartime regulation, and at a temperature of exactly 104 degrees Fahrenheit. At that time he had a four inch telescope, which he used for stargazing; he also produced crayon drawings of pottery and vases, which he signed.

We learnt to make a range of dishes for him. His salad was always the same: chopped egg white, waxy potatoes, hand made mayonnaise from olive oil specially sent from the USA in the Diplomatic Bag, skinned sliced tomatoes and lettuce. Eggs were from the Clarendon or from a chicken run in the Meadow, and we had to feed the chickens each day with the scraps from the Christ Church kitchen. We were expected to obtain milk from the kitchens, remove the cream and make butter by hand, churning it for what seemed hours, to make a small pat of butter. Peas were specially grown and picked when half way between *petits pois* and the normal size; Prof also liked asparagus. Breakfast, always in bed with the day's papers, included scrambled eggs with chopped truffles from Fortnum & Mason. Although Prof was very largely a teetotaller he often enjoyed a glass of liqueur, such as Green or Yellow Chartreuse, after his dinner. When we had guests we would arrange for the Christ Church kitchen to send over food at the appropriate time.

He dined at Wadham occasionally; he also dined in Christ Church but not before we had obtained a list of those dining at High Table; if there was anyone he did not like he wouldn't go.[11]

Lindemann was later described as having, at this time of his life, 'a head like a grey stone bust of Cicero, of striking, malicious, virile handsomeness, with sombre brown eyes'. [12] His excursions sometimes took on a stately air. Lindemann would emerge from his rooms in Meadow Buildings, and Topp, in uniform, would stand ready by the car. A procession would draw near: Dinah the dog would lead, a few paces ahead of the imposing figure of Lindemann, followed in turn at a respectful distance by Harvey, usually carrying suitcases; finally would come Dennis Rosborough, bringing up the rear and clutching the daily papers and a carton of sandwiches. He later recalled his amusement at being fourth in rank, behind the dog.[13]

It seemed surprising to many that Dinah, an elderly cairn terrier that had been a present from F. E. Smith, was there at all. Lindemann never took it for a walk, or stroked it, or appeared in any way to take much notice of it, and when he and Dinah passed each other in the passageway there would not be the slightest reaction from either party.

He was lucky to receive the olive oil that Rosborough mentioned, as it was a scarce commodity during the war. Lindemann claimed that it was essential for his well-being, and it was therefore sent by his brother Charles, who had become a counsellor at the British Embassy in Washington, in succession to Professor Hill. Oil deliveries were made rather under sufferance, as Charles became convinced that on arrival it was requisitioned by the Churchills' cook and was used to enliven the wartime dishes she had to prepare.

Lindemann saw little of his elder brother now; in the pre-war years Charles had been a consultant to the Anglo-Persian Oil Company, and at the start of the war had become a liaison officer in Paris. The journalist Geoffrey Cox recalled meeting him with a friend in the Paris Ritz early in the war:

Claire Boothe Luce was indeed lovely, in her late thirties or early forties, with fair hair and a slightly worn, well pressed, well dry-cleaned American face, a little lined but still beautiful . . . With her was a general in British uniform with red tabs. He was Lindemann, brother of the Professor I had met at Oxford . . . Lindemann was talking of the German tank columns. 'They spend the nights in a sort of korral with their transport in the middle. I can't understand why we don't take a few bombers and smash them at any cost. I'd take a bomber and crash it down on them if they would let me', and I knew he would, and felt better.[14]

Lindemann's younger brother, Sepi, had married a rich French woman and was settled in the South of France where, until the war, he had lived the life of a playboy. He 'made a splash', even in the colourful English colony of those days, not least by keeping two Rolls-Royces, a white one driven by a negro, and a black one driven by an albino. Nevertheless, when war came he rose to the challenge: aided by his fluency in three languages, he moved around Occupied and Vichy France in disguise, sometimes as a French officer, gathering information which he passed to MI6. Had Adolf Lindemann lived, he would no doubt have been proud of Sepi's contribution to Britain's war effort, as well as that of his two other sons. However, he had died in 1931, having spent his last years at a house above Marlow, overlooking the Thames Valley, where he had been looked after by the family's devoted servant of many years, Fräulein Anna Thalmann.

When in Oxford, Lindemann would often dine in his own rooms and later walk over to join his colleagues in the common room. His paramount mental relaxation seemed to be his work on prime numbers, expressed in letters to mathematics professors, or in learned articles to magazines such as the *Quarterly Journal of Mathematics*. Close acquaintances of Lindemann at this time included the master of Balliol, A. D. Lindsay, his erstwhile political opponent Sir Farquahar Buzzard, besides Professor Ayr, Robin Barrington-Ward and Frank Pakenham.[15] Lindemann would often invite guests to dine at High Table. Usually they were people of importance – civil or military – and the talk would be mainly of the war; at other times there would be just a handful of elderly colleagues and a few guests, when the dialogue would reflect more academic interests. It would also sometimes display an engaging unworldliness. Lindemann used to recall with pleasure how one evening the talk turned to racing, and he heard an elderly don address his guest, an equally elderly clergyman, saying:

'I've never actually been to The Derby, have you?'
'No,' came the reply, 'I have not. But once, though, I very nearly did: I happened to be in Derby that very day.'

Unworldliness in Lindemann's life was not at this time confined to Oxford. As the Prime Minister's scientific adviser, his opinion and help were sought in countless matters concerning the application of science to the war. Some were less practicable than others. One such was an idea, perhaps more a vision, known as 'Habakkuk'. Lindemann first heard of this notion when he received a letter from Lord Louis Mountbatten, enthusiastically setting out a proposal that he had received for 'the provision of air-bases which are intermediate between land-bases and aircraft carriers; the method proposed being virtually the construction of large iceberg ships, which would not only be unsinkable, but could be built without a strain on existing sources of raw material'.[16]

These aircraft carriers, to be made of ice treated with a special ingredient, were to sit in the remote Atlantic and support the aeroplanes that hunted the German U-boats. Their proposed size was enormous: 2,000 feet in length, 300 feet across, carrying a 'useful load' of 800,000 tons, and driven by 10,000-horse-power engines. Their influence on the course of the war, Lord Louis believed, would be decisive.

Soon a Habakkuk Committee was formed, and a considerable amount of energy was expended on the concept, with Churchill urging it on, although, as he put it, 'I do not of course know anything about the physical properties of a lozenge of ice 5000 feet by 2000 feet by 100 feet.'[17] Lindemann remained wholly sceptical, and at length interest in the project petered out, partly because Portugal had offered the Azores as an Atlantic base, so that there was no longer any need for giant ships of ice. Geoffrey Pyke, Habakkuk's mercurial and imaginative inventor, committed suicide shortly after the war had ended.

Meanwhile, the scale and tragedy of the waste of effort devoted to Bomber Command's raids over Germany was about to be revealed. Lindemann had long been pressing for research along any lines that might lead towards improved target-finding powers for Bomber Command. This had led to the fitting of cameras in a certain number of bombers, although by 1941 they had been installed in only about one in four. To analyse the photographs with which the crews were now returning, a Central Interpretation Unit had been established at Medmenham, where photographic data was beginning to be amassed.

Lindemann's success in getting cameras installed in aeroplanes led almost at once to an unpleasant surprise. In the summer of 1941 he visited Medmenham to examine photographs taken on raids over Germany. He was aghast at what he saw: instead of being cheered by pictures of the bombers' targets either on fire or reduced to rubble, he found himself bleakly contemplating acres of green pastures that had been cratered by wasted bombs. As one RAF wag put it: 'Last night we made a determined attack on German agriculture.'

Lindemann knew at once that something must be done to rectify this grievous situation. Daylight attacks were out of the question, while by night German fighters and air defences were taking a grim toll of the British raiders, with the survival rate of those who baled out of the stricken aeroplanes being not more than one in ten.

Without delay, therefore, he arranged for a member of his department to visit Medmenham and carry out a comprehensive survey of the evidence. He chose for the job his secretary, David Bensusan Butt, a young Cambridge economist who already had a distinguished academic record and who had compiled the index for Keynes' seminal work, the *General Theory*. On 30

July 1941 Lindemann sent Butt down to Medmenham to examine a large number of air photographs. In the words of the official history:

> Others outside the Air Ministry and Bomber Command also had doubts about the accuracy of bombing. They included Lord Cherwell, who had special facilities for the investigation of such problems, and it was on his initiative that a more searching enquiry into the question was undertaken.[18]

When he arrived at Medmenham, Butt examined nearly 650 photographs, taken on a hundred raids over Germany in the preceding months. What he found was to change the course of the war.[19] Professor Thomas Wilson, another young economist in Lindemann's department, recalled Butt's devastating revelations:

> Of the sorties recorded, only one in five got within 5 miles of the target – that was within seventy-five square miles of it. Some planes did not attack at all, but of those that did, only one in three came within 3 miles of the target. These were the average of actual results, which varied with the target and the weather.[20]

The conclusion, both immediate and unavoidable, was that in night operations the Royal Air Force was largely unable to find – let alone destroy – its targets.

Lindemann at once gave Butt's report to the Prime Minister, commenting that 'however inaccurate the figures may be, they are sufficiently striking to emphasise the supreme importance of improving our navigational methods'.[21] Churchill sent the report straight on to the chief of the Air Staff, adding: 'This is a very serious paper, and seems to require your most urgent attention. I await your proposals for action.'[22] A week later he added the obvious but sombre comment: 'It is an awful thought that perhaps three quarters of our bombs go astray. If we could make it half and half we should have doubled our bombing power.'[23]

If the Royal Air Force could not successfully carry out selective attacks, there remained two alternatives. One was to stop bombing altogether, which was out of the question; the other was to aim for a larger target – a policy that was to gain notoriety as 'area bombing'.

In the first month of the war Chamberlain had assured Parliament that 'whatever the lengths to which others may go, His Majesty's Government will never resort to the deliberate attack on women and children and other civilians for the purpose of mere terrorism'. At that time towns were not considered proper targets. As the chief of the Air Staff reported to the Prime Minister in October 1940, 'Berlin is the only town which we bomb as a town; the bombing of other towns is incidental to the pursuit of our main objectives.'[24]

Since the early 1920s Sir Charles Portal,[25] who had become chief of the Air Staff in October 1940, had been a believer in the military value of strategic, or 'area', bombing. It was he who had been primarily responsible, after the threat of invasion had receded, for the expansion in bombing policy so as to include industrial centres. Accordingly the Air Staff had directed, on 30 October 1940, that Bomber Command should make a definite attempt to 'affect the morale of the German people', and had specifically referred to the selection of targets in the centres of towns or populated districts.[26]

Feelings hardened when it was discovered that the Luftwaffe pilots who bombed Coventry in the notorious raid in November 1940 had been instructed to attack the centre of the city, as well as workmen's dwellings and similar areas, and that the raid had been deliberately aimed at the morale of the civilian population. A few weeks later the RAF carried out a heavy raid on Mannheim, in reprisal for that on Coventry. 'Area bombing – though as yet only as a secondary policy, and at this stage based on attacking a known objective like a power station within an industrial area – was thus officially enjoined.'[27] At the same time operations planners gave weight to two other factors: first, the large variety of targets for selective attack, together with the growing realisation that they were extremely difficult to find by night; and second, the mood of the people. Both these factors argued the case for area bombing.

Area bombing had also been endorsed by the army and the navy, whose respective chiefs had written a paper for the guidance of Churchill at his planned meetings with Roosevelt in August 1941. In that paper they had stated:

As our forces increase, we intend to pass to a planned attack on civilian morale with the intensity and continuity which are essential if a final breakdown is to be produced. There is increasing evidence of the effect which even our present limited scale of attack is causing to German life. We have every reason to be confident that if we can expand our forces in accordance with our present programme, and if possible beyond it, that effect will be shattering.[28]

A further move towards a policy of area bombing was endorsed by a clear statement from the Air Staff of the size of bomber force it required for the purpose. Portal had replied to Churchill's minute about the Butt Report by setting out a number of longer-term remedies for the bombers' inaccuracy. 'For the short-term,' he admitted, 'there appeared to be only one solution – a sacrifice of the concept of precision bombing, and an acceptance of that principle of indiscriminate plastering of German cities which, it had once been laid down, was "contrary to British policy".' The Air Staff had drawn up a list of towns that were suitable for destruction; on it were forty-three containing fifteen million people; and, as Portal told the Prime Minister:

> Judging by our own experience of German attacks, the strength required to obtain decisive results against German morale may be estimated at 4000 heavy bombers, and that the time taken would be about six months.[29]

The way was now clear for a bolder statement of the place of area bombing in official policy, and accordingly a directive was issued to Bomber Command by the Air Staff on 14 February 1942, saying:

> . . . a review has been made of the directions given to you in Air Ministry letter dated 9.7.41, and it has been decided that the primary object of your operations should now be focused on the morale of the enemy civil population and in particular, of the industrial workers.[30]

Already therefore, and quite independently of Lindemann's advice, area bombing had gained priority over other methods of air attack.

Yet although the subject had already been well aired, Lindemann was to spark off an acrimonious debate on bombing policy by sending a minute to Churchill on the matter, on 30 March 1942, after a period in which both he and the Prime Minister had been the subject of strong criticism in Parliament.

Lindemann's supposed influence had been coming under general attack, not least from other leading scientists, so much so that towards the end of 1941 questions about him had been asked in the House of Commons. At that stage the war was not going well and Churchill himself was coming under increasing pressure, partly as a result of his direct involvement in so many military decisions.

There had been a particularly difficult moment for the Prime Minister when two battleships, intended to bolster the defence of Singapore, were lost within a few hours of each other. Churchill had suggested that the ships leave the war zone, but they had not done so, and the news of their destruction by the Japanese came as a severe shock. Although Churchill himself was not to blame, tongues turned against him. An example is given by Lady Mosley,[31] whose husband, Sir Oswald, had been closely involved in politics before the war:

> I went to lunch with the Churchills specifically to tell Winston about Hitler. That was in 1936, and I remember something very interesting about that lunch. At that time the great terror was Mussolini and Abyssinia, and I said might it not be dangerous for our warships in the Mediterranean, if we put oil sanctions on, might they not be attacked by almost suicide bombing from the Italians, because that's the kind of thing they might do, as they're no good in the field, as we know.
>
> Winston said 'No: an aeroplane cannot sink a battleship'. I said 'why not?', and he said 'because the armour is too thick'. Well, a few years later there was a Cabinet meeting about whether – this was during the war – to send the *Prince of Wales* and the *Repulse* to the China Sea with no air cover. And the Service Ministers said it was a mad thing to do, and the only person who supported Churchill, who wanted to do it – in order to intimidate the Japs, really – was Eden, who was a complete wash-out, as we know. Well, they sent them into the China Sea without air support, and they were both sunk. And what the Japanese did was they attacked them with torpedoes under the water-line, where the armour is less thick; and not on deck. By then one knew about torpedo-carrying aeroplanes, and Churchill shouldn't have risked them. He said in his memoirs that it was the most terrible night of his life when he heard the news. And of course he was, really, person-ally responsible.[32]

By extension, Lindemann had come to be regarded in many quarters as an evil genius behind the Prime Minister, with too much influence and not enough accountability to Parliament. The first attack on his position had come in the summer of 1941 when a senior Conservative backbencher, Sir John Wardlaw-Milne, had asked a pointed question in the Commons about Lindemann's role; that had been followed the next day by a question to the Prime Minister asking for an explanation of Lindemann's duties – a ques-tion that had gone down badly with Churchill, who had described it as 'offensive'.

Later in the year the challenge was taken up by another backbench MP, Sir Waldron Smithers, member for Chislehurst. On 11 November he tried to get the Prime Minister to admit that Lindemann was a power behind the scenes, and he followed that up with a supplementary question about why he had accompanied the Prime Minister to America to meet President Roosevelt. Smithers intervened to ask: 'If Lord Cherwell was one of the members of the party, does not my Right Hon. Friend think it unwise . . .' The question was left unfinished, however: at that point uproar broke out, with barracking, jeers and shouting on all sides. The Commons Report described the scene by means of the word 'Interruption', a parliamentary euphemism for commotion, cacophony and general disorder. Churchill was seriously affronted. He became more so later on when he came upon Smithers in the Smoking Room. George Harvie-Watt, Churchill's Parliamentary Private Secretary, and MP for Richmond, recalled the occasion:

Waldron Smithers, a bumbling sort of chap with his heart in the right place, asked some critical questions in the House about Lord Cherwell, and hinted that he was an alien. The Prime Minister was livid, and rightly so, and said in an aside to me 'Love me, love my dog, and if you don't love my dog you damn well can't love me'. Afterwards Winston left the Chamber of the House and went to the Smoke Room. I've never seen him in such a temper before. Later, Waldron Smithers came up with his tail between his legs and started grovelling to Winston who told him to get the hell out of here and not to speak to him again. Poor Smithers got the shock of his life.[33]

Chips Channon also witnessed what happened:

In the Commons the Prime Minister was in a bellicose mood: he answered Questions ungraciously, especially one about the 'Prof', Lord Cherwell. Alan and I went to the smoking-room and ordered brandy and ginger ale. Nearby sat Waldron Smithers, an ass of a man, alone. Suddenly the Prime Minister, attended by Harvie-Watt, entered and they, too, sat down. Suddenly the Prime Minister saw Smithers, and rose, and bellowing at him like an infuriated bull, roared: 'Why in Hell did you ask that Question?' 'Don't you know that he (Lord Cherwell) is one of my oldest and greatest friends?' – the unfortunate Member for Chislehurst tried to defend himself – but the Prime Minister, still shaking, refused to listen or be pacified, and went on 'You make protestations of loyalty – I won't have it. President Roosevelt was most impressed by him.' And so forth – It was an extraordinary scene. The 'Prof' otherwise 'Baron Berlin', or, correctly, The Lord Cherwell, has long been a subject of speculation to the House, and from time to time there have been questions and veiled innuendos reflecting on his

Teutonic origin. But Winston's blind loyalty to his friends is one of his most endearing qualities.[34]

Such a reaction was a rather public demonstration of how Churchill stood by friends and supporters. Another example was given by Lord Beaverbrook, who recalled that during the war a Member of Parliament had said in private conversation that Cherwell was a German spy. Churchill forced the member to make an apology, on threat of expulsion from Parliament, and would, it was believed, have required it to be public, had he not felt that attention should not be drawn to the incident.

Early in 1942 a much more significant dispute was to blow up when Lindemann, with widespread repercussions for his reputation, entered the fray in support of the area bombing of Germany.

Two grave concerns, crucial to the whole success of the British war effort, had arisen in parallel, and now came together to force a debate in the highest military and political circles. The first was mounting discontent with the performance of Bomber Command, and the second was whether too large a proportion of war production was being devoted to bombing Germany – while the army's goal was still a force of not less than fifty-five divisions, and the navy was calling for more aircraft for Coastal Command and an expansion of the force of escort vessels protecting the shipping lanes.

The disquiet was brought dramatically to the fore by Sir Stafford Cripps, formerly British Ambassador in Moscow, who had joined the War Cabinet in February 1942. Cripps was at that moment a powerful figure and was seen in some quarters as a possible replacement for Churchill. That month he told the Commons, in a speech that was sufficient at least to unsettle the Prime Minister, that the original policy of bombing Germany – 'instigated at a time when we were fighting alone against the combined forces of Germany and Italy' – had come under review, partly because of the 'enormous access of support from the Russian Armies'.[35]

In the words of the official history: 'Bomber Command was in danger not only of being denied the resources needed for its expansion, but it was also existing under the threat of having its established squadrons taken away and, perhaps, even re-equipped for other purposes.'[36]

The question concerned the policy (later highlighted by Lindemann's 30 March minute) of delivering all-out attacks on the housing of German industrial workers so as to break the spirit of the German people, and thereby providing, in Churchill's words, the 'design and theme for bringing the war to a victorious end in a reasonable period'. The broad policy had been laid out in the directive of 14 February 1942 – and was to be confirmed by the Combined Chiefs of Staff at the conference on war strategy held in

Casablanca in January 1943. It was interpreted by Bomber Command as meaning, according to the official history, 'general attacks necessary to render the German industrial population homeless, spiritless and, as far as possible, dead'.[37]

Churchill and Lindemann both believed that the bombing offensive should be maintained, despite its disappointing performance up until then, and Lindemann's minute on the potential for bombing Germany was written to provide Churchill with a short, sharp and simple argument in favour of doing so. It caused a furore at the time, and has been widely held against Lindemann ever since. Since the war, attempts have been made to blacken his name, and commentators, led notoriously by C. P. Snow,[38] have suggested that it was he who was mainly responsible for the policy of area bombing, which they regarded as evil and of little help to the war effort. They have further suggested that Lindemann instigated it because of unworthy prejudice against the Germans.

That approach is both anachronistic and wholly unfair to Lindemann. In March 1942, when he sent his celebrated minute to Churchill, the alternatives facing Britain were either general area bombing – or nothing. Had it been nothing, Hitler would have gained a huge advantage and the Allies would have foregone a means of attack that was ultimately to prove decisive.[39]

The intensity of this controversy can be explained by reflecting upon the awful fate that befell the victims of area bombing. Even during the war it was a subject of emotion and dispute, although its effects were not then generally realised. Later knowledge of what actually happened in the bombed cities has meant that the policy has been sensitive ever since.

The report of the Police President of Hamburg on the raids of July and August 1943 graphically describes what was in store for the inhabitants of the German cities that were selected as targets for area bombing:

> The catastrophes of Chicago and San Francisco, the fire in the Paris Opera House, all these events, of which the scenes of fantastic and gruesome terror have been described by contemporaries, pale beside the extent and the uniqueness of the Hamburg fire of 1943. Its horror is revealed in the howling and raging of the firestorms, the hellish noise of exploding bombs and the death cries of martyred human beings as well as in the big silence after the raids. Speech is impotent to portray the measure of the horror, which shook the people for ten days and nights, and the traces of which were written indelibly on the face of the city and its inhabitants.
>
> And each of these nights convulsed by flames was followed by a

day which displayed the horror in the dim and unreal light of a sky hidden in smoke. Summer heat intensified by the glow of the firestorms to an unbearable degree; dust from the torn earth and the ruins and the debris of damaged areas which penetrated everywhere; showers of soot and ashes; more heat and dust; above all a pestilential stench of decaying corpses and smouldering fires weighed continually on the exhausted men . . .

The streets were covered with hundreds of corpses. Mothers with their children, youths, old men, burnt, charred, untouched and clothed, naked with a waxen pallor like dummies in a shop window, they lay in every posture, quiet and peaceful or cramped, the death-struggle shown in the expression on their faces. The shelters showed the same picture, even more horrible in effect, as it showed in many cases the final distracted struggle against a merciless fate. Although in some places shelterers sat quietly, peacefully and untouched as if sleeping in their chairs, killed without realisation or pain by carbon monoxide poisoning, in other shelters the position of remains of bones and skulls showed how the occupants had fought to escape from their buried prison.[40]

The havoc of those nights is estimated to have resulted in the death of some 45,000 people.

The human suffering sustained in saturation raids such as that on Hamburg, and most notoriously on Dresden in February 1945, darkened Lindemann's reputation for many years after the war, when some of the factors that drove events at the time, and which were compelling reasons for the area-bombing policy, had faded from people's memory. An accurate précis of the forces at work can nevertheless be found in the words of R. V. Jones:

So Hamburg in a sense was the nearest the area bombing policy came to success. We had started the war morally opposed to the bombing of civilian populations, and now we were pursuing it on a horrifying scale. How had this come about? It was convenient at one time to blame Lord Cherwell, but the fact is that in 1940 he was as keen as any of us to make precision raids on pin-point targets of strategic importance. Portal, too, was of the same mind; through 1941, so long as the myth of our bombing accuracy persisted, he pursued the policy of attacking oil installations, on the argument that if the German Armed Forces could be deprived of fuel their fighting ability would be destroyed. Then had followed the realisation that we could not even guarantee to hit towns, let alone individual factories, and yet Bomber Command was the only weapon that we had which could reduce the German war potential. Given the fact that the Germans had bombed our towns more or less indiscriminately, the decision to bomb German towns was an emotional certainty.[41]

As Professor Thomas Wilson wrote:

Apart from any crude desire for revenge, there was the feeling that, if bombing could be made effective in winning the war Britain should not hesitate to use it in defence of freedom, as the Germans had already used it for the malign purpose of suppressing freedom. There was also a feeling that the Germans, who had started two world wars, should be given a lesson in the meaning of war which they would not, thereafter, ever forget.[42]

Such were the feelings that had spread throughout the country, and they were shared in large measure by Lindemann. As it happened, he had direct knowledge of the matter: one of his staff, Herbert Robinson, had sent him a memo describing an air raid in Hull during which a mine had floated down on a parachute and had exploded outside an air-raid shelter, killing and maiming dozens of its occupants and flattening the nearby house of Robinson's parents. They had come to him in great distress and said: 'Herbert, tell Mr Churchill we cannot stand this and he should negotiate an end of the war with Hitler.' Robinson had told Lindemann how many working people were being killed or made homeless, and were becoming defeatist. He suggested that German morale would suffer painfully if British bombing attacks were expanded so as to cause huge losses of German housing and community services, leaving the population in misery.[43]

The memorandum that Lindemann gave to Churchill, on 30 March 1942, aimed to fulfil three requirements: to respond to the nation's desires; to provide Churchill with a succinct case for the policy of area bombing; and to set out how to attack the enemy with the greatest effect. Its detailed ideas had sprung from a conversation that had taken place in Oxford the previous August between Lindemann and a young physiologist, Solly Zuckerman,[44] who was employed at the Ministry of Home Security, analysing the results of air raids. Zuckerman later recalled the occasion:

What happened was that one weekend I found myself at the High Table in Christ Church sitting next to Cherwell, who soon started talking about the arguments which were then being levelled against

RAF Bomber Command because of its navigational and bombing shortcomings, and consequently about the fruitlessness of its attacks on targets in Germany. Some of those in authority were already urging that the national resources which the Command consumed could be far better used for other purposes. Cherwell's view, however, was that the case against the Command had not been proved and, furthermore, that bombing was the only way open to us to hit back at Germany.[45]

Zuckerman's idea was to get a measure of what bombing could achieve, by surveying in detail the damage caused by air raids on Britain. Lindemann at once took to the idea, and gave Zuckerman suggestions for the sort of questions that might be asked, such as: 'How many tons of bombs does it take to break a town?' and 'How should the bombs be delivered – should it be in one sharp attack, or in what ratios should the total load be distributed, and over how many nights?'[46]

The resulting survey was carried out by Zuckerman and Desmond Bernal, a scientist from Cambridge who at the time was Britain's leading crystallographer. Birmingham and Hull were chosen partly because they could be regarded as typical of manufacturing and port towns, and partly for the practical reason that there was an almost complete tally of the bombs that had fallen on them in air raids. Because of Lindemann's close interest in the survey, information from it was fed to David Butt in the Statistical Department, as soon as it became available.

S Department analysed the results of the survey in preparing data for Lindemann, who paid considerable attention to it in framing his minute to the Prime Minister, which read:

PRIME MINISTER

The following seems a simple method of estimating what we could do by bombing Germany.

Careful analysis of the effects of raids on Birmingham, Hull and elsewhere have shown that on the average one ton of bombs dropped on a built-up area demolishes 20–40 dwellings and turns 100–200 people out of house and home.

We know from our experience that we can count on nearly 14 operational sorties per bomber produced. The average lift of the bombers we are going to produce over the next fifteen months will be about 3 tons. It follows that each of these bombers will in its lifetime drop about 40 tons of bombs. If these are dropped on built-up areas they will make 4,000–8,000 people homeless.

In 1938 over 22 million Germans lived in 58 towns of over 100,000 inhabitants, which, with modern equipment, should be easy to find and hit. Our forecast output of heavy bombers (including Wellingtons) between now and the middle of 1943 is about 10,000. If even half the total load of 10,000 bombers were dropped on the built-up areas of these 58 German towns the great majority of their inhabitants (about one-third of the German population) would be turned out of house and home.

Investigation seems to show that having one's house demolished is most damaging to morale. People seem to mind it more than having their friends or even their relatives killed. At Hull signs of strain were evident though only one-tenth of the houses were demolished. On the above figures we should be able to do ten times as much harm to each of the 58 principal German towns. There seems little doubt that this would break the spirit of the people.

Our calculation assumes, of course, that we really get one-half of our bombs into built-up areas. On the other hand, no account is taken of the large promised American production (6,000 heavy bombers in the period in question). Nor has regard been paid to the inevitable damage to factories, communications, etc., in these towns and the damage by fire, probably accentuated by breakdown of public services.[47]

Churchill at once asked for the opinion of the chief of the Air Staff and of the Secretary of State for Air. Their response was enthusiastic, and they told him: 'We both find Lord Cherwell's calculations simple, clear and convincing, and we suggest that they might be of general interest to the Defence Committee.' However, they did emphasise that the conclusions would not be valid without certain conditions being fulfilled – in particular, that enough bombers would actually be deployed, and that at least half the bombs carried would be dropped on built-up areas in Germany. This was a crucial qualification and lay at the heart of Lindemann's estimates, but it has been largely ignored by those who have attacked him.

In any event, six days later the minute was circulated to the Defence Committee of the War Cabinet, in effect the highest authority in the land, which accepted Lindemann's argument and endorsed the policy that his paper implicitly advocated.

The stakes at issue were high. Not only would an extended policy of area bombing result in death and destruction of almost biblical proportions among German civilians, but it would restrict the number of bombers that would be available to meet the deadly threat posed by German submarines in the Atlantic. There might therefore be a grave risk of Britain losing the war at the hands of the submarine wolf-packs that were encircling her shores. On the other hand, if the policy were successful, and the German spirit broken, the enemy might sue for peace and bring the war to an early conclusion. Moreover, Russia had been fighting bitterly against the Germans since she had been invaded, in the summer of 1941, and Churchill was under great pressure to help her. For that reason the Prime Minister had asked the Air Staff to write an appreciation of the possibility of assisting, in Blackett's words, 'our sorely tried Russian allies in their great land battle', by extending the British bombing offensive against Germany.[48]

With so much depending on which area was given priority – Germany or the Atlantic – Lindemann's advice to Churchill came under fire almost immediately. Initially there were two separate quarters from which he was attacked: the authors of the report on the raids on Hull and Birmingham, and the scientific establishment – between Lindemann and whom there was now little love lost.

The essence of the first of these challenges, from Bernal and Zuckerman, was that Lindemann's conclusions – and the advice that he had tendered to the Prime Minister – could not be sustained by their findings, although he had appeared to rely on them. They also complained that Lindemann had not waited to read their report either in summary or in full, before sending his minute to Churchill.

That is certainly true. Lindemann sent his minute not only before the release of the full survey, but even before publication of the preliminary report, which appeared on 8 April. This left him open to the charge that the Statistical Department had extrapolated the report's figures in a way that put a false gloss on them, and in particular that it had used one significant issue in a misguided fashion.

The objections of Bernal and Zuckerman centred on the fact that Lindemann advised Churchill that it was likely that area bombing would break the spirit of the German people, whereas they themselves had found little evidence to support that contention. What their report did not exclude was the possibility that there might be quite a different result in the case of very much heavier raids – and that was a central assumption of Lindemann's paper to Churchill. Bernal and Zuckerman's conclusions certainly weaken Lindemann's case for claiming that bombing would break the spirit of the enemy and have allowed his detractors at least to press the point that his advice was based not on empirical evidence, but on a vindictive desire to attack the Germans.

Lindemann, said the report's authors, drew almost diametrically the wrong conclusions from their evidence, and they felt that the result of his error was of great importance. Bernal later derided Lindemann's interpretation of their report:

> Lord Cherwell claimed that it proved that as German bombing of Birmingham had produced little effect, a very much heavier bombing of German cities must produce a decisive one . . . it was this kind of wild extrapolation that made most scientists who served under both prefer the careful logic of Tizard's approach to such problems.[49]

There was another, wholly different, angle from which Lindemann was attacked. It related to the arithmetic that he had used, on which depended whether or not his estimate of the scale of bombing that might be achieved was in fact realistic. It was on this point that Lindemann's other scientific adversaries opposed him.

The first salvo came from Sir Henry Tizard, who had seen Lindemann's minute and who wrote to him, in language that might conventionally be described as 'full and frank':

> My dear Cherwell,
> . . . I am afraid that I think that the way you put the facts as they appear to you is extremely misleading and may lead to entirely wrong decisions being reached, with a consequent disastrous effect on the war. I think, too, that you have got your facts wrong.[50]

Tizard continued: 'I don't really disagree with you fundamentally but only as a matter of timing . . .' – a comment that rather weakened his case – but then made two points that went straight to the heart of the matter. First he questioned, in effect, whether the RAF would be able to deliver attacks on a sufficiently heavy scale to justify Lindemann's advice and predictions. Second, he went on to say:

> My trouble is that I don't see a decisive effect being caused by this wholesale bombing before the middle of 1943 [the time frame referred to by Lindemann]. In the meantime, we must preserve command of the seas, and it is difficult for me to see how we are going to do this without strong support of the Navy by long range bombers.[51]

This point was highly relevant, and it heralded a fierce debate that was about to break out over the allocation of scarce bomber resources, and whether a significant number should be withdrawn from operations over Germany, to be used instead against the U-boat threat. Tizard explained his objections to the Air Minister, with the authority gained from his position at the Ministry of Aircraft Production:

> . . . I think that Cherwell has overestimated the probable effects of using the whole of our heavy bombers and most of our Wellingtons on Germany by a factor of at least 4, and probably by a factor of 6 or over.[52]

Blackett now lent his weight to this argument, no doubt venting his feelings with relish, both as a strong supporter of the Russians and as one who cordially disliked Lindemann. He was also believed, in Sir John Slessor's words, to be 'intellectually and temperamentally opposed to the bomber offensive'.[53]

This eminent but radical scientist now poured cold water over the claims made for Bomber Command's proposed offensive. He bleakly calculated that during the period of the heaviest air raids over Britain, 0.8 people had been killed per ton of bombs; he then established that British bombs were less effective than the enemy's and that German targets were harder to find and hit. The RAF could therefore expect, he said, to kill 0.2 people per ton of bombs, which would in practice work out at 400 per month. Blackett pointedly compared this with the normal rate of civilian road deaths in Germany of 700 per month.[54] He concluded by dismissing Lindemann's estimate of what could be achieved as being at least six times too high.

However, there were many with whom this type of slide-rule science cut no ice, and Blackett was made aware of it. As he admitted: 'By this time a certain allergy to arithmetic was spreading in Whitehall and our arithmetical forebodings went unheeded . . . The story goes that at that time in the Air Ministry it was said of anyone who added two and two and made four: "He is not to be trusted; he has been talking to Tizard and Blackett."' For his part, Tizard was making the wholly valid point that, if the policy were not to be decisive, the risk of losing the war – by losing the Battle of the Atlantic – would be very great; and in his view that was insupportable.

Although Lindemann's emotions were at one with his belief in area bombing – in which he reflected the will of a majority of the nation – he also believed it to be the soundest (if not the only) way both of hitting back at the enemy and of responding to the urgent pleas from the Russians, who were already demanding a 'second front'. However, the maintenance of the policy throughout the rest of the war was a consequence not of further recommendations from Lindemann (although he did, with certain important exceptions, continue to support it), but of the objectives agreed by the War Cabinet, and expressed in directives from the Air Staff to Bomber

Command. Contrary to what his critics have said, Lindemann was wholly flexible in his approach to changes in the war situation and the policies needed to meet them, and was far from wedded to a single policy through thick and thin.

For example, at the end of March 1944, as plans developed for 'Overlord', the Allied invasion of Europe, the Chiefs of Staff Committee asked Lindemann to examine the proposed use of the Strategic Air Forces to assist the invading armies. The chief of Bomber Command, Air Chief Marshal Harris, resisted proposals designed to assist Overlord, on the grounds that they would reduce the scale of area attacks and that his bombers could not hit precision targets. Lindemann, by contrast, spoke up for the main objective of keeping the German Air Force away from the invasion area, although it would involve the diversion of aeroplanes from the area-bombing offensive.

However, the secondary target that had been chosen was the German transportation capacity, with a large number of French marshalling yards selected for obliteration. Lindemann told Churchill that he was dubious about this idea, as it seemed to be what was described as 'attritional', being a long-term policy and not one that would deliver the immediate result of protecting the invading armies. Yet Lindemann's counter-proposal was not – as might have been supposed, and indeed as Harris' own was – for area bombing, but for a concentrated attack on Germany's oil resources.

Churchill then asked Lindemann to draft a paper for the Supreme Allied Commander, General Eisenhower, setting out his objections to the proposed bombing of the marshalling yards. In his note Lindemann warned Eisenhower of the possible French attitude to the inferno that was about to be visited upon their land:

> The Marshalling Yards Plan involves the killing of 10,000 to 15,000 Frenchmen, and the maiming of as many more. As this is apt to poison our relations with the French people not only during the invasion but for a generation afterwards, the Government feel justified in asking to be convinced that this plan will actually bring great military advantages.[55]

It is noticeable that although Lindemann's initial brief for advising the Prime Minister specifically excluded military strategy, as the years passed he seemed to become closely involved in giving such advice.

This flexibility in his approach, and the varied nature of the advice that he gave on bombing policy, has on the whole been ignored in the furore that developed, long after the war, when Lindemann was assailed in the same way as Air Chief Marshal Harris, who was remembered for ever after as 'Bomber Harris'. It has also been suggested, although without any evidence to support it, that Lindemann believed that the war could be won by bombing alone and without invading Europe.[56]

The details of Lindemann's opinions have been blurred by the effect of his broad support for strategic bombing, and because his famous minute undoubtedly had great effect, aptly summarised by Zuckerman when he said: 'In my view the outcome would have been very different if Lindemann had not been there to put the weight of his authority, and his influence on Churchill, behind a bombing policy.'[57]

This view is supported by the official history of the war in the air, which stated:

> . . . because of the position which he occupied at the time at which he submitted his minute, Lord Cherwell's intervention was of great importance. It did much to insure the concept of strategic bombing in its hour of crisis.[58]

Nor did Lindemann shrink from expressing strong views about the treatment that the Allies should mete out to the Germans. In his response to an Air Staff proposal designed to minimise unnecessary damage to historic towns in Germany, and to preserve their architectural and artistic treasures, Lindemann was quick to suggest that the approach was entirely misconceived, and in doing so he displayed some almost Teutonic trickery of his own. Writing to Air Vice-Marshal Bottomley, the deputy chief of the Air Staff, he said:

> . . . the intention as I understood it was only to select one city, which we would be unlikely to bomb anyhow, and only to promise immunity provided that we were satisfied no munitions were being made there. I cannot help thinking that this would render life intolerable in the said city and that it would lead to innumerable quarrels and recriminations.
>
> After two or three months, if it suited us, we could declare ourselves unsatisfied with the fulfilment of the manufacturing side of the bargain, nominate some other town and chase half the refugees in the first town across Germany.
>
> If by some mischance we did drop a bomb or two into the selected town, which I would have thought unlikely as we would obviously pick one near the limits of our range, we could always attribute it to the

Germans and say that they were trying to make mischief, as they did when they bombed the Vatican.

Quite frankly, I do not regard this proposal as a way of sparing cultural monuments or saving German lives; on the contrary, I regard it as a way of adding to the confusion which prevails in that country.[59]

In order to assess the praise or blame that should properly attach to Lindemann, and to evaluate his contribution to the outcome of the war, it is right to consider not only how large a part he played in the shaping of bombing policy, but also whether the area-bombing policy was in fact justifiable and matched the needs of the hour.

This remains a matter of controversy, partly because area bombing did not achieve the objectives that were originally expected of it – the collapse of German morale and of war production. The ultimate objective of the policy was to deliver victory as soon and as decisively as possible, and to be justified it had to be demonstrably better for that purpose than any alternative policy. Among the reams of information on the effects of the bombing of Germany there are two unimpeachable sources that are a helpful guide towards judging its merits: one is the official history, *The Strategic Air Offensive Against Germany 1939–1945*, and the other is the testimony of the man who might almost be described as 'the horse's mouth': Reichsminister Albert Speer, to whom the Führer gave the Herculean task of countering the effects of the Allied offensive.

Although charges have been levelled at Lindemann from many different quarters, two in particular – *The Spectator* and the *New Statesman* – attracted widespread comment. The first wrote:

> . . . and with Lindemann came strategic bombing, saturation bombing, the policy – incredible at the time and totally disproved by post-war analysis – of forcing the Germans to surrender by bombing Germany out of house and home. It added six months to the war.[60]

In the judgement of the *New Statesman*:

> Tizard and several experts from operational research challenged Cherwell's theory. They proved on the basis of existing evidence of bomb destruction that Cherwell's estimates of devastation were five or six times too high . . .
>
> A post-war survey showed that the raids led to no significant decline in morale and still less to a decline in production . . . Cherwell's figures were shown to be not five or six but ten times too high . . . It is at

least arguable that had the all-out bombing offensive been accorded lower priority, the allies might have won the war in 1944 and denied Eastern Europe to Russia.[61]

Alluring though the latter vision is, the argument is not valid. In the words of the biographer of Lord Portal, chief of the Air Staff for the whole period under consideration:

> Without the work of the strategic air forces, victory could never have crowned the Allied arms in 1945. Doubtless it would have come years later, but only at infinitely greater cost. It is possible to believe, with the official historians, that a more concentrated and rigidly enforced bombing policy would have shortened the war by two or three months; but this would remain a belief, and not a fact.[62]

It was Lord Zuckerman who supposedly produced the 'existing evidence' quoted by the *New Statesman*, but on being presented with the allegations, he said:

> The 'New Statesman' suggestion that Tizard and several experts challenged the Prof on the basis of 'existing evidence of bomb destruction' is complete nonsense. The rest is equal rubbish.[63]

Unfortunately that sort of 'nonsense' has often been quoted and copied, and an entirely false impression about Lindemann's role has thus been formed. In contrast, the official history highlights a point of the greatest importance: the area bombing of towns and cities was not an unattached policy, separate from other operations, to be judged entirely on its own; it was part and parcel of a composite plan, so that when one part could not be operated – for example, when there was not enough moonlight for night attacks on a specific target – another part (area bombing) took its place. The Air Staff's directive to Bomber Command, in July 1941, set this out quite clearly:

> . . . for approximately ¾ of each month it is only possible to obtain satisfactory results by heavy, concentrated and continuous area attacks of large working class and industrial areas in carefully selected towns.[64]

The official historians confirm this in their central verdict on the area-bombing policy:

Moreover the continuing area offensive, apart from assuming almost unmanageable proportions in many towns, contributed important by-products to the achievements of the main plans for oil and transport. These direct results had a decisive effect upon the outcome of the war and there were also continuing and accelerating indirect results which were scarcely less important.[65]

In his famous minute Lindemann had told Churchill of the harm that he envisaged being done to the fifty-eight principal German towns, concluding: 'There seems little doubt that this would break the spirit of the people.' It was this forecast that was far from realised. The important point here, however, and a valid defence of Lindemann's stance, is that the bombing intensity that he had envisaged never in fact came to pass: the number of bombers available to Harris fell far short of the production and use that Lindemann had employed in his calculations.

The other factor about which he was wrong was the will to resist shown by the German people. As Albert Speer recounted:

> The powers of resistance of the German people were underestimated and no account was taken of the fatalistic frame of mind which a civil population finally acquires after numerous raids. Other people, as perhaps the Italians, would have certainly collapsed under a similar series of night attacks and would have been unable to undertake further war production.[66]

Speer later confirmed the resilience of German morale, writing from his prison cell:

> These air raids carried the war into our midst. In the burning and devastated cities we daily experienced the direct impact of the war. And it spurred us on to do our best.
>
> Neither did the bombings and the hardships that resulted from them weaken the morale of the populace. On the contrary, from my visits to armaments plants and my contacts with the man in the street I carried away the impression of growing toughness. It may well be that the estimated loss of 9% of our production capacity was amply balanced out by increased effort.[67]

In this assertion there is an understandable element of patriotism. As Professor Thomas Wilson has remarked: 'Both Churchill, on the British side, and Speer, speaking about the German side after the war, made fine statements about morale in their respective countries but both may have closed their eyes to some less agreeable signs of weakening.'[68] Speer did not, for example, draw attention to the fact that many of the workers in the Fatherland comprised slave labour and were not permitted the luxury of morale. In fact, right at the end of the war German morale did more or less collapse, and it was established that when the catastrophe at Dresden became known to the whole of Germany, morale disintegrated everywhere, in spite of the best efforts of the Gestapo.[69]

As it was, doubts about the policy began to be expressed vocally in the last months of the war, particularly after the raids in February 1945 that consumed Dresden in a dreadful inferno, and there are strong arguments for saying that the saturation bombing of cities should have been halted earlier than it was. Churchill certainly became equivocal. He called for 'basting' of the Germans by bombing, so that at his forthcoming meeting with Stalin at Yalta he could demonstrate the vigour of the British effort. Yet shortly afterwards, in March 1945, he wrote to the Chiefs of Staff:

> It seems to me that the moment has come when the question of bombing of German cities simply for the sake of increasing the terror, though under other pretexts, should be reviewed. Otherwise we shall come into control of an utterly ruined land . . . The destruction of Dresden remains a serious query against the conduct of Allied bombing.[70]

Lindemann, it may be assumed, did not share this opinion. He had all along maintained that his often-quoted minute to Churchill was written to show what could be done with a given use of force. As he told Tizard at the time:

> The whole point of my note was to show what damage would be possible with a given number of bombers devoted to attack on the large German cities. I did not say that we could carry out the desired devastation by a given date, nor did I say that we should necessarily devote all our bombers to this purpose.[71]

Furthermore, even in early 1945 it was thought that the war could drag on for many more months. Hitler had already produced V-weapons and jet-propelled aircraft, and the Schnorkel submarine was on its way: there could be no let-up, it was felt, if Allied lives were to be saved. This necessity would surely have matched Lindemann's emotions, and to justify them he could have pointed to the violence of the enemy, the nature of whose own bombing policy had been clearly depicted in a speech made by Hitler in 1940:

> Have you ever looked at a map of London? It is so closely built up that one source of fire alone would suffice to destroy the whole city, as happened once before, two hundred years ago. Goering wants to use innumerable incendiary bombs of an altogether new type, to create sources of fire in all parts of London. Fires everywhere. Thousands of them. Then they'll unite in one gigantic area conflagration. Goering has the right idea. Explosive bombs don't work, but it can be done with incendiary bombs – total destruction of London. What use will their fire department be once that really starts![72]

THIRTEEN

Science at War

Within a few weeks of Churchill becoming Prime Minister there arose a scientific problem with potentially disastrous results for Britain, for which Lindemann, by means of his position, was able to help devise the solution.

In 1940 Dr R. V. Jones, usually known as 'Doc', was on the staff of the Air Ministry, but at Tizard's suggestion he had been seconded to Intelligence duties at the Air Ministry Directorate of Intelligence. He had heard a fragment of conversation between two German prisoners of war, discussing something called an X-Apparatus. He had also seen a scrap of paper, salvaged from an enemy aircraft that had been shot down in March, which referred to 'Radio Beacon Knickebein'. A few weeks later Jones was handed the transcript of a German wireless message that read: 'Knickebein Cleves established fifty-three, twenty-four north, one degree west.'

By happy coincidence, in October 1939 a Heinkel aeroplane had come down near Edinburgh, after a raid on the Firth of Forth, and Jones had discovered that this aeroplane's Lorenz blind-landing receiver was much more sensitive than would normally be needed for its purposes. As a result of Enigma Intelligence work at Bletchley Park, with which he had recently become involved, Jones was able to piece together all this information. His conclusion was that the Germans had set up a radio beam transmitter called Knickebein, at Cleves – about the nearest bit of Germany to England – with a new and deadly purpose.

Jones had not seen Lindemann for some time, partly because Tizard was also working at the Air Ministry and Jones wished to avoid becoming a pawn in their squabble. However, Lindemann had at length tracked him down and a meeting had been arranged for 12 June 1940, the morning on which Jones was handed the note about Cleves. Lindemann had asked to see Jones to find out what he knew about German radar, but at their meeting Jones, armed with the various scraps of information about Knickebein, also told Lindemann that he thought the enemy had established an intersecting beam system, using beams narrow enough to allow for accurate bombing of targets in England.

At first Lindemann was disbelieving. He objected that the system could not possibly work, as the necessary short waves would not bend around the curvature of the earth between Germany and England. The distance involved was over 200 miles, and received scientific wisdom at that time – at any rate in England, although presumably not in Germany – held that waves transmitted on a frequency of around thirty megacycles (which Lorenz receivers used) travelled in straight lines. However, the next day Jones talked to Lindemann again, and this time showed him a paper written by the scientific adviser to the Marconi Company, an expert on radio-wave propagation. This paper suggested that in certain circumstances it would be possible for aircraft flying over England to pick up signals transmitted from Germany. So Lindemann was persuaded that there was at least a chance that the system might work.

The situation was fraught with peril. Not only might it now be possible to transmit waves successfully from Germany; even worse, France had just collapsed, and it would not be long before the Germans might be using French airfields much nearer to Britain. If their bombers could be directed by the use of beams, they would be able to mount night air raids, against which British air defences were in poor shape. Jones believed that the Knickebein would enable the Germans to 'place an aircraft within 400 yards over a point in this country'.[1] British cities suddenly looked extremely vulnerable.

Lindemann now used his influence for all it was worth, and the same day sent a minute to Churchill:

Prime Minister   13th June 1940

There seems some reason to suppose that the Germans have some type of radio device with which they hope to find their targets. Whether this is some form of RDF and they have IFF beacons planted by spies to guide them, or whether it is some other invention, it is vital to investigate and especially to discover what the wave-length is. If we knew this we could devise means to mislead them; if they use it to shadow our ships there are various possible answers; if they rely on IFF we could lead them astray; if they use a sharp beam this can be made ineffective.

With your approval I will take this up with the Air Ministry and try and stimulate action.[2]

In his memoirs, Churchill described the 'painful shock' that he received on hearing of the radio beams:

It now appeared that the Germans had developed a radio beam which, like an invisible searchlight, would guide the bombers with considerable precision to their target. The beacon beckoned to the pilot, the beam pointed to the target. They might not hit a particular factory, but they could certainly hit a city or town. No longer therefore had we only to fear the moonlight nights, in which our fighters could see at any rate as well as the enemy, but we must even expect the heaviest attacks to be delivered in cloud and fog.[3]

The next day Churchill sent Lindemann's minute to the Air Minister, Sir Archibald Sinclair, his former companion-in-arms in the trenches on the Western Front. He wrote upon it: 'S of S for Air: This seems most intriguing and I hope you will have it thoroughly examined.' Sinclair immediately appointed Air Chief Marshal Sir Philip Joubert to take charge of the investigation and a meeting was held the following day, attended by both Lindemann and Jones. They decided upon immediate action.

Jones, who could imagine the dangers ahead probably more vividly than any of the others, was concerned about the risk of delays and recorded that 'despite the priority we already had, progress might be held up because of insufficient scientific manpower'.[4] Even though he was a master of his subject, it must have seemed daunting to a young man of twenty-eight (Jones' age) now to be surrounded by grey-haired men with gold braid on their hats and exuding a general atmosphere of gravity and importance. It must have been especially so as he knew very well how vital was the discovery that he had made, and how urgent a matter for the country.

However, Lindemann was at hand. He knew and liked Jones, understood the nature of the problem and, crucially, had the Prime Minister's ear. It was a fortunate combination. Straight away Lindemann wrote to the Prime Minister:

In view of the extreme urgency of investigating radio methods likely to be used against us by the enemy in the air or elsewhere, it would seem desirable to have a ruling that such investigations take precedence, not only as regards materials but especially the use of men, over any research whose results are not liable to affect production in the next three months.

On this minute Churchill wrote on the same day, 17 June, the vital words:

'Let this be done without fail.'[5] He then summoned a meeting, to be held in the Cabinet Room four days later. As he subsequently wrote:

> Being master, and not having to argue too much, once I was convinced about the principles of this queer and deadly game I gave all the necessary orders that very day in June for the existence of the beam to be assumed, and for all counter-measures to receive absolute priority.[6]

Jones was ordered to attend the meeting. He has written a memorable account[7] of how, having at first believed that his invitation was a practical joke, he found himself at the Cabinet table among some of the country's most senior officers and politicians. When Jones entered, Churchill was on one side of the table, with Lindemann on his right and Beaverbrook on his left. Opposite them were half a dozen of the topmost men in the air force, as well as Tizard and Watson-Watt. Jones quietly told the story from the beginning – and from that moment Churchill was to hold him in the highest esteem. Tizard, by contrast, was disbelieving, although his attitude was undoubtedly coloured by Lindemann's involvement; he had already commented unfavourably on Lindemann's advancement, writing in his diary for 4 June:

> Thence to see Lindemann at 10, Downing Street. Apparently he has been told by the PM to 'drive ahead' with anything new that may be of use this summer, and there is enough overlapping of responsibility to hinder almost anything being done.[8]

His unfortunate scepticism was to damage his future wartime career. As it was, far from Lindemann being a hindrance, his influence was to prove the very reverse. Tizard obviously felt a certain dismay at these developments, and immediately after the meeting on 21 June resigned from his posts as adviser to the Air Staff and chairman of the Scientific Advisory Committee. Churchill was later in the war to shrug off another threatened resignation from Tizard, saying: 'If we had listened to Sir Henry Tizard in 1940, we should not have known about the beams.'[9]

Later that day – and even then not without the opposition of Air Ministry sceptics – a flight was laid on to search for the beams. The following morning the pilot and observer made their report: it was a triumphant vindication of all the detective work, the hard scientific thought, and the manner in which Churchill was persuaded of the danger. Orders were given that the threat should be dealt with at once.

It turned out that Goering had decided that among the prime targets of the Luftwaffe should be the Rolls-Royce aero-engine works at Derby, the only factory producing the engines for the Spitfires and Hurricanes without which the RAF would be crippled in its fight to protect the British skies. The beams that Jones had discovered, and which Lindemann had so quickly brought to the Prime Minister's attention, led straight to Derby.

Science was now being harnessed to war with a vengeance, but the counter-measures were not at first uniformly successful, even though the scientists were able to pass on warnings of impending raids. On 24 October 1940, for example, Lindemann wrote to Churchill:

> On many occasions recently it has been possible to inform Fighter Command in advance what targets were going to be attacked and approximately what course the first raiders would take. E.g. last night it was known that Coventry would be attacked by KG100, using one of the beams in the four metre region. It must be assumed that everything was done to warn the AA batteries so that they could concentrate a barrage in the right place and that it was really impossible to lay mines in the path of the advancing aircraft.[10]

He added: 'The counter measures in this wave-length region do not seem to be progressing as fast as might be hoped. In my view they should take precedence of any other radio work.'

Despite the warning, the Luftwaffe flew over Coventry in force, and the city suffered a night of death and destruction. Churchill passed Lindemann's minute to the chief of the Air Staff, who replied:

> Professor Lindemann implies in his minute that we are not pressing on with our radio countermeasures to the German beam system as fast as we might. I can assure you that this is not the case . . . we have an organisation covering the whole of the Southern Counties and the Midlands, including Liverpool. So far as we can make out, this organisation is having some effect in upsetting the German navigational aids.[11]

It was not long before Goering was thwarted by the remarkable abilities and insights of physicists on the British side:

> The counter-measures, introduced just in time during the coming weeks, were to limit severely the value of the German technique. This was never used successfully for the night bombing of Fighter Command's airfields, an operation suggested by early investigations, and one which might have had the most fearsome consequences.[12]

In the struggle to master the beams, Knickebein was given the codename 'Headache', while the ensuing antidote received the name 'Aspirin'. The counter-measures against Knickebein and its successors included both jamming and widening the beams, which often caused the bombers to deviate unwittingly from their path and drop their bomb-loads harmlessly over green fields, instead of over densely populated cities:

> On a recent occasion the NCO in charge of the 'Aspirin' transmitter at Hagley reported that aircraft approaching Birmingham from the south, when aiming within the vicinity of his Lorenz transmitter, slewed off to the north-west and in each case missed Birmingham . . . During this period, as an experiment, the Hagley operator was instructed to change the frequency of his transmitter. Immediately after doing so the next aircraft approaching in his direction went straight over the 'Aspirin' and dropped its bombs on Birmingham. The operator was instructed to revert to his original frequency, when once again the aircraft appeared to be diverted to the north-west.[13]

In Birmingham and elsewhere civilians were maimed or killed as a result of such experiments, and many unknowingly had a lucky escape; but such necessities were part of the price of enabling the scientists to get the measure of the peril.

Lindemann's minute to Churchill was an example of the lucidity that did so much to keep the Prime Minister well informed and enthusiastic about such complex matters. He described to the Prime Minister the enemy's plan to use radio beacons established in Germany, Norway and northern France, writing:

> There are two ways of dealing with such beacons. The first is to jam them, i.e. to make so much disturbance in the ether that their signals cannot be received. If one compares them with lighthouses, it is like turning on the sunlight so that they would become invisible. This method is difficult because they operate on so many different wave-lengths that we must produce very strong signals in each band to cover the lot. Furthermore, operators become very skilful in recognising signals through the general glare . . . Further, each lighthouse has its own colour (wavelength) which has to be out-matched, so that the general glare must be produced over the whole spectrum, ranging from 30 metres to 1800 metres . . . This brings us to the second method, called 'Masking'. For this purpose, we require a number of small stations in England which pick up and repeat the German signals

exactly in phase. If this is done, the wireless operator in the German machine cannot distinguish between the signals from his beacon and the echo signal from our station, and his direction-finding is completely set to nought. Since these echo stations are in exact phase with the ground stations it is impossible to home on them, so that they cannot be used as a navigational aid by the enemy as a German station could.[14]

It was this sort of help that Churchill later referred to when he wrote:

There were no doubt greater scientists than Frederick Lindemann, though his credentials and genius command respect. But he had two qualifications of vital consequence to me. First . . . he was my trusted friend and confidant of many years. Together we had watched the advance and onset of world disaster. Together we had done our best to sound the alarm. And now we were in it, and I had the power to guide and arm our effort. How could I have the knowledge?

Here came the second of his qualities. Lindemann could decipher the signals from the experts on the far horizons and explain to me in lucid, homely terms what the issues were . . . What I had to grasp were the practical results, and just as Lindemann gave me his view for all it was worth in this field, so I made sure that by turning on my power-relay that some at least of these terrible and incomprehensible truths emerged in executive decisions.[15]

Afterwards Churchill was to tell Jones: 'It makes me very proud of our country that there were minds like yours playing so keenly around the unknowable, and I am also glad that through my friendship with Lindemann I was able to bring these deadly beams into relation with the power of the British State.'[16]

The battle against the Luftwaffe was a paramount factor in Lindemann's advocacy of a sustained offensive from Bomber Command. It was only twenty-five years since he himself had been grappling with the hazards of flying aeroplanes in wartime, twisting his 'Night Experimental' through the skies to test primitive bomb-sights, or spinning towards the ground in his BE2E. The memories of those pioneering flights would have given him an understanding of the courage and endurance required of the crews of Bomber Command.

Operations over Germany were uncomfortable and hazardous in the extreme for airmen. They involved cold, strain and exhaustion, accompanied by the ever-present fear of blinding searchlights and anti-aircraft fire, or of German fighters appearing suddenly out of the black night. The anxiety that the crews must have felt is starkly illustrated by the statistics for Bomber Command's casualties: whereas a total of 5,582 operational aircrew were killed during the war, about eight times as many were 'presumed dead'; that is, no remains were ever found.

Lindemann was conscious of all these difficulties, and would frequently talk to the crews to learn of their problems at first hand. As Lord Sherwood commented: 'Prof was extremely good with the bomber crews, who were fascinated by him and his gigantic knowledge of their problems.'[17] He knew that scientific aids would lessen the chances of mishap, and he energetically encouraged their development; indeed, he was described as being 'almost emotional about the theme of a scientific instrument in every bomber'.[18] Fortunately, as the war progressed, more such instruments became available; every square inch of each aeroplane was pressed into service, until at one stage Air Chief Marshal Harris was moved to complain of the dangers of aircraft being sent over Germany 'decked out like Christmas trees'.

In his famous 'de-housing' minute to Churchill, Lindemann had referred to '58 German towns of over 100,000 inhabitants, which, with modern equipment, should be easy to find and hit'. The Butt Report had shown that, without scientific aids, towns were very far from 'easy to find and hit'; but, with Lindemann's backing, that report had spurred research into new methods of target-finding and bomb-aiming, and he was encouraged in his advocacy of area bombing by his knowledge that significant developments were in train.

Much of the work was done at the Telecommunications Research Establishment (TRE) in Malvern, with other research being carried out at the Clarendon Laboratory. Particularly important navigational aids were Gee, G–H and Oboe, the last getting its name from the crews, who thought that, when in use, it sounded like an oboe – whether by the musical among them, or the reverse, is not recorded. Lindemann's continuing support for the Clarendon indirectly ensured that inventions designed to help the bombers were pressed forward with all speed. For this purpose he made frequent appearances at the TRE research meetings, which became known as 'Sunday Soviets' and at which many valuable ideas were conceived.

Since the beginning of the war his team at Oxford had been working on the development of short-wave radar. Lindemann knew that a reduction of wavelength to 10cm or below would be invaluable: it would enable a narrow beam to be used, which would lead both to the concentration of transmitter power and to the elimination of unwanted return echoes. It would also lead to much smaller objects being reflected by the radio waves, so that it would be possible to detect the most important prize of all – submarine conning towers. The scientists searching for a breakthrough had already had a moment of great exhilaration at a demonstration of an experimental 10cm radar set at Swanage in 1940, when they had picked up the reflections from a submarine's conning tower at a distance of four miles.

However, the revolutionary invention that eclipsed all others in value was that of the cavity magnetron. This thermionic device, invented by two physicists at Birmingham University, made outstanding strides in meeting three vital requirements for radio detection that had not yet been solved: first, that the transmitted beam should be as narrow as possible, so as to discover the bearing of enemy aircraft; second, that the transmitted pulse should be as sharp as possible, so as to define the position of the aircraft; and third, that the pulse should be powerful enough to detect aircraft at a great distance.

The magnetron was a small block of copper with cavities machined in it, through which electrons circulated while being subjected to a magnetic field, resulting in intense magnetic radiation. It was usually only about ten cubic centimetres in size, yet it could produce pulses of one-millionth of a second's duration, and kilowatts (and later megawatts) of power. It therefore made radar sets much more effective, and enabled them to be designed and produced for airborne use; there was a further advance with the invention, at the Clarendon Laboratory, of a single cell that would both transmit and receive.

The cavity magnetron was a breakthrough of enormous significance. Although Air to Surface Vessel radar equipment (known as ASV) had already been issued to the navy and to Coastal Command, it operated initially on a 1.5-metre wavelength, which meant that enemy submarines were able to pick up the signals in time to avoid attack. Airborne Interception equipment (or AI), which had been issued to the RAF, also had limited use. Microwave radar equipment, by contrast, besides being very powerful, had the inestimable advantage that its short wavelength meant that it could not be detected by enemy submarines, which therefore had no time to dive to safety when approached by British aircraft. An added bonus came when a captured English pilot deceived the Germans into thinking that the British could hear the German receivers in their vessels and aeroplanes, with the result that the enemy wasted much time in modifying them.

In August 1940 Sir Henry Tizard had led a mission to the United States to discuss progress in scientific inventions of war, and he had given a magnetron to the Americans for them to copy. One American historian described it as 'the most valuable cargo ever brought to our shores. It started the whole development of microwave radar and constituted the most important item in reverse lease-lend.'[19]

Lindemann took a deep interest in these scientific developments and ensured that they received high-level support. It was fortunate that he did so: they proved of the greatest value in enabling bombing missions to be carried out with accuracy, besides saving the lives of very many aircraft crew.

He was particularly closely associated with the development of H2S, for the success of which the cavity magnetron was responsible. This marvel of science permitted accurate bombing through cloud cover and led to the successful detection of submarines on the surface by night. Its original code-name was 'TF', but Lindemann considered that its purpose – loosely described as 'Town Finding' – could be deduced from that name, so he rechristened it H2S, and it became known as 'Home Sweet Home'.[20] It was to prove an invaluable weapon of war, and Lindemann hastened its development in the face of many setbacks. Writing to the Prime Minister in February 1942, he said of H2S:

> I think everything is going forward on the right lines and that it is really receiving the high priority that it deserves.
>
> I have been in close touch with Freeman about it in your absence, and with your permission will continue this so as to make sure that navigational training etc. is directed in good time towards the special problems involved.[21]

H2S was in effect an aerial map-reader, displaying on a screen in the aircraft a picture of a large area of the land beneath the aeroplane. It can readily be understood what a boon it was for the bomber crews. Instead of uncertainly weaving around over Germany, or desperately trying to find their way home, they could use H2S to tell them with accuracy where they were – and it was not thrown out of kilter, as other devices had been, by violent ducking and banking when avoiding enemy defences. H2S was only made possible by the development of the cavity magnetron, which generated centimetric waves on a sufficiently large scale for towns to be distinguished from countryside, and coastline from the sea. It was developed by Bernard Lovell,[22] in association with Philip Dee, who wrote to Lindemann paying tribute to his support:

> . . . for a long time now I have realised the enormous part you played in furthering the project on its initiation. But for your bold policy of driving for production before the experiment was fully developed, I am sure that it would never have been ready for the crises when they occurred.[23]

The accuracy provided by H2S made it an obvious piece of equipment for the new Pathfinder Force, which had been strongly encouraged by Lindemann, together with Air Commodore Bufton,[24] and which was established in August 1942. Lindemann had long cherished the idea of such a force, and he had called for Bomber Command to re-examine most carefully the possibilities of making specially expert navigators, or bombers equipped with special navigational aids, fly ahead of the main body to light fires to guide those following, as the Germans did. It might be wondered how the pathfinders themselves were to find their targets, despite the special aids, especially as the Germans had become experts at lighting decoy fires, and Lindemann pressed for 'the use of marker bombs dropped in daylight, made to light up or emit radio signals in the night'.[25]

In contrast to his vital encouragement of these developments, and his pushing them over the bureaucratic obstacles that were inevitably placed in their way, Lindemann was responsible for what nearly became a very costly mistake; it would have become one, were it not for the ingenuity of R. V. Jones and the Intelligence Services.

It had to be decided whether H2S was finally to be designed with a klystron output valve or with a magnetron. The leader of the newly formed Pathfinder Force, for which H2S was expected to be particularly valuable, found after taking part in trials that the magnetron version was preferable. However, there was strong opposition from those who said that the magnetron would be much more useful in the anti-submarine war, and that if an aeroplane equipped with magnetron H2S flew over the Continent, its precious cargo might fall into German hands. If that happened, it was argued, the enemy would be able radically to improve their RDF night-fighting equipment and ground warning systems, and become a much greater threat to Bomber Command. Lindemann, however, backed by Watson-Watt, discounted that idea, believing that it would take the Germans twelve to eighteen months to develop a magnetron from the time they first acquired one from a British aeroplane. At the same time Air Chief Marshal Harris bluntly stated both that H2S would be essential to the success of the Pathfinder Force and that it was viable only with the magnetron. Lindemann backed him, and at a meeting to decide the issue, held with the Air Minister on 15 July 1942, that support proved decisive.[26]

It was an important decision, with the risk that in this case Lindemann's influence might have cost many lives, both in the air and at sea. The magnetron, with its solid anode block and surrounding bulky magnet, was very difficult to destroy, even with an explosive charge, in cases of threatened capture. If its secret got out, the Germans would discover what wavelength was being used in the detection of their submarines by ASV.

The Intelligence Services expressed great anxiety on hearing of

Lindemann's stubbornness, thinking it dangerously obsessive, as the device had a quite different and possibly far more important use as a U-boat detector. They felt it was essential to keep H2S out of enemy hands, especially while it was still new. The Germans were by no means lacking in radio technology, and although they did not at first have the magnetron, they became aware that the British had a device that could produce short wavelengths. Jones tried to persuade the Air Staff of the risk, but nothing he or the service chiefs said could alter Lindemann's mind.

Inevitably, after a short time the Germans did retrieve a magnetron from a crashed aeroplane. By great good fortune and 'almost incredible slowness on the part of the Germans',[27] Jones and his intelligence staff were ingenious enough to fool them into thinking that their submarines were being detected by infra-red, and not by radar. Nevertheless, Lindemann's single-minded determination to give priority to Bomber Command could have proved expensive.

Lindemann was also closely involved with the development and use of 'Window' (or 'Chaff', as the Americans called it), the codename for specially prepared aluminium foil strips which, when dropped from aeroplanes in certain shapes and sizes, jammed radar detectors. Its use saved countless Allied lives by confusing enemy fighter and ground defences when bombers approached targets in Germany. This ingenious invention was originally a consequence of the technical air-defence work that Jones, as Lindemann's pupil, had been doing at the Clarendon Laboratory before the war. As a result of Jones' work, Lindemann had drawn Churchill's attention to the vulnerability of radar to jamming. Churchill later wrote:

As early as 1937 Professor Lindemann had prompted me to make a very simple suggestion to the Air Defence Research Committee. This was to scatter from the air packets of tin-foil strips and other conducting material cut to a specific length so as to simulate a bomber on the enemy's radar screen. If a cloud of these were dropped by our aircraft the enemy fighters would not be able to tell which were our bombers and which were our tinfoil strips. This was later called 'Window'. The experts were doubtful and the idea had not been tried till four years later when, early in 1942, at Lindemann's instigation, highly secret trials were held.[28]

Although Lindemann was a strong supporter of research on radar, equally he believed it to be incautious to abandon the development of alternative ideas for air defence, in case the Germans were also developing radar systems. Accordingly, in March 1938 he prepared for Churchill a note warning of various difficulties with radar, 'lest too much reliance,' as he said, 'be placed upon RDF methods':

> Great difficulties may be encountered when large numbers of aeroplanes attacking and defending are simultaneously in the air, each sending back its signals. This difficulty may be very naturally increased if the enemy chooses to blind the RDF operator by strewing numbers of oscillators in the appropriate region.
>
> It is quite true of course that a single oscillator of this type could after a few minutes be distinguished from an aeroplane, since it would only move with the velocity of the wind, instead of approaching or receding at several miles per minute. But if some hundreds or thousands were scattered . . .
>
> It is known that a system similar to the RDF was patented in Germany a good many years ago . . . they will have observed and interpreted our signals and may adopt some simple counter method.[29]

R. V. Jones himself wrote:

> . . . a month or two later Lindemann told me that Churchill had said that he understood from the Sub-Committee that they were going to shut down my infra-red work. I replied that infra-red certainly had its limitations of not being useful through cloud and of not giving an indication of range, but that radar, too, was vulnerable, especially to a 'smoke-screen' of spurious radar reflections which only need be lengths of wire half a wavelength long. Lindemann told me that he would get Churchill to raise this point at the Sub-Committee. When I subsequently asked him what had happened he said that Tizard and Watson-Watt had rather 'looked down their noses' at the suggestion.[30]

After Churchill became Prime Minister, Lindemann was able to resuscitate the matter and in 1941 he pressed for trials. They showed that Window was highly effective and would act as a smoke screen for attacking aircraft. Development therefore went ahead, and all seemed set fair for its use. It was actually loaded on to aeroplanes for an operation as early as May 1942, but Derek Jackson,[31] then Fighter Command's airborne radar officer, called a halt until calculations were made of the effect on British night fighters if the Germans discovered its secret and used it themselves. In this, Jackson was strongly supported by both Tizard and Watson-Watt, and Lindemann was persuaded to withdraw his support.

The misgivings arose from the fact that the effects of Window were so

striking that its use might at once show the Germans an easy way of neutral-
ising British radar defences – as it happened, an exactly parallel argument
was taking place in Germany.[32] However, the proponents of Window claimed
that German offensive air operations were now so weak, partly because many
of their aeroplanes were engaged against the Russians, that any damage they
could do would be dwarfed by Allied operations made successful by using
Window against German radar defences.

An intelligence report of a conversation in a German train, suggesting
that knowledge of Window was in any event widespread in Germany, further
reduced the need to keep it secret. Lindemann, however, was reluctant to
change his mind, and poured scorn on the idea of changing policy on the
basis of a conversation overheard on a train. So the argument over when,
or even whether, to introduce it continued. One minor by-product of the
dispute was recorded by Jones, who said that during the discussions a further
meeting was called by the chief of the Air Staff, and Jones told Lindemann
that he would continue to oppose him on the issue, to which Lindemann
replied: 'If you do that you will find Tizard and me united against you.'
Jones could not help replying, to Lindemann's amusement: 'If I've achieved
that, by God, I've achieved something.'[33]

Mulish as ever, Lindemann maintained his opposition to the use of
Window, advising the Prime Minister that 'Bomber Command would probably not gain very greatly by using it, whereas Fighter Command would be
ham-strung if it were used against us.'[34] He also feared that its use might
jeopardise the invasion of Sicily, intended for July 1943. Eventually, at a
meeting called by Churchill and attended by Watson-Watt, Lindemann and
the Chiefs of Staff, the Prime Minister ruled that Window should be brought
into use, declaring: 'Very well, let us open the window.' It was first used on
a raid on Hamburg on 24 July, with devastating effect. The German defences
were wholly confused, and the British Intelligence operators were able to
intercept heated controversies between German ground operators and their
pilots, demonstrating utter disorder in the defence organisation. Bomber
Command's aircraft loss rate fell to a quarter of that on previous attacks on
Hamburg.

The success of scientific aids, especially H2S, intensified what became a
fierce debate, begun in 1941, about whether the prime target for air attack
should be the German U-boat fleet or Germany itself. Lindemann remained
a leading advocate of giving priority to bombing the German homeland. Yet
the arguments for devoting extra resources to combating the U-boat menace
were on the face of it strong. As Churchill himself was to say: 'The U-boat
attack was our worst evil. It would have been wise for the Germans to stake
all upon it.' His concern was so great that he issued a specific directive to

the Air Staff in March 1941, giving top priority to defeating the attempt to strangle Britain's food supplies:

> We must take the offensive against the U-boat wherever we can and whenever we can. The U-boat at sea must be hunted, the U-boat in the building yard or in dock must be bombed. The Focke Wulf, and other bombers employed against our shipping, must be attacked in the air and in their nests.[35]

A few weeks into the war, at the German U-boat yards in Wilhelmshaven, there had been an historic meeting between Hitler, Grand Admiral Raeder, head of the German Navy, and Admiral Dönitz, the flag officer in charge of submarines. Dönitz had laid his plans before the Führer, proudly telling him:

> After a careful examination of the whole question of U-boat warfare, I am convinced that in the U-boat we have, and always have had, a weapon capable of dealing Britain a mortal blow at her most vulnerable spot.
>
> The U-boat war, however, can only be successfully waged if we have sufficient numbers available. The minimum requisite total is 300 U-boats . . . Given this number of boats, I am convinced that the U-boat arm could achieve decisive success.[36]

During this period Britain had to import two-thirds of her food and all her raw materials except iron, and Dönitz had become convinced that U-boats were the way to prevent Britain from conducting any military offensives overseas – a prelude to starving her into surrender. They seemed well placed to do so: although the Germans started the war with only fifty-seven U-boats, numbers quickly began to increase and shipping losses rose dramatically.

The first 'wolf-pack' attacks had started in the autumn of 1940, and were based on Dönitz's theory that 'the concentration which a convoy represents must be attacked by a like concentration of U-boats acting together'. After twelve months of war German submarines had sunk more than 2.25 million tons of shipping, including an aircraft-carrier, a battleship, three destroyers, two submarines, five auxiliary cruisers and 440 merchant ships. Disaster threatened, and food imports to Britain had almost halved.

The Statistical Department, using detailed information on individual sinkings, produced an ingenious chart for Churchill, revealing how U-boats timed their attacks, whether in daylight or in good or poor moonlight. The development of these charts, an early form of operational research, played a part in gradually helping the navy and RAF to force submarines from the surface by day, and eventually for long periods both by day and by night.

However, from an early stage Bomber Command had made persistent demands on aircraft production and use, and in August 1941 Air Chief Marshal Joubert, the head of Coastal Command, felt compelled to put the case for giving priority to the Battle of the Atlantic:

> . . . At any moment we may suffer a major shipping disaster. [The German] submarine building programme is such that the enemy can flood the Atlantic with U-boats . . . I am making this point because I hear rumours of attempts to remove the aircraft from Coastal Command which are vitally necessary to its work . . . Coastal Command must retain, and indeed increase, the numbers of its aircraft if it is to help the Navy to keep our lifeline going . . . we could lose Egypt and not lose the war, but if we lose the Battle of the Atlantic we are done.[37]

The proponents of the campaign against submarines concentrated their demands on increased patrolling over the Bay of Biscay, through which the German submarines came and went from their bases on the French coast. The most persistent advocate of this was Blackett, from his eyrie at the Admiralty. There he had already successfully introduced the new discipline of operational research, whereby scientists were sent on operations to gain practical experience of combat, so as to enable them to marry the theories of science to the practice of warfare. Blackett had been a great success at his first posting, with London's anti-aircraft defences, where his introduction of scientific controls had reduced from 20,000 to 4,000 the number of shells needed to bring down an aircraft – or 'rounds per bird', as it was known.

However, Lindemann scorned Blackett's arguments as much as he did the man himself, and typically proposed instead a much simpler and less expensive solution to the submarine problem. Writing to the Prime Minister in June 1942, he commented:

> Certain people are constantly urging that yet more squadrons should be transferred from Bomber Command to Coastal Command . . . if it is decided that a greater operational effort by Coastal Command in the Bay of Biscay is really essential, we must consider how this can be achieved with least damage to our bombing offensive.
>
> My suggestion is that the least harmful method would be to raise the number of crews in Coastal Command, so that the number of

sorties could be increased without augmenting the number of machines.[38]

Lindemann pointed out that there were plenty of crews available, and that if they were double-banked, each aeroplane could make twice as many sorties per month. As usual, he backed up his argument with concise numerical details, and concluded: 'the net result would be that by sacrificing a small fraction of its monthly allocation of about 200 machines, Bomber Command would enable Coastal Command very greatly to increase its rate of effort. This would be equivalent to, and certainly far less painful than, handing over complete squadrons.'

As on so many occasions, he had analysed the data and prepared the case, and Churchill had only to endorse the minute. In this case he sent it straight to the chief of the Air Staff, only adding: 'CAS, Lord Cherwell wrote this by my direction and I should be obliged if you will look into it. It is very much in the RAF interest to avoid further inroads as are constantly threatened. Please give it favourable consideration. W. S. C.'[39]

Lindemann's view was that the best role for the aircraft of Coastal Command would be for the protection of Atlantic convoys, and not for chasing elusive submarines in the Bay of Biscay. He also thought that neither operation justified diverting aircraft from operations over Germany. With logic and mathematics at his fingertips, he put the case to the War Cabinet's Anti-U-boat Committee, to which he had been appointed, together with Watson-Watt and Blackett. Noting the Admiralty's estimate that a U-boat in its life sinks seven or eight ships, he said:

Any particular U-boat we sink will probably have done half its fell work. Hence sinking a U-boat should in the long run be equal to the saving of $3\frac{1}{2}$ or 4 ships. The immediate saving of threatened ships by sending aircraft to protect a convoy is often far greater than this, quite apart from any U-boat which may be sunk . . . Since each aircraft only makes about 50 sorties, it has lately cost us something like 15 aircraft to sink a U-boat in the Bay. We are therefore expending 4 or 5 of these great machines for every ship saved. Admiralty practices show 16 ships saved in the life of one aircraft on convoy patrol: it is evident where the balance of advantage lies.

Nor is the Bay Patrol comparable in value with the immediate attack on Germany. To drop 1000 tons on a German town has cost us in recent months about 15 bombers (the equivalent of one U-boat sunk). It is difficult to compare quantitatively the damage done to any of the 40-odd big German cities in a 1000 ton raid (Coventry got 180 tons), with the advantage of sinking 1 U-boat out of 400, and saving 3 or 4 ships out of 5500. But it will surely be held in Russia as well as here that the bomber offensive must have more immediate effect on the course of the war in 1943.[40]

Nevertheless, some bomber squadrons were diverted to the Bay Patrol to release long-range aircraft for convoy protection. Lindemann's efforts to prevent any drain of resource away from Bomber Command were spiced by his cynicism whenever he was confronted with expensive or elaborate solutions to a problem. One of his workers in S Department, who was on secondment to the navy, noticed that when ships saw a conning tower they tended to escape, but that the reverse equally applied. It transpired that most merchant ships were equipped with poor binoculars, and that they were mostly little opera-glasses provided by the public. Word got back to Lindemann, who discovered that the Admiralty were sitting on a horde of good ones, against the naval building programme. He persuaded the Prime Minister to instruct that the Admiralty binoculars should be distributed at once, and thereafter many lives were saved. Others in the Statistical Department added similar zest to their work on these matters, partly stimulated by the firmly held belief that Blackett was partisan in his approach:

> He was then working for the Admiralty, and he wanted more bombers assigned to Coastal Command, with a view to using more bomber strength against submarines, especially in the Bay of Biscay, and less against the inside of Germany. It is to be noted that Blackett was doing his stuff on behalf of the Admiralty, and it was up to him to make the best possible case for Admiralty interests.
>
> The arguments of Blackett were examined with the greatest care, and found wanting. We had statistics about the number of Coastal Command sorties, and the number of casualties of German submarines claimed. While certain successes were achieved, the figures for the number of sorties required to get a kill were so enormous that it was pretty obvious that the amount of resources devoted to this kind of attack should not be too great.
>
> In the judgment of our office, which was as highly skilled as any group in the country in the interpretation of statistics, Blackett's case was completely demolished.[41]

The Statistical Department's contention that the U-boat threat could be contained without depredation of Bomber Command was developed by Lindemann into a paper that he submitted to the War Cabinet in February

1943. In it he argued against paying too much attention to reports in the press and elsewhere that U-boat sinkings might lead to the war being lost. He explained that in the first year of the war each U-boat used for operations had sunk about nineteen ships, but in the third year that figure had fallen to seven and a half: 'a striking illustration of the resource and efficiency of the Royal Navy'. He continued: 'it seems difficult to justify on merits the numerous alarmist statements which have in the last month or two been assiduously propagated throughout the country', and he concluded by impressing on his Cabinet colleagues his view that the 'facts did not justify the assertion that the U-boat may yet win the war for Hitler'.[42]

Air Chief Marshal Harris also attacked the Admiralty case, claiming that to use bombers to patrol the Bay of Biscay would be 'chasing wild geese'. At a conference called by Churchill to resolve these issues, emotions bubbled high until pricked by the engaging humour of the Prime Minister, as R. V. Jones recorded:

After some intense arguments, Harris burst out with: 'Are we fighting this war with weapons or slide-rules?' To this, after a shorter than usual pause and puff of his cigar, Churchill said: 'That's a good idea; let's try the slide-rule for a change.'[43]

As it turned out, once centimetric radar was introduced against U-boats, the battle turned sharply against the Germans, depriving them of their invisibility when attacking by night, and forcing them under water for long periods both by day and by night, so that they could no longer operate as wolf-packs. Dönitz considered that by itself it had swung the balance in the Battle of the Atlantic, and Hitler said that the 'setback' in the Atlantic war was due to a single technical invention of the enemy.

Although for a time the Germans were led into believing that they were the victims of infra-red devices, at length they concluded that the British were once more using radar. This had the satisfactory by-product of helping to preserve the secret that British Intelligence had by then broken the German naval codes. In early 1943 the cipher experts at Bletchley Park made great advances in decrypting enemy signals and, armed with new sources of information, the British changed their tactics from trying to divert convoys away from known U-boat concentrations to 'fighting them through', especially with American very long-range aircraft. By the summer of 1943 the Germans had lost the battle. As Bernard Lovell wrote:

Success was so clear that the pessimists in Coastal Command and elsewhere were transferred to other posts. In May 1943 there was a slaughter of U-boats. Shipping losses fell from 400,000 tons in March 1943 to a comparatively trifling 40,000 tons in August that year . . . The trial of wits, of measure and countermeasure, was not over but never again was the U-boat a menace and a threat to our existence . . . It is not surprising that some important judges have seen in the change in the U-boat struggle, brought about primarily by the use of not more than fifty sets of H2S radar equipment, the most significant single event which happened in the whole war of 1939–45.[44]

By opposing calls to channel more resources into the war against the U-boats, Lindemann has faced the charge that he gave advice to Churchill that might have resulted in the loss of the Atlantic battle, and consequently of the whole war. The official historian of the war at sea wrote that:

In the early Spring of 1943 we had a very narrow escape from defeat in the Atlantic; and that, had we suffered such a defeat, history would have judged that the main cause had been a lack of two more squadrons of very long range aircraft for convoy escort duties.[45]

Such a charge has not been proved. Although at one point the losses caused by submarines reached a critical level, it can be seen that Lindemann's reasoning was embedded in logic. In the event, he was correct to advocate the use of bombers for Atlantic escort duties, rather than the Bay Patrol, and particularly to maintain that it was not more bombers that would prove decisive, but the 'radio aids' that he so persistently championed, and especially the supremely effective magnetron.

These remarkable scientific aids led to victory both in the Atlantic and over Germany, and at length, with devastating effect, in the Far East. In the words of the joint author of the official history: 'Cherwell did for Bomber Command what Tizard did for Fighter Command – he gave it the scientific means of becoming an effective instrument of war.'[46]

Lindemann achieved this partly through his ability to make Churchill understand how science could affect the use of such weapons of war as U-boats and night fighters. As General Ismay said, without Lindemann's advice to Churchill we would have lost the radio war.

FOURTEEN

Follow My Leader

In 1940, as the sun glinted on German binoculars trained on the cliffs of Dover, Britain alone stood in the path of the Axis powers as they sought to paint their New Order on the map of the world. Yet within eighteen months a Grand Alliance had been formed of three world powers, and they were to march forward together until the enemy was vanquished. Their path to victory was charted by a series of conferences, at which the Allied leaders forged a bond with which they planned not only their strategy, but also the shape of the post-war world.

The fact that Lindemann accompanied Churchill to a number of these gatherings, and that he was at the Premier's side at the momentous meetings of world leaders at Quebec, Potsdam and Yalta, demonstrates how closely he had become involved in Britain's decision-making process, and that Churchill had seen fit to lead him on to the world's political stage. At several of the crucial meetings with Roosevelt and his senior advisers, the Prime Minister was accompanied not by the Foreign Secretary or the Chancellor of the Exchequer – nor even by both, as might have been expected – but by Lindemann.

The first encounter between Premier and President took place in August 1941, in Placentia Bay, Newfoundland. Churchill and Roosevelt had not set eyes on one another since a brief meeting in 1918, but the result of their first wartime meeting, on the American battleship *Augusta*, was the historic declaration that became known as the 'Atlantic Charter'. On this journey Churchill's entourage included the First Sea Lord, the chief of the Imperial General Staff, the vice-chief of the Air Staff and Lindemann.

Their first destination was Scapa Flow, where the party was to board the battleship *Prince of Wales*. Churchill was in buoyant mood, and as the train steamed north he turned to Lindemann and asked for one of the instant calculations for which the Prof had become renowned:

Just as lunch was finishing the PM suddenly jumped up in his place, put his head over the back of his seat and said: 'Prof, what is 24 times 365?' Out came the Prof's slide-rule, and the answer was given as nearly 9000. 'Well,' said the Prime Minister, '9000 bottles of Champagne is not too bad. I can look back on a well-spent life. Prof, what size swimming bath would that amount of Champagne fill?' More slide-rule: 'Well it could easily get inside this compartment.' 'Oh,' said the Prime Minister, 'I do not think much of that. I shall have to improve on that in the future.'[1]

A further cameo of Lindemann on this journey showed him on board the battleship:

The Prof is a grand sight strolling leisurely up and down the deck in a yachting cap which, in the Army expression, is 'asleep'. He frequently succeeds in buttonholing one of the Chiefs of Staff for a long discussion of figures, just when the latter particularly wants to go off and have a sleep. He is, therefore, not entirely popular.[2]

Three days later Lindemann had his first meeting with President Roosevelt, at dinner on board the USS *Augusta*, where he also met senior American figures including Harry Hopkins, General George C. Marshall and Averell Harriman.[3]

His next journey with Churchill was twelve months later, when he accompanied the Prime Minister to Quebec, for a meeting that laid the plans for the invasion of Europe, Operation Overlord; but the conference at which Lindemann was to play his greatest part, and at which he had detailed discussions with the President himself, was the Second Quebec Conference, known as 'Octagon'. This took place in September 1944, and among the problems facing Churchill in his talks with Roosevelt was the state of Britain's economy – a grave prospect, not only while the country was struggling on an all-out war footing, but in the aftermath of the victory that was, with growing confidence, expected.

One of the tasks that had fallen to Lindemann was to negotiate a satisfactory agreement from the Americans on lend-lease aid. His objective was a favourable grant to Britain for the period between the anticipated German surrender and the end of the war with Japan. This had become known as 'Stage II', and was expected to last for about eighteen months. Lindemann was fully aware that during this time not only would Britain need a constant flow of munitions from America, with which to fight in the Far East, but she would need other goods and materials to enable her to make a start on repairing the ravages of five years of war. The conference at Quebec was therefore intended to be largely economic in subject. It was also to consider plans for the post-war world.

It may seem strange that Lindemann, who was not trained as an economist, should head the British negotiating team. In fact his work in the economic field ranged very widely indeed, and during the course of his career he was responsible for significant and influential advice on economic matters, both as Churchill's adviser and in his own right as a Cabinet minister. However, save for one exceptional matter arising during Churchill's second administration, treatment of Lindemann's work in the field of economics is beyond the scope of this book – indeed, it would fill a book of its own.

He had become well versed in economic theory and practical developments long before the Second Quebec Conference – his Statistical Department was staffed with first-class economists – and he was well able to absorb a mass of detail and present it lucidly to the Prime Minister. An example concerned the Mutual Aid Agreement, which, after prolonged and detailed discussions in Washington, was signed by Britain and America in 1942. It committed Britain to working with the United States towards the elimination of discriminatory treatment in international commerce, a goal that Lindemann believed would work to the advantage of Britain as a trading nation. In a clear summary he had set out for Churchill the main advantages and objections involved in proceeding along the lines suggested by the Americans in Washington:

After the war, as the result of our loss of shipping and the piling up of debts to other countries, we shall only be able to pay for our normal imports if we can increase our exports to about 1½ times the pre-war level . . . This will mean not only arresting, but reversing on a grand scale, the declining trend in our exports since 1913, which has been greatly accentuated by wartime developments overseas. We cannot hope to succeed in this immense task without a general and drastic reduction in the artificial barriers to our exports. Even so, it will certainly take a good many years to achieve the required expansion in our exports, and in the meantime we shall have to restrict our imports to make both ends meet.

The problem is to find a scheme, acceptable to other countries, which will entitle us to retain import restrictions, and if necessary depreciate the pound to improve our competitive power, so long as we cannot pay for all we should like to import; and at the same time oblige other countries, whose exports are more than enough to pay for their imports, to moderate their import restrictions, and refrain from retaliating should we find it necessary to depreciate the pound.

This is precisely what the Washington proposals ensure. They are thus highly advantageous to us, and, since they are eminently sensible on general grounds, they may appeal to other countries, as they appear to appeal to at least some Americans.[4]

At Quebec the Prime Minister felt comfortable in receiving from Lindemann advice on economic matters that were of prime importance for Britain's survival. He therefore called on his Paymaster-General (as Lindemann now was), rather than on the Chancellor of the Exchequer or any of his expert advisers, to lead the talks.

Lindemann was given close support by his own experts, particularly Donald MacDougall, who had accompanied him to Quebec and who furnished him with all the information necessary to make a cogent case. One of Lindemann's objectives was to ensure that Churchill, who would present Britain's needs to the President, should clearly understand the gravity of what was at stake. He therefore wrote to Churchill as they set off for Quebec:

This is not just a minor financial question to be settled or shelved on the last day of the Conference. It is a matter of the utmost importance not only because it will determine the scale of our effort against Japan and the part we play in Europe, but also because our whole economic and political future depends upon the arrangements we make now.[5]

Although Lindemann led the British economic team in the opening negotiations, which took place at the highest level in Quebec, in due course the Treasury delegates moved to Washington, where they worked out the details of what the leaders had agreed in principle. Maynard Keynes, the most famous economist of all, had been in America during the summer, attending the Bretton Woods Conference, at which the blueprint for the financing of a new world after the war had been forged. In due course Keynes arrived to represent the British Treasury, and Lindemann handed over to him the detailed management of the British case. He remained in America until November. He had other pressing business there, much of it of an entirely different nature.

When they arrived in Quebec, the British were surprised to find that the Americans had placed at the top of the agenda not lend-lease arrangements, but the future of Germany itself. As a result of his part in the discussions on this thorny problem Lindemann was to come under sharp attack from many quarters, and it is one of the reasons why his name has ever since been associated with an apparently implacable hatred of Germany.

On the evening of 13 September 1944 Roosevelt and Churchill held a small dinner party at The Citadel, the Governor-General of Canada's summer residence. Lindemann was invited, along with the Secretary of the US Treasury, Henry Morgenthau. Earlier in the day the President had asked Morgenthau to tea, telling him that he had been asked to Quebec so that he 'could talk with the Prof'. Morgenthau had devoted the past weeks to drawing up a plan for the treatment of Germany after the war and, although it had been intended that the main subject at dinner should be Britain's shipping requirements, the talk quickly turned to Germany. Roosevelt explained that he had asked Morgenthau to talk to Lindemann about the American plans the following day, but suggested that he should now 'explain the program he had in mind for Germany'.[6]

Morgenthau's explanation exploded like a grenade upon the dining-table. He had just returned from a trip to London – that bombed city with its courageous people, as he described it – and what he saw had filled him with a determination to support Britain. His belief that the country would need a thriving export trade in order to prosper after the war chimed with his views on what should become of Germany. With most leading Americans, he shared basic assumptions about the peace to come: they included a prosperous Great Britain, a co-operative and friendly Russia, and a liberal community of democratic nations in a world free from war. However, in common with the other leaders of the Grand Alliance, he had superimposed upon that creed an animosity towards the Nazis, who had 'brutalised Germany, annihilated millions of human beings, stormed across Europe, and mistreated those whose lands they conquered'.[7]

Morgenthau explained his ideas. He believed that the youth of Germany would have to be re-educated and that huge numbers of Germans who had taken part in the war must be transported to clear up the mess in the countries they had invaded. The core of his thinking was that the heart of industrial Germany, the Ruhr, should be entirely dismantled, so that for generations Germany would not be capable of re-arming for another war. Although his staff had pointed out that such a plan would entail putting at least fifteen million people out of work, Morgenthau was adamant, saying that if the Ruhr was put out of business, the 'coal mines and steel mines of England would flourish for many years'. As he had told his US Treasury colleagues:

The only thing you can sell me, or I will have any part of, is the complete shut down of the Ruhr . . . Just strip it. I don't care what happens to the population . . . I would take every mine, every mill and factory and wreck it . . . Steel, coal, everything. Just close it down . . . I am for destroying it first and we will worry about the population second.[8]

On hearing all this, Churchill's initial reaction was hostile. He described it as unnatural, unchristian and unnecessary. He looked on the plan, he said, as he would on chaining himself to a dead German. Morgenthau recorded that he had never seen the Prime Minister more irascible and vitriolic. The atmosphere at the President's table grew tense. Nevertheless, dinner continued, the discussions proceeded and it was agreed that the next day Lindemann and Morgenthau would consider the question of Germany.

Those present recorded that Lindemann seemed to be much more in sympathy with the American plan than the Prime Minister, and the following day he told Morgenthau that the proposal could be dressed up in a way that would be more attractive to Churchill. Lindemann did not think Churchill had fully taken in the crucial point that if the industrial regions of Germany were pastoralised, as the US Treasury Secretary proposed, it would present Britain with an immense opportunity to rebuild a sustainable export trade and to take from Germany the markets that she had captured in the 1930s by undercutting her neighbours as she was preparing for war.

Lindemann believed that Morgenthau's plan would be an economic life-line for Britain. Accordingly, at some point after the dinner at the Citadel, he seems to have put this viewpoint to Churchill, painting an alluring picture of a strong revival of Britain's exports. As he told Churchill's doctor, who had also been at dinner with Roosevelt:

I explained to Winston that the Plan would save Britain from bank-ruptcy by eliminating a dangerous competitor. Somebody must suffer for the war, and it was surely right that Germany and not Britain should foot the bill. Winston had not thought of it that way, and he said no more about the cruel threat to the German people.[9]

The idea of turning Germany into a predominantly agricultural society appealed also to Stalin. At the Tehran Conference ten months earlier, he had put to Churchill the demand that Russia should dismantle and expro-priate large quantities of machinery in the Ruhr and use it to replace the wreckage left in the wake of the German Army. Like Morgenthau, Stalin feared that the Germans might start a new war within a comparatively short time, and had therefore asked Churchill whether he would prohibit such businesses as watchmakers and furniture factories, which, said Stalin, could easily be turned over to military purposes.

Roosevelt also had in mind the risk that German munitions production could be revived, wherever manufacturing companies were situated, and not just in the Ruhr or the Saar. He expressed his fears by amending the draft plan that Churchill drew up when he, Roosevelt, Lindemann and Morgenthau met at noon the day after the dinner at The Citadel. At that meeting Churchill, following a talk with Lindemann, dictated a memorandum which did not at all reflect his initial reaction to the presentation at dinner. Morgenthau himself was pleased but surprised by Churchill's apparent change of heart, but the wider interpretation was that the subsequent memorandum was the result of influence by Lindemann and went against Churchill's finer instincts.

That memorandum, initialled by Roosevelt and Churchill on 15 September, included the following passage:

The ease with which the metallurgical, chemicals and electric industries in Germany can be converted from peace to war has already been impressed upon us by bitter experience. It must also be remembered that the Germans have devastated a large portion of the industries of Russia and other neighboring allies, and it is only in accordance with justice that these injured countries should be entitled to receive the machinery they require in order to repair the losses they have suffered. The industries referred to in the Ruhr and the Saar would therefore be necessarily put out of action and closed down . . .

The program for eliminating the war-making industries in the Ruhr and the Saar is looking forward to converting Germany into a country primarily agricultural and pastoral in its character.

The Prime Minister and the President were in agreement upon this program.

In fact the concept of a pastoral Germany had been favourably received by the President at a meeting a week or so earlier at the White House. There he had ruminated on the days of his childhood, and of 'Dutchess County and how it was back in 1810, and how the people lived in home-spun wool . . . there is no reason,' he had mused, 'why Germany couldn't go back to 1810, where they would be perfectly comfortable but wouldn't have any luxury.'[10]

Roosevelt's fond images of Dutchess County were not in fact very far removed from the Germany to which the Nazis themselves apparently aspired, judging by the propaganda films of the 1930s, with their scenes of lithe, healthy, smiling *Volk*, exercising with hoops and medicine balls, in pastures set against snowy peaks and foothills dark with the resinous forests that are so close to the German soul.

In the event the American Treasury plan, entitled 'Program to Prevent Germany from starting a World War III', failed to survive its initial acceptance by the two leaders. It received a hostile response from the British Treasury, who thought that, far from benefiting Britain, it would mean that world trade would suffer and that it would lessen Germany's ability to buy British exports. There was also a widespread feeling in Whitehall and some American state departments that in economic terms it would drive Germany towards Russia, and would increase the Soviet sphere of influence in Europe. Lindemann flatly disagreed and fought a rearguard action, writing to Churchill six months later:

> But why should we agree to restore German industries at all in order to compete with us in the markets of the world? The only notable compensation that we can hope to receive from her for all the evil she has inflicted on us is her export markets.
>
> In my view we could persuade the Russians to be content with any existing German machinery and such forced labour as they want while leaving us the German export markets.
>
> I agree with the Chancellor that the more Germany is dismembered, the less will she be able to pay in reparation; but, as I have said, the fewer manufactured goods she exports, the better it will be for us.[11]

In this paper to Churchill, which summarised the issues in the Anglo-American trade discussions, Lindemann had given a stark example of the effect of the war on Britain's exports: the cotton trade, only recently the pride of Lancashire and a significant source of earnings for Britain, had by 1942 fallen to a quarter of its value five years earlier, while that of the USA, India and Brazil had in aggregate increased by more than two and a half times.

Yet cold economics could not compete for the hearts and minds of those, including – after some reflection – Churchill and Roosevelt, who were unwilling to speed Germany back to the early nineteenth century.

Meanwhile, as discussions continued in Quebec, far from the home-spun comfort of Dutchess County a new and deadly weapon had been unleashed and directed towards the long-suffering inhabitants of London. Early in the evening of 8 September 1944, silently, without warning and as if from nowhere, a high-explosive rocket descended on Staveley Road, in the leafy suburb of Chiswick. It completely demolished nearby houses, rendered others uninhabitable, killed three people and seriously injured a further ten. Preceded by a blinding flash, the report echoed like a clap of thunder across London – in the words of the official history, startling 'Londoners travelling home from work or preparing their evening meals'.[12] A few minutes later a second rocket blasted into the middle of Epping Forest. Four days after that, disaster struck again, when a rocket landed on the Chrysler factory at Kew, killing ten and injuring three times as many. The long-feared German rocket attack had begun in earnest.

For more than eighteen months it had been accepted in high military circles that the Germans might be building long-range rockets (subsequently known as V2s). Lindemann became closely involved with these developments at an early stage, both because of his position as Churchill's scientific adviser and because of his close contact with R. V. Jones, who from the start had been a recipient and co-ordinator of Intelligence reports on rockets, and who was at the heart of plans to meet the threat.

However, Lindemann's counsel in the battle against the V2 weapons, as they became known,[13] was to harm his reputation. Because of his pivotal position, and his high scientific ability, great attention was paid to his recommendations. Unfortunately he formed the opinion that long-range rockets were not a practical proposition or, consequently, a dangerous threat. He obstinately maintained this view almost until the first rockets landed in the streets of London.

A rather strange twist to Lindemann's record in this story is the suspicion that he allowed personal animosity to colour his advice. That ought to seem unlikely, in the case of a man as dispassionate as Lindemann, and in a context of the highest importance, in which the main subject-matter was physics – close both to his heart and to his understanding. There is no unequivocal evidence for the idea that he was swayed by emotion, but it is a view that became current at the time; and in some of the minutes that he addressed to the Prime Minister there is the suggestion that his opinion was tainted by disdain for others, in particular for the man placed in charge of investigating the rocket threat.

On 15 April 1943 Churchill received a minute from the Chiefs of Staff, in which they warned him of reports of German experiments with long-range rockets and proposed that the facts should be established with all despatch, so that counter-measures could be devised. They also recommended that one man should be given charge of the task, and they proposed Duncan Sandys. In 1943 he was the Joint Parliamentary Secretary to the Ministry of Supply, the department responsible for much of the important scientific work in progress, although he was not a scientist himself. He was also Churchill's son-in-law, and on 20 April he was directed by the Prime Minister to review the evidence for believing that the enemy was building long-range rockets.[14]

From the outset, Lindemann seems to have treated this appointment with scorn. Moreover, his contempt for the layman's grasp of physics was spiced with a desire, reasonable enough in this case, that the man in charge should be a scientist – despite Lord Trenchard's[15] often-quoted dictum that scientists should be 'on tap and not on top'.

Without delay Lindemann made known his scepticism about the existence of German rockets, let alone missiles of the size that were being talked about. Two days after Sandys' appointment he wrote to Churchill:

German long-range rockets.

Though this possibility cannot be ruled out a priori, I have the impression that the technical difficulties would be extreme, and I should be rather surprised if the Germans had solved them . . . If the launching rails were above ground they would be easily observed and not very difficult to destroy by bombing. If below ground, there would be terrible problems of bringing forward and handling these ten ton projectiles . . . The rocket would emerge at comparatively slow speed, so that accuracy would be severely impaired by wind. Moreover, since the long range could it seems only be achieved by using two rockets in tandem, at worst something about equivalent to a 2000 bomb would arrive in London at the end of it all.[16]

He concluded: 'without hearing all the evidence my opinion is not worth very much, but as at present advised I should be inclined to bet against such rockets being used'.[17]

Some of the advice that Lindemann was himself receiving was coming from Jones, who had been primed initially by a remarkable document that came to be known as the 'Oslo Report'. This paper, apparently from a disaffected but extremely well-informed German, had reached the hands of British Intelligence early in the war, and had set out a number of details of great significance, and which proved as the war progressed to be substantially correct. One of the items in the report referred to a remote area called Peenemünde on the Baltic coast. When Jones and his colleagues had, through subsequent Intelligence reports, added to the initial information given in the Oslo Report, they were able to identify Peenemünde as a probable testing-ground for long-range rockets.

By May 1943 expert opinion had reached the provisional conclusion that rocket development was not impossible. Such missiles, it was believed, could be multi-staged, with a high-explosive warhead of up to ten tons, and a total weight of up to seventy tons. With a range of up to 150 miles, the obvious target was London. As the debate intensified, it became a matter of great importance that Lindemann's advice should be correct, partly because it stood a high chance of being accepted, and partly because on this might turn not only progress on the military fronts, but also the scale of death and injury among helpless civilians. In the event, casualties from German rockets would exceed 21,000 in the main target area, the south-east of England.

By June British Intelligence had acquired photographs which indicated strongly that the construction of rockets was in progress. Yet they did not convince Lindemann. He scorned such conclusions, and appeared to be stuck in his view that such rockets were technically too difficult for the Germans to make. Even so, his advice to Churchill did not exclude the possibility of some unidentified threat, and on 3 June he wrote to the Prime Minister:

There are photographs which show that the Germans are erecting very large structures similar to gun emplacements in the Calais region. Whether or not we take seriously the story about new weapons for bombarding London, would it not be a good thing to bomb these emplacements before the concrete roofs over them are finished? If it's worth the enemy's while to go to all the trouble of building them it would seem worth ours to destroy them before it's too late.[18]

A week later Lindemann again poured cold water on the idea of rockets of the size that the experts were forecasting, saying that they would require vaults as large as a church. 'I cannot conceive,' he said, 'that the Germans could carry out such elaborate installations in the neighbourhood of Calais without being observed and having their work nipped in the bud.' However, with notable insight he went on to suggest: 'the old scheme of unmanned radio directed aeroplanes, jet propelled or otherwise, would seem more feasible'.

Lindemann then took an implied dig at Sandys, by drawing Churchill's attention to R. V. Jones, continuing: 'Jones, who you may remember is in charge of Scientific Intelligence, has been following these questions closely, and I do not think there is any risk of our being caught napping.'[19] Here again Lindemann was to play the role that probably only he could fulfil, ensuring that the often invaluable work of quite junior scientists reached the notice of those who wielded power.

The Prime Minister now called a meeting of the War Cabinet Defence Committee to review the facts. At this meeting Lindemann was quite undaunted by the impressive body of evidence pointing to German rocket development. Weight of opposition *per se* never had much effect on his opinion. He told the meeting that 'the impression that he had formed was that the rocket story was a well designed cover plan'. It had been 'going the rounds for years and was thus very suitable for use as a cover plan'. Nevertheless, in a crucial concession, he agreed with the conclusion of the meeting that Peenemünde should be bombed as soon as possible.

As the summer progressed, more photographs and reports reached England, strengthening the evidence of German rocket activity. Yet Lindemann remained sceptical, telling a further meeting of the Defence Committee that 'he could not believe that it was possible for a weapon such as the long range rocket to be developed from the experimental stage to one at which it was fit for operational use in only 8 or 10 months'. Faced with photographs of objects with fins that looked very like rockets, he insisted, using a phrase that was to be levelled against him in later years:

> . . . the relatively low initial acceleration and the very large fins would result in the projectile being liable to deflection by the wind. He still felt that at the end of the war, when we knew the full story, we should find that the rocket was a mare's nest.[20]

It was at this meeting that the celebrated South African statesman, Field Marshal Smuts, attending as a member of the War Cabinet, gave an instance of his worldly wisdom that Churchill so admired. Asked to comment on the cloudy and conflicting evidence swirling around the long-range rockets, Smuts replied with simple directness: 'Well the evidence may not be conclusive, but I think a jury would convict.' That seemed to put the matter in a nutshell, and shortly afterwards Churchill displayed similar sound sense in summing up the arguments:

> Unless it could be shown that scientifically a rocket was impossible, we could hardly ignore the existence of unexplained facts. There was no doubt of the presence of an overpowering urge on the part of the German Government to retaliate for our bombing.[21]

Still the obstinate streak in Lindemann's nature, which could be destructive as well as the reverse, prevented him from looking at the facts in a new light. He set out once more for the Prime Minister his reasons for continued disbelief:

As there are various techniques well known to the enemy which could be used for dropping bombs on London, I think it unlikely that he would devote great effort to developing a rocket weapon, whose success must be problematical, whose accuracy is bound to be bad, and whose launching points could be observed and destroyed. That he should already be in a position to operate seems to me even more unlikely.

Succumbing to a dangerous hubris, he concluded: 'As I am often believed to be responsible for giving you scientific advice, it would perhaps be well to mention the fact that I am sceptical about this particular matter.'[22]

His implication was that talk of rockets was a hoax: referring to the body of Intelligence reports that supported the opposite case, he said:

The only comment I have on this is that the Germans have been particularly careful not to give us advance information about their real new weapons, like the radio directed glider bomb and the acoustic torpedo, so the fact that they are spreading the giant rocket story does not enhance its probability.[23]

Such tortuous logic betrayed perhaps the desire to fit fact to theory, rather than the other way round – the converse of what Lindemann usually recommended.

He had, however, clearly raised the possibility that the Germans were developing pilotless aircraft and, even if he was wrong in some of the detail that he forecast, his warnings of this peril were to ensure that countermeasures were set in hand. Consequently, what were to turn out to be the V1 flying bombs were, if not contained, at least prevented from doing much worse damage than in fact occurred.

Lindemann was customarily generous with the scorn that he poured on those taking the opposite view to his own. He described the scientist leading the investigation as a man 'who has hitherto not been conspicuously successful in rocket design', and to Churchill he rather cattily described the rockets as 'the weapon with whose supposed existence Duncan Sandys has been dealing'. Deprecating the 'various bits of information that have been collected so painstakingly by Mr Sandys',[24] whom he depicted as an amateur, Lindemann said that 'all this gossip . . . would probably not have been taken seriously had Mr Sandys not discovered on photographs of the German Air Force experimental station at Peenemünde large torpedo shaped objects . . . which he identifies with the Giant Long Range Rocket.'[25]

However, he did appear to shift his ground as the argument progressed, by emphasising less the unlikelihood that the Germans had succeeded in developing rockets at all, but rather that they could not have made one that would deliver a ten-ton warhead. In this context Sir Ian Jacob recalled:

> I remember going to see Cherwell and asking him why a ten-ton warhead was out of the question. He said: 'If you came and told me that you had in your company a man 10 feet tall I should call you a liar. If you said you had a man who was 7 feet tall I might believe you. A rocket of the size and weight suggested is so far beyond present capability that I regard it as out of the question now. A one-ton warhead is a possibility.'[26]

Lindemann did at least have logic on his side when he urged that the rockets should not be allowed to distract from proceeding with 'counter measures against other forms of bombardment which involve no serious difficulties, which are in line with the proved course of German development, and which I therefore consider much more likely to happen'.

In the event, when they did eventually land on London, the V2 long-range rockets carried the same-sized warhead as the V1 flying bomb, although their effect was the greater because the speed on impact was much higher. Another reason why the V2 caused so much damage was that its powerful bow wave moved linearly and not according to the inverse square law, as with an explosion. Nevertheless, there were good reasons for Lindemann to think that the Germans would have been more sensible to use other methods of bombing London – as he put it: 'When it's remembered that each rocket carries a thousand-horsepower turbine and the same warhead as does a flying bomb, Hitler would, I think, be justified in sending to a concentration camp whoever advised him to persist in such a project.[27]

Perhaps by the very strength of his dismissal of the rocket potential, Lindemann had given a greater credence to the possibility of flying bombs than he himself would allow. At any rate, Churchill now ordered the Ministry of Aircraft Production to hold an inquiry into the evidence for rockets, but he added: 'At the same time it would be well to assemble what arguments there are for and against (a) the pilotless airplane and (b) the glider bomb operated by a directing aircraft from a distance.'

To his credit, Lindemann did cause to be rectified without delay one unrelated but serious failing that came to light, only by chance, in the course of discussions on the V-weapon threat. As a result of receiving a letter from Herbert Morrison, the Minister for Home Security, Lindemann discovered that the explosive used in RAF bombs was very much less efficient than that in German bombs. He immediately instigated an inquiry into this anomaly:

It is news to me that our explosive is only $5/_9$ as efficient as the German, and if it is true it seems a most shocking thing. I have asked the Chief of the Air staff to look into it as it would be deplorable if our bombs have been filled with an inferior explosive when a better type appears to be perfectly well known.[28]

It turned out that the Germans had been using aluminium powder to enhance the power of their ammonium-nitrate explosives. The superiority of this filling had for some time been recognised by the British, but those responsible had failed to realise that the aluminium that was scarce at the beginning of the war had long since become more freely available. Within a day or so Lindemann had the culprit 'on the mat' and saw to it that enough aluminium powder could be produced, and that Britain was using it herself, within a fraction of the time that the 'official channels' would have taken.[29]

By December 1943 he had become convinced of the existence of pilot-less aircraft (V1s), although he could not accept that the threat was a very serious one. He furnished the Prime Minister with a detailed warning of what might be in store, starting his minute by saying: 'Some 10 days ago I sent you a note about the ski sites. This time I think the threat is real, but I believe the scale to be comparatively insignificant.'[30] He went on to esti-mate that the useful load carried by the pilotless aircraft would be small, writing: 'My guess would be about half a ton.'

Accordingly, the next month Lindemann submitted to the War Cabinet a paper on 'Crossbow', the codeword that had been given to the flying-bomb threat. In it he analysed the potential launch rate of the bomb, the production effort entailed and the German production capacity, and drew conclusions as to the probable consequences of attack. He had a particular purpose – to use his paper to argue against what he regarded as the exag-gerated fears of some of his colleagues. His particular target was Herbert Morrison, the Home Security Minister, who appeared anxious to begin a large-scale evacuation of London, with all the damage to public morale and official business that would cause. As was his custom, Lindemann quanti-fied the risk:

Bombardment on this scale implies that the average Londoner would be exposed to one explosion within a mile's distance about once a week, or within half a mile once a month. Even if my calculations are out by a factor of 2 the prospect does not appear unduly alarming. It seems important that these facts should be emphasised lest discus-sions about evacuation . . . be allowed to consume too much valuable time.[31]

Some months later, when flying bombs had begun to fall on London, Lindemann put forward plans for dissimulation in order to mislead the Germans as to the effect that their missiles were having. He had noticed that obituaries in *The Times* and the *Daily Telegraph* had been describing their subjects as 'killed by enemy action' and giving the borough in which death had occurred. He moved to have such information withheld. He also recommended disinformation to make the Germans think that far more people would be killed if the mean point of impact of the missiles was moved to South Bermondsey. This would have had the result of increasing the number of bombs that fell harmlessly in open country. However, Morrison resented this suggestion – South Bermondsey being in his constituency – and was unmoved by its logic. The proposal was rejected.

In retrospect, if Lindemann were to be put in the dock for his handling of the V-weapon threat, he would probably admit that he believed that long-range rockets were a bluff to disguise the preparation of flying bombs and that the rocket story was a deliberate hoax; also that he maintained that attitude despite the evidence presented to Duncan Sandys; further, that he did not advise the Government to prepare for a rocket attack – to which he could answer that no panic ensued – although he did at length know of the rocket base at Peenemünde.

However, he did maintain, with at least some justification, that he regarded the vital issue to be not his disbelief in a long-range rocket, but his disbelief in a rocket with a ten-ton warhead, as had been predicted by the experts. On that issue it was Lindemann who was proved correct. He also deserves credit for being the one who exposed the risk of attack by flying bombs, even if in the event they were to do more damage than he believed possible.

On balance, it was lucky for Britain that Lindemann's advice on the V2 rocket was not taken, as it would have meant that no counter-measures were effected, and that British morale would probably have been struck a severe blow when the rockets started to arrive. Moreover, Lindemann cannot escape the charge that in framing his counsel he appeared to drive himself into an indefensible corner, partly it would seem because of lack of sympathy for, and perhaps jealousy of, Duncan Sandys.

Lindemann was fortunate that Churchill's long years of admiration meant that he overlooked this lapse, as is borne out by another of Churchill's 'Secret Circle', Sir Leslie Hollis:

> . . . of all such pilotless planes or flying bombs to be launched, Cherwell was sure that only a few would ever reach their target area. He reckoned that the payload of such planes would be half a ton, and fore-

cast that the launching of each flying bomb would result in no more than one casualty in London.

In actual fact nearly 1,500 flying bombs equipped with automatic pilots came over in the first twelve days of attack; in the last six days – June 21st to June 27th, 1944 – 275 flying bombs hit London out of a total of 594 launched. The weight of their war-heads was one ton, not half a ton as he had calculated, and each bomb caused an average of four casualties.

On the morning after the first flying bomb landed, the Cabinet met at the House of Commons, when the 'Prof' was at pains to remark that 'one swallow does not make a summer'. But the explosions had irreparably damaged his arguments against such missiles. Rather sadly, Churchill said to him afterwards, 'Why did you stick your neck out so far?'[32]

FIFTEEN

Heavy Metal

Far-reaching plans for the future economic shape of the world were hammered out by the British and the Americans through the summer and autumn of 1944. Although for a time they had closely involved Lindemann, after Keynes' arrival in Washington he handed over leadership of the British delegation and turned to other matters. Yet although the Second Quebec Conference, at which he had played such an important part, ended in September 1944, he remained in the United States for a further two months. One clue to the reason for his prolonged stay can be seen in a telegram that Churchill sent Roosevelt at the end of November:

> Cherwell has told me how very kind the US Army and Navy were in showing him their latest developments in many fields and in entertaining him at their various establishments. Perhaps if you thought it well, you would transmit my thanks to them and especially to General Groves who went to so much trouble to show Cherwell the latest developments in his particular field.[1]

General Groves was in charge of what became known as the Manhattan Engineering District, or more simply the Manhattan Project. It was a highly secret undertaking, but as the Prime Minister's scientific adviser, Lindemann became very closely involved. Its purpose was to develop an atomic bomb.

This momentous development was the legacy of a concept that had originally been born in Ancient Greece. The idea that the various forms of matter were arrangements of tiny particles was first developed by Leucippus of Miletus in the fifth century BC. He and his followers had described such particles as *atomos*, meaning 'indivisible', and the name 'atom' has remained with the concept ever since. For lack of means of empirical proof, these ideas lay dormant for many centuries, until they received a new consideration in the eighteenth century and more detailed analysis in the nineteenth;

and in the early years of the twentieth century there emerged the conviction that matter itself contained a great force that might one day be harnessed.

Early in the 1920s Lindemann had given Churchill the idea that a bomb 'no larger than an orange' might have a destructive force far beyond any contemporary experience, and as far back as 1903 the great Rutherford had forecast that if a proper detonator could be found, a wave of atomic disintegration might be started through matter, which 'would indeed make this old world vanish in smoke'. Before too long such fantasies had entered the pages of popular fiction. In 1909 H. G. Wells had begun a series of science-fiction romances depicting what might broadly be described as nuclear forces at work, and in 1932 – known as the *annus mirabilis* of nuclear physics – Harold Nicolson had published a novel that contained an uncannily accurate description of an elemental atomic bomb, which Churchill described as astonishingly prescient when he read it many years later:

> Further experiments . . . had led to the surmise that this new alloy which transformed aluminium into what was to all intents a new metal, might itself be refined and made to yield an element which could have revolutionary possibilities. If that proved true, here was a find of incalculable importance. It was averred that it might produce in large quantities an element so unstable that beside it radium would be as dull as lead; an element, some physicists began to speculate, that as soon as it was reduced to its pure state must transmute itself, as radium transmutes itself into lead, but with infinitely more violence; in fact with an explosion that would destroy all matter within a considerable range and send out waves that would exterminate all life over an indefinite area.[2]

As physicists began to contemplate the awful potential of releasing the forces inherent in matter, they became conscious of the dangers it might involve. As the official historian of Britain's atomic-energy development in the war said: 'Moreover, how could a uranium bomb be prepared that would not blow up immediately? "Hoist with his own petard" would almost certainly be the fate of the first man successful with the process.'[3] Gatherings of physicists began increasingly to dwell on the problem, as the *New York Times* reported:

> Tempers and temperatures increased visibly today among members of the American Physical Society as they closed their Spring meeting, with arguments over the probability of some scientist blowing up a

sizable portion of the earth with a tiny bit of uranium, the element which produces radium.[4]

Perhaps it was most succinctly put by the popular novelist P. G. Wodehouse, when one of his characters described the moment when an important decision had to be made:

It was a dashed tricky thing, of course, to have to decide on the spur of the moment. I was reading in the paper the other day about those birds who are trying to split the atom, the nub being that they haven't the foggiest as to what will happen if they do. It may be all right. On the other hand, it may not be all right. And pretty silly a chap would feel, no doubt, if, having split the atom, he suddenly found the house going up in smoke and himself torn limb from limb.[5]

Lindemann himself expressed his forebodings about the speed of scientific advance in an article published in *Nature*:

When one observes the geometrical character of this progression and realises the even more serious and, perhaps, sinister interventions which advances in the biological sciences almost certainly will render possible, one cannot but be anxious about the future. The world picture has been fundamentally modified. Rightly or wrongly, the restraints of religion have been thereby to a great extent swept away. The facilities which science has provided have made it easy to substitute plausible but superficial and often half-baked theories, and infect whole nations with beliefs and ideologies which in soberer times would have been scorned.[6]

A vital breakthrough had been made in 1932 at the Cavendish Laboratory when James Chadwick[7] had discovered the neutron, which, having no electric charge, could be used to bombard the nuclei of elements. Experiments in neutron bombardment, particularly of the nuclei of uranium, the heaviest element and most unstable metal, were soon being conducted by the leading physicists of the day, first by Enrico Fermi and then by others such as Niels Bohr in Denmark. In Germany also the quest was on, led by Otto Hahn and by Lise Meitner, subsequently a friend of Lindemann, who was later to entertain her in Oxford. Meitner, however, was an Austrian and a Jew, and had been forced to interrupt her experiments and flee Germany after the *Anschluss* had automatically cloaked her with German citizenship. She went to Sweden and spent Christmas 1938 at Kungälv with her nephew

Otto Frisch, another highly distinguished physicist. There she received a letter from Hahn telling her with enthusiasm of his latest experiment, conducted in the Kaiser Wilhelm Institute in Berlin – in a special enclave known as the Virus House, to discourage visitors.

The story of Hahn's letter, its impact on Frisch and Meitner and the developments that stemmed from it, are part of physics legend. Aunt and nephew went for a walk in the snow and talked over Hahn's findings, applying them to the idea first developed by Niels Bohr – regarded in many quarters as the father of nuclear physics – that the nucleus of an atom could best be compared to a drop of liquid. This is because whereas the mutual electrostatic repulsion of the charges in a nucleus tries to drive the nucleus apart, its surface tension tends to hold it together. If, by an external influence, such as the impact of a neutron, the shape of the nucleus is distorted and becomes, like a liquid drop, elongated instead of spherical, then the electric forces can become dominant and the nucleus will split.

They began to realise what Hahn had discovered. Frisch recalled what happened next:

At this point we both sat down on a tree trunk and started to calculate on scraps of paper. The charge of an uranium nucleus, we found, was indeed large enough to destroy the effect of surface tension almost completely; so the uranium nucleus might indeed be a very wobbly, unstable drop, ready to divide itself at the slightest provocation.[8]

They also deduced that splitting the nucleus caused mass to be lost, and calculated the mass difference between a uranium nucleus before it has been split and the two nuclei of about half the original mass that result from the splitting. They worked out the energy acquired by the fragments as a result of the repulsion, in accordance with Einstein's famous equation $E = mc^2$, and found that it came to the staggeringly large figure of 200 million electron-volts.

They had realised that when a uranium nucleus was penetrated by a neutron, it effectively exploded, splitting into two fragments of roughly equal size and releasing secondary neutrons. This was an entirely new phenomenon, as hitherto nuclear disintegration had been thought to involve only very small changes in mass and charge. Later Frisch was to ask an American biologist what he called the process by which single cells divide into two, and was told 'fission', so Frisch coined the phrase 'nuclear fission' for the process that Hahn had described.

These developments were published in the columns of *Nature* in February 1939, and were soon read all over the world; yet even before that the news spread like wildfire, the match being lit by Niels Bohr, whom Frisch and Meitner told of their findings, and who left almost at once to attend a conference of physicists in Washington. When, at that conference, in January 1939, Bohr delivered the news of the discovery of fission, members of the audience were hurrying back to their laboratories even before he had finished speaking.

That year was to see a rapid series of crucial advances in the understanding of nuclear fission, as investigations were started in Britain, America, France, Canada, Russia, Germany and Japan. As scientists began to contemplate these discoveries, it became apparent that their uses might be military as much as civil. In a world where the clouds of war were visibly gathering, the need to decide how to proceed – or indeed whether the research was too dangerous to take any further – moved from the realm of science to that of politics.

One scientist who was prominent at this time was Leo Szilard, who was also exceptionally pragmatic and perceptive. Having been driven from his native Hungary by anti-Semitism, he had in due course reached England, where in 1933 he had been struck by Lord Rutherford's famously untimely remark that 'anyone who looked for a source of power in the transformation of atoms was talking mere moonshine'. Szilard had stumbled upon the concept of a nuclear chain reaction when, walking through the streets of London, he watched motor cars responding to traffic lights changing in Southampton Row. As he recorded, 'it suddenly occurred to me that if we could find an element which is split by neutrons and which would emit two neutrons when it absorbs one neutron, such an element, if of sufficiently large mass, could sustain a nuclear reaction'.[9]

Szilard had at length been taken on by Lindemann at the Clarendon, and had been exploring how neutrons interact with atomic nuclei. He was a colourful addition to the laboratory, brilliant but hard to work with. He had shared a room with C. H. Collie until his apparatus had all but crowded out his colleague, who in exasperation had finally exclaimed: 'And what is more, Szilard, I can't work with you in this room', to which Szilard replied mildly: 'I've noticed that!'

It was not long before Szilard became acutely concerned about the dangers lurking behind the forces in matter, and feared that unravelling the great mysteries might end up putting tremendous power in the wrong hands. In June 1935 he had expressed his fears in a letter to Lindemann, in which he talked of taking out patents as an alternative to enforced secrecy about the subject:

> . . . even if I am grossly exaggerating the chances that these processes will work out as I envisage at present, there is still enough left to be

deeply concerned about what will happen if certain features of the matter become universally known. In the circumstances I believe an attempt, whatever small chances of success it may have, ought to be made to control this development as long as possible.[10]

He did take out a patent on his idea of a chain reaction, but assigned it to the Admiralty on being told by Lindemann that it was the only way in which the idea could be protected.

When, therefore, Szilard learnt of Hahn's discovery of fission, he realised that a chain reaction had become a practicable possibility. 'All the things,' he said, 'which H. G. Wells predicted appeared suddenly real to me.' He was by then in Princeton, and in order to test the theory he set up an experiment, of which he later wrote:

Everything was ready and all we had to do was to turn a switch, lean back, and watch the screen of a television tube. If flashes of light appeared on the screen, that would mean that neutrons were emitted in the fission process of uranium, and this in turn would mean that the large-scale liberation of atomic energy was just around the corner. We turned the switch and saw the flashes. We watched them for a little while and then we switched everything off and went home. That night there was very little doubt in my mind that the world was headed for grief.[11]

Many leading scientists remained sceptical about this astonishing idea, among them Lindemann and Tizard. Lindemann in particular was appalled at the idea of such power being harnessed, saying at first that 'he could scarcely believe that the universe was constructed in this way'.

However, by the spring of 1939 others were also becoming uneasy at the strange new knowledge that was being acquired, and to politicians one obvious way of containing its possible dangers was to attempt to secure the supplies of uranium, or at least take steps to deny them to a potential enemy. In April, Sir Horace Wilson had received from Kenneth Pickthorn, MP for Cambridge University, a memorandum explaining how Professor George Thomson, now at Imperial College, London, had carried out research on uranium and had come to believe that there was at least a chance that the metal might have an explosive quality very much greater than anything so far known to mankind. Wilson had asked General Ismay to investigate Thomson's proposition, so Ismay approached Henry Tizard, in his capacity as chairman of the Committee for the Scientific Survey of Air Defence (CSSAD), and had raised the possibility of buying up all the available supplies of uranium.

Tizard expressed his scepticism that anything would come of the research, at least in the reasonably near future, but with characteristic caution suggested that:

> the possible outcome of research was so important that it was wise to take steps to investigate and if possible to secure an option on existing supplies, and particularly to prevent them from being secured by possible enemy countries.[12]

The largest deposits of uranium were at the Shinkolobwe mine, in the Belgian Congo, and consequently in May Tizard met the managing director of the Union Minière de Haut Katanga, which owned the mining rights, in an attempt to corner the market.

Lindemann, meanwhile, had allowed his dismay at the thought of these stupendous discoveries to reinforce his scepticism that they could have any practical effect, although he appeared to shift his ground slightly from denying absolutely their potential to denying their possibilities in the short term. In August 1939, as war fever raged, rumours of a strange new bomb had appeared in a popular newspaper; Lindemann had therefore drafted a reply setting out the facts about the nuclear possibilities as he then understood them, and gave it to Churchill to send to the Air Minister. He also added a liberal measure of cold water, partly on the basis that it would take several years to extract U235 (the most excitable part of uranium), and that if anyone else had been successful, the secret would have got out. Churchill wrote accordingly:

> Some weeks ago one of the Sunday papers splashed the story of the immense amount of energy which might be released from uranium by the recently discovered chain of processes which take place when this particular type of atom is split by neutrons. At first sight this might seem to portend the appearance of new explosives of devastating power. In view of this it is essential to realise that there is no danger that this discovery, however great its scientific interest, and perhaps ultimately its practical importance, will lead to results capable of being put into operation on a large scale for several years.
>
> . . . the fear that this new discovery has provided the Nazis with some sinister, new, secret explosive with which to destroy their enemies is clearly without foundation. Dark hints will no doubt be dropped and terrifying whispers will be assiduously circulated, but it is to be hoped that nobody will be taken in by them.[13]

These sentiments echoed those of Tizard, who appeared to have little faith in the theories involved. Although Lindemann was for a time sceptical, he seems – unlike Tizard – to have based his doubts on the practicalities rather than the theory: after all, he had produced with F. W. Aston a groundbreaking paper on the separation of isotopes as long ago as 1919. Nevertheless, he felt that he could play on his old enemy's doubts, and early in the war he was to send his scientific adviser, James Tuck, to a demonstration of new weapons at which he knew Tizard would be present. He told Tuck:

> Tizard is sure to pump you as to what I am up to here. You say that our big line is a uranium bomb. This is just the sort of thing Tizard would expect me to be thinking about. You know enough about it to make a plausible story.

Tuck was in fact buttonholed, just as Lindemann had predicted, and told him the story; on hearing it, Tizard exclaimed: 'Ha, just what I would expect. It will never be used in this war, if it works at all!'[14]

Churchill's a priori acceptance of Lindemann's views on scientific matters obviously meant that it was greatly important for the country that his advice should be wholly correct, and in few matters could that be said to apply more than to the question of Britain's programme of atomic development. Even in the year or so since the discovery of fission, ideas and conclusions, claims and denials, had begun to follow each other with bewildering rapidity, and in 1940 a wide body of scientific opinion, especially in America, still discounted the value of the latest discoveries. Professor A. V. Hill, by now counsellor at the British Embassy in Washington – a post he was shortly to hand over to Lindemann's brother Charles – cabled the British Government with a synopsis of the prevailing American views on the matter:

> It is not inconceivable that practical engineering applications and war uses may emerge in the end. But I am assured by American colleagues that there is no sign of them at present and that it would be a sheer waste of time for people busy with urgent matters in England to turn to uranium as a war investigation . . . the Americans feel that it is much better that they should be pressing on with this than that our people should be wasting their time on what is scientifically very interesting, but for present practical needs is probably a wild goose chase.[15]

Lindemann, however, was beginning to receive advice from which very different conclusions could be drawn. Franz Simon, whom he so admired and whose work had largely helped advance the status of the Clarendon Laboratory since his arrival there in 1933, had repeatedly spoken to the Prof on the matter. In his diary he recorded:

> Discussions with Lindemann about isotope separation since beginning of 1939 . . . urge Lindemann again and again, last time letter 7th May, 1940 . . .
>
> Beginning of June Peierls visits me. Tells me that now uranium research is under way, after he and Frisch developed new ideas about the possibility of bomb with fast neutrons . . . asks whether I would co-operate. Yes. Had met in the meantime by chance Tizard . . . Had mentioned also uranium business. He does not believe in it.[16]

The reference to fast neutrons highlighted a significant development. The great Dane, Niels Bohr, had by now published a paper that was to help transform the perception of uranium as material for an atomic bomb. He explained how natural uranium was made up of two distinct isotopes: U238 nuclei, making up 99.3 per cent, which were not readily fissionable, usually absorbing any neutrons that hit them; and the balance of 0.7 per cent being made by U235 nuclei, which were.

It also appeared that the minimum, or 'critical', mass that would be necessary to engender a chain reaction would be so large as to make any bomb too heavy to deliver to a target. Even if a chain reaction occurred, if the bombardment was by slow neutrons, it seemed that the reaction would spread slowly and the resulting explosion would be not much more violent than a chemical explosion. While the huge amount of energy released in fission soon turned people's minds to thinking in terms of a bomb, there seemed to be enormous – if not insuperable – obstacles in the way of making one.

The situation was summed up by O. R. Frisch, who had been working in Bohr's laboratory in Copenhagen before the war but had now accepted an offer from Birmingham University, where he was a colleague of Professor Rudolf Peierls. As Frisch put it: 'there are now a number of strong arguments to the effect that the construction of such a super bomb would be, if not impossible, then at least prohibitively expensive and that furthermore the bomb would not be so effective as was thought at first'.[17] Early in 1940 he assessed what he thought was the paramount difficulty:

> One could think of separating the isotopes on a laboratory scale but the quantities involved in the various methods were minute. To ask that this should be done on an industrial scale, producing pounds of

a separated isotope, was entirely different. It was like getting a doctor who had after great labour made a minute quantity of a new drug and then saying to him: 'Now we want enough to pave the streets.' The differences were really of that order.[18]

These were some of the conclusions that Lindemann might reasonably have had in mind when giving his early advice to Churchill. But a very short time after Frisch had expressed his preliminary conclusions, Lindemann had a radical change of heart, and this was to shed an entirely new light on the subject.

Frisch and Peierls began to consider what might be the result of producing a lump of pure U235 and bombarding it with fast neutrons. They worked out from the theory that there would be no need to slow down neutrons, as with pure U235 they would not merely be absorbed unproductively, and when approaching uranium nuclei they would have a higher chance of success in producing fission. With a bomb, this would mean that a chain reaction would develop very quickly, enabling a great amount of energy to be liberated before the reaction was stopped by the expansion of the casing. The energy liberated by five kilograms of U235 would, they calculated, be equivalent to several thousand tonnes of TNT.[19]

Frisch described his approach:

If one could produce enough uranium 235 to make a truly explosive chain reaction possible, not dependent on slow neutrons, how much of the isotope would be needed? I used a formula derived by the French theoretician Francis Perrin and refined by Peierls to get an estimate. Of course I didn't know how strongly fission neutrons would react with uranium 235, but a plausible estimate gave me a figure for the required amount of uranium 235. To my amazement it was much smaller than I had expected; it was not a matter of tons, but something like a pound or two.

Of course I discussed the result with Peierls at once . . . we came to the conclusion that . . . one might produce a pound of reasonably pure uranium 235 in a modest time, measured in weeks. At that point we stared at each other and realised an atomic bomb might after all be possible.[20]

Lindemann now began to hear opinions which not only explained that a bomb might after all be feasible, but which by the same token suggested the alarming possibility that the Germans might also be on the trail. The original discovery of fission had after all been made in the Kaiser Wilhelm

Institute in Berlin, and some of the world's leading physicists, such as Werner Heisenberg, were known to be working in Germany.

One such warning came from Professor Simon, who in May 1940 wrote to Lindemann drawing his attention to an article in the *New York Times*, which asserted that the German Government had heard about the latest American research into uranium and had ordered large numbers of scientists to drop all other experiments and devote themselves to this work alone. Simon continued:

> You know that I have often emphasised that in my opinion Germany will spend any amount of money even if they would not give a higher probability than 10% to the successful working of the uranium bomb. I would not be astonished at all if they were not already engaged in erecting a big factory for the separation of U235.
>
> Should not something be done in this country also?[21]

Simon was an affable man and had an excellent relationship with Lindemann. The previous month he had given the Prof a birthday present of a new type of loose-leaf notebook with many sample leaves: logs, constants, prime numbers, the periodic system. 'If one uses the book properly,' he had said, 'it is quite impossible to forget anything except, of course, the things one wants to forget (there is an extra page for them).' Simon was to do good service by getting Lindemann to listen to the new evidence that had suddenly appeared concerning the feasibility of a bomb.

Even if Lindemann was heartily disliked by some of the scientific establishment, it was by now accepted that he was effective in ensuring that those in power addressed these problems, which were potentially crucial to whether the war was won or lost. Peierls had himself written to Lindemann at the beginning of June, in answer to a request for a statement of the reasons why the uranium bomb should now be taken seriously. He had answered that the probability of the bomb working 'is sufficiently high to make it important to investigate the matter as rapidly as possible', and had continued:

> Another important aspect of the matter is that, while there is no evidence that the Germans realise the potentialities of a U235 bomb with fast neutrons, it is quite possible that they do, and for all we know they may have almost completed its production.[22]

Simon then arranged for Peierls to present the case in person to Lindemann. Although Peierls afterwards said, on being asked about Lindemann's reaction, 'I do not know him sufficiently well to translate his grunts correctly', he had in fact convinced the Prof that the uranium bomb was now a proposition that could no longer be ignored.

Lindemann then arranged for Simon to lead a team to investigate methods of separating U235. The main work at the Clarendon had hitherto been the development of radar, but this research was restricted to British nationals, and many of them in 1940 were at their battle stations on the coast in preparation for an invasion. Among the scientists barred from this work were three very able men whom Simon was now to recruit: Kuhn, Kurti and an American, Schull Arms. This team set about the exceptionally difficult task of separating uranium isotopes; it was described as being comparable to sorting a vast number of sand grains from their identical companions on the seashore. At the same time they had to report their movements to the local police, in accordance with the defence regulations for aliens.

The theory which they started to test held that if uranium was converted to gaseous form, it could be filtered though a sieve, or 'membrane', and that in the process the U235 isotopes – having three fewer neutrons in their nucleus and therefore being lighter – would pass through the barrier more quickly than the U238. Therefore, although the process would have to be undergone a very great number of times, the lighter isotopes would eventually be separated from the heavier and could be collected and used for a bomb. Uranium hexafluoride, the relevant gaseous compound, was very scarce, so they started by testing the process with 'Dutch Cloth' and a mixture of carbon dioxide and water – experiments that were transformed, in the telling, into Mrs Simon's kitchen strainer and soda water.

Antony Croft, who was at the Clarendon at the time, recalled:

The team working on radar on the north side of the Clarendon Laboratory knew that work of some kind was going on under Dr Simon on the south side – a group of physicists under Dr Kurti and H. G. Kuhn – but had no idea what it was. Everybody else, including the undergraduates, were kept out of the north side by little wooden barriers with naval pensioners scrutinising passes, and had to make their way along the south side where they peered in, wondering why these people were not also doing something important. Only after the uranium and plutonium bombs were dropped in August 1945 did the real business of these people come out. Naturally, it was a big joke that this very highly secret work had been carried out by aliens or one-time aliens who could not be put on to the highly secret radar work.[23]

Detailed examination of the prospects for a bomb were now taken in hand by a special committee of scientists, with the camouflage title of the MAUD Committee,[24] which was put under the auspices of the Ministry of Aircraft Production. In August 1941 this committee delivered a comprehensive report to the minister, and the same month Lindemann, by now fully convinced of the urgency of the matter, sent a minute of paramount importance to Churchill, in effect advising the Prime Minister to put his full weight behind the production of an arsenal of atomic weapons.

The researchers at ICI had also been active, and their chairman, Lord Melchett, had written to Lindemann summarising the arguments in favour of proceeding with a plan to build a bomb. In it he compared, unfavourably, the cost of producing and delivering to their targets conventional explosives of equivalent destructive effect with a one-ton uranium bomb, and concluded:

The position must also be viewed in the light of the fact that it is known that the enemy are working on similar lines. As there is no defensive answer to this form of attack the first side to perfect this scheme will gain a decisive and crushing victory.

It therefore seems that the question of proceeding with the scheme is determined by this issue rather than the calculation of the chances of failure or success.[25]

Lindemann's minute to the Prime Minister was a lucid exposition of a complicated subject:

Prime Minister

I have recently spoken to you about a super-explosive making use of energy in the nucleus of the atoms which is something like a million times greater, weight for weight, than the chemical energy used in ordinary explosives.

A great deal of work has been done here and in America and probably in Germany on this, and it looks as if bombs might be produced and brought into use within, say, 2 years. Owing to various complications it will probably not be quite as effective as might at first seem, but if all goes well it should be possible for one aeroplane to carry a somewhat elaborate bomb weighing about one ton which would explode with a violence equal to about 2000 tons of TNT.

There are two questions which arise:

(1). Will the explosive really do this?

So far we have only had microscopic quantities in our hands, but they seem to confirm theory and calculations.

(2). Can we make the explosive?

Natural uranium consists of two components chemically so excessively similar that they are extremely difficult to separate from one another. It is the rarer component which according to all physical theory will in its pure form explode with extreme violence if brought together in quantities of 20 lb or so. The difficulty is to extract this rarer component from its admixture of 99% of the commoner.

A process has been devised by which it seems almost certain that this can be done; but it is an extremely elaborate and costly process involving repeated enrichment of the rarer component in something like 70,000 stages. Nevertheless it seems feasible and it is certainly the most hopeful proposal which has been made.

We have plenty of uranium in Canada and the Congo; The Germans have less (in Czechoslovakia) but I fear sufficient.

Lindemann then stated that Britain should prepare a plant, and that he was strongly of the opinion that the plant should be in England, or at worst in Canada. He felt this partly because he believed that the secret would be better kept in England than in America – which at this stage of the war was still neutral – but above all because:

Whoever possesses such a plant should be able to dictate terms to the rest of the world. However much I trust my neighbour and depend on him, I am very much averse to putting myself completely at his mercy. I would not, therefore, press the Americans to undertake this work; I would just continue exchanging information and get into production over here without raising the question of whether they should do it or not.

People who are working on these problems consider the odds are 10 to 1 on success within two years. I would not bet more than 2 to 1 against, or even money. But I am quite clear that we must go forward. It would be unforgivable if we let the Germans develop a process ahead of us by means of which they could defeat us in war, or reverse the verdict after they had been defeated.[26]

Churchill accepted Lindemann's advice, and at once sent his minute to the Chiefs of Staff Committee, adding: 'Although personally I am quite content with the existing explosives I feel we must not stand in the path of improvement, and I therefore think that action should be taken in the sense proposed by Lord Cherwell.'[27] The Chiefs of Staff agreed, and urged that no expense of time or money should be spared.

It was decided to place the project in the hands of the Department of Scientific and Industrial Research, but led by William Akers, the head of research at ICI. The decision not to put the development into the hands of ICI or another private company was particularly wise, because of the suspicions that were growing in America that the British were as much interested in the post-war potential of nuclear development as in winning the war with a bomb. Such thoughts might have been encouraged by the large map that hung on the wall of the project's office in London – it depicted ICI sales divisions.

At Lindemann's suggestion the minister appointed to oversee the work was Sir John Anderson; he and Akers between them came up with the name 'Tube Alloys' as a disguise for the project, partly to avoid having to type 'Secret' on all its correspondence. Once it was established, Lindemann joined the small advisory council of the 'Directorate of Tube Alloys'. The project to make a British atomic bomb was born.

The question of whether the project should go forward jointly, or independently in each country, now grew in importance. Lindemann was strongly in favour of an independent British project, and advised the Prime Minister accordingly. Initially there seemed to Lindemann little reason not to base the project in England: most of the recent theoretical advances had been made by scientists now working in Britain, and the Americans, it seemed to him, had not pushed ahead with any sense of urgency.

However, several factors came together to spur the Americans to a far greater interest in the project, not least their own entry into the war, following the attack on Pearl Harbor in December 1941. By then the MAUD Report had been sent to America, and at a stroke it opened their eyes to the advances that had been made.

As it was to turn out, the cost and overall magnitude of the task of building the bomb was to prove too great for war-torn – and still vulnerable – Britain to manage on its own, and by the summer of 1942 Sir John Anderson reluctantly told Churchill:

It has now become clear that the production plant will have to be on such a huge scale that its erection in this country will be out of the question during the war. Even the erection and operation of a pilot plant would cause a major dislocation in war production.[28]

Anderson therefore proposed that the British design work and personnel should be moved to the United States, and that work on the bomb should be pursued as a combined Anglo-American effort. He concluded by suggesting that, in case there were any doubts, he should come and talk to the Prime Minister, and would bring Lindemann, who had taken part in the discussions leading to this proposal.

Lindemann himself took no practical part in the progress of Tube Alloys, but he was kept fully informed, not least because he was the only member of the Cabinet who could really understand what was going on. After the 'Octagon' Conference in Quebec, in September 1944, he stayed on in America and spent many days in New Mexico, where the Manhattan Project was proceeding. There, in July 1945 at Alamogordo, the first test explosion successfully took place – thereby sealing the fate of the Japanese the following month, and leading swiftly to the end of the Second World War.

Lindemann did, however, become involved in the arguments with Churchill about which countries should share the atomic secrets after the war. One of the great advocates of letting the Russians, at least, into the secret – and thereby perhaps promoting world stability – was arguably the greatest nuclear physicist at the time, Niels Bohr. In September 1943 he had escaped from his native Denmark and the clutches of the Gestapo and had fled to Sweden. As his son recalled: 'The stay in Stockholm only lasted a short time; a telegram was received from Lord Cherwell with an invitation to come to England. My father immediately accepted and requested that I should be permitted to accompany him.'

Having been briefed about Tube Alloys, Bohr had gone to America to inspect the workings of the Manhattan Project. But for all his brilliance as a physicist, Bohr was a philosopher with an international vision, and while in America he had become concerned at the risks to the world posed by the atomic bomb. He had therefore communicated to President Roosevelt his anxiety about the need for great safeguards if a nuclear arms race was to be avoided.

His views had also been passed on to Sir John Anderson who, with Lindemann's help and agreement, had drafted a minute to Churchill warning of the dangers of nuclear proliferation and proposing the establishment of a form of international control of nuclear development. This suggestion was emphatically turned down by the Prime Minister, who was very alive to the importance of secrecy in such matters and felt that keeping the knowledge of the bomb closely guarded by a small number of British and American leaders, and by the scientists who obviously had to be involved, was the best path to safety.

On Bohr's return to England in 1944, Lindemann was asked to take the eminent scientist to meet Churchill, so that he could present his views in person. The President of the Royal Society, who had encouraged the meeting, retained doubts about it on account of Bohr's 'mild, philosophical vagueness of expression and his inarticulate whisper' – not the sort of attributes to stir Churchill at any time, let alone when he was dealing night and day with the problems of the impending Allied invasion, Operation Overlord. In any event, the occasion was a disaster, with Churchill spending much of the allotted time talking rather irascibly to Lindemann, and failing to heed the points that Bohr had come to make. 'I did not like the man,' Churchill told Lindemann, 'when you showed him to me, with his hair all over his head.'

Lindemann was unable then or later to persuade the Prime Minister to consider international control: Churchill felt that far too much was at stake. 'You may be quite sure,' he was to say, prophetically, 'that any power that gets hold of the secret will try to make the article, and that this touches the existence of human society.'[29]

As scientific adviser to the Prime Minister, Lindemann was also closely in touch with developments on other offensive fronts. One of these concerned contingency plans for biological warfare. Early in the war Lindemann had advocated the development of chemicals to burn German crops and defoliate the Black Forest. However, ideas for biological warfare, and for the use of gas, had since remained quietly in the background, mainly to develop counter-measures to any enemy biological offensive. For these reasons the Allies developed a small anthrax bomb, of largely British design, which bore the codename 'N'. Lindemann gave Churchill an account of it in February 1944:

> N spores may lie dormant on the ground for months or perhaps even years but be raised like very fine dust by explosions, vehicles or even people walking about . . . this appears to be a weapon of appalling potentiality; almost more formidable, because infinitely easier to make, than Tube Alloys. It seems most urgent to explore and even prepare the counter-measures, if any there be, but in the meantime it seems to me we cannot afford not to have N bombs in our armoury.[30]

Fortunately, during the Second World War no action was required in this field, but the idea of biological warfare has remained a threat, and countless British soldiers since those days have had to go through rigorous and extremely uncomfortable training in case they have to meet it.

At length the V-weapon attack came to an end and in the spring of 1945 the Allied armies surged into Germany. High above them the Allied air forces were making their 'round-the-clock' deliveries of incendiaries and high explosives to German cities, and it was clear that the war in Europe could last for only a few more months. The only possible reversal of the Allies' fortunes could be caused by German development of the atom bomb. Lindemann was closely in touch with the Intelligence Services, and in April 1945 he was alerted to a scare caused by unusual activity in an area south of Stuttgart. It was a district in which Werner Heisenberg and his team of atomic physicists were known to be working, and the Intelligence reports indicated unusual use of electric power. It was an alarming moment. It suddenly seemed possible that the Germans might after all be producing a bomb. Lindemann at once examined the evidence and advised Churchill accordingly, and arrangements were made for intensified bombing of the area under suspicion.

It turned out to have been unnecessary: the German physicists were captured a short time later, and in due course it transpired that they had not come anywhere near making or delivering atomic weapons – hindered partly by the chaotic ideas of organisation that prevailed in the Nazi hierarchy.

On 9 May listeners to German radio – in Germany almost all wireless sets were made so as to receive only German wavelengths – heard the following announcement:

> Since midnight, all weapons are silent on all fronts. On the orders of the Grand Admiral, the armed forces have ceased fighting which has now become hopeless, thus ending a heroic struggle which lasted almost six years. This struggle brought us great victories, but also heavy defeats. In the end, the German Wehrmacht succumbed with honour to an enormous superiority.
>
> In this grave hour, the Wehrmacht remembers its comrades who have remained in battle. The dead impose on us an obligation of unconditional loyalty, obedience and discipline towards the Fatherland which is bleeding from countless wounds.[31]

For them, the war was over.

Lindemann had already begun to consider the pressing problems of peace. Britain's financial plight now loomed large in his mind, and the Statistical Department was gazing upon a bleak picture. He aimed to give Churchill and the Cabinet economic advice that addressed two issues: that those who had caused the war, and the consequent chaos in world affairs, should be the ones who paid for it; and that a strong economic framework for the future should be agreed by the Allies, so that world trade could revive and bring in its path some relief to the nations injured by war.

He took the view that the paramount requirement would be to revive Britain's export trade – in effect, this was the lifeline to save her from bankruptcy. In April 1945 he prepared a memorandum for the War Cabinet in which he countered the argument that failure to restore German industry would impoverish Europe and the world:

> The question now is not whether German factories should be destroyed or not. They *have* been destroyed. The question is whether they should be rebuilt in Germany and employ German labour or whether the goods they could produce for export should be made here . . .
>
> . . . as a result of her fight to save liberty, Britain has become the greatest debtor nation of the world. We have the right to demand that our interests be considered in the post-war settlement. Let us not forget that a weak Britain, struggling with unemployment and a low standard of life, her foreign trade reduced and her exchanges constantly threatened, might well impoverish the world far more than a contraction in German industry.[32]

In his view – a theme that he was to pursue in future years in his advice to Churchill – gaining export share was the principal road to prosperity, and should be pressed hard as the dust of war settled in Europe and the Far East. He concluded:

> It is far more important to this country to re-establish British exports than to obtain German manufactured goods as reparations. For this reason alone, we should discourage the restoration of German industry. But quite apart from this, such a policy would give far greater military security than any other scheme likely to be devised . . . Britain must expand her exports or starve. Germany can live without. Everyone agrees that she should face sacrifices in order to repair the damage she has done to other countries. Who then can condemn Britain if she seeks restitution in the German export markets?[33]

His final task of the war was to accompany the Prime Minister to Potsdam, where Churchill was to grapple with Stalin in shaping the post-war world, hoping for support from President Truman, who had taken office following Roosevelt's death on 12 April 1945. Lindemann – whom Churchill described to Stalin as his 'Gestapo', which rather puzzled the Russian – contributed to Churchill's brief for his preliminary talks with the Americans. He focused again on the grave weakness of Britain, which, after six years of war, had been fighting for longer than any other Allied country and was now drained of resources. Having set out the themes that he believed the Prime Minister should adopt, Lindemann concluded his letter of advice to Churchill:

> It is vital for us to get American help after the war unless we are to submit for many years to austerity more severe than we have suffered in wartime. And as a pauper nation the part we could play in world affairs would dwindle rapidly.
>
> If the President discusses relief it might be well to point out that in our desperate plight we are in no position to subscribe to charity. The USSR, which has probably twice as much gold and dollars as we have and has only negligible debts, is making no contribution. Nor is France, although she too is much better off than we are.[34]

The idea of Britain's part in world affairs dwindling rapidly was anathema to Lindemann, as no doubt it would have been to Churchill. However such, for a time, was to be their own fate. On Wednesday, 25 July, before the Potsdam Conference was over, the results of the British General Election came through. By the end of the week Churchill and Lindemann were out of office and the Statistical Department had been abolished.

Wearily, but one suspects with great relief, Lindemann travelled home to Christ Church.

SIXTEEN

Home from the Hill

With the war over, and his work in Whitehall finished, Lindemann could with reason look forward to some years of contented existence at Oxford, overseeing the Clarendon Laboratory and taking part in collegiate life as much or as little as he pleased. Year followed year in placid verisimilitude, to paraphrase Harold Nicolson writing of King George V when there did not seem much else to say about the royal life; and although that hardly bore true for Lindemann's vigorous mind and the intellectual atmosphere of Oxford, he could reasonably feel, in the words of the liturgy that he admired, that 'the evening shadows lengthen, the busy world is hushed, the fever of life is over and our work is done'.

Churchill had gone off to Lake Como, to paint and to reflect on the fickleness of man, at least in the polling booth, and a new age had dawned with a Socialist Government swept into office by a landslide of votes. The ideals and aspirations of the people and their Government did not one whit appeal to Lindemann. Even before the war, when the land that he moved in was infinitely more stable and graceful than the one in view in the post-war era, he always sounded gloomy about the survival prospects of capitalist society. Now, with a radical government at the helm of a near-bankrupt country crying 'We are the masters now', he might well have been filled with foreboding. All the more attractive, therefore, was the prospect of concentrating on science, and turning from the turbulence of politics to the calm of Christ Church.

The outlook at Oxford was bright. At the Clarendon valuable research had been done during the war, with its scientists unhindered by the need to teach undergraduates; and the research on radio and nuclear physics made necessary by the war was to be a springboard for developments in new fields in peacetime. Lindemann, who returned older and mellower, complemented this, and his power and prestige were to benefit Oxford physics in large things, while he himself was less inclined to interfere in minor ones or disturb the routine.[1]

In the 1930s, interested in the design of the new laboratory, Lindemann had kept in mind the expansion of research in both low-temperature work and nuclear physics; consequently a large part of the building, from the basement to the second floor, had been lined with copper sheeting in order to house a million-volt generator. Now that the war was over, plans could be made to take that work forward, and Lindemann suggested that experiments should also be made in the field of nuclear fusion. As these developments progressed, the Clarendon, to Lindemann's delight, moved much closer in reputation to the Cavendish.

The austerity that soured post-war Britain disturbed Lindemann far less than it did his colleagues. He still had Harvey to look after his every need, and assistants for Harvey whenever they were wanted. He did not for a time travel much, but when he did so there was still a comfortable car and a chauffeur. Now that he had returned full time to Oxford, his surroundings became warmer and more comfortable. A friend reported that:

The tables were littered with files and documents. The bookshelves were filled in jumbled confusion with learned periodicals and books which a severe scholar would undoubtedly dismiss as trash: ephemeral novels, yellow-backed thrillers, casual biographies and the general reminders of a railway bookstore. There were no works of literary merit. On the mantelpiece was a signed photograph of Winston Churchill, and the only other pictures were enlarged scenic photographs which crowded every wall – photographs taken by Prof on his travels: Venice and Constantinople, Athens and Mycenae, Rome and the Kremlin. That aspect was not very uplifting, reminding one of the cabin of some luxury ship, showing the passengers where the ship called.[2]

In those drab days of scarcity, his strange diet was supported by a cow called Holly, which he bought from the estate at Ditchley Park and installed near Oxford, on a farm belonging to Derek Jackson. Harvey would be sent off to the farm to collect the milk, cream and butter that would help sustain Lindemann while the shops remained empty.

However, he was not to be left entirely in peace, for before long Churchill returned. Soon Lindemann had been persuaded to rekindle his interest in politics and give his practical support to the much-battered remains of the Conservative Party. In due course he became a member of the Conservative Shadow Cabinet:

He had been at the heart of policy for so long that it is unlikely that he was now willing to relinquish all contact with great affairs, and he made brilliant contributions to the House of Lords, mainly on economic and scientific matters, when he acted as Opposition spokesman, and delivered an annual speech on the Economic White Paper.[3]

Perhaps surprisingly, the Labour Government had decided when it took office after the war that atomic development for both civil and military purposes should be continued in Britain, and this project was placed under the control of the Ministry of Supply. In 1946 Lindemann was appointed to the ministry as a consultant on atomic energy, and although the development proceeded with great success, he began to feel sceptical that a Government agency would prove to be the proper authority to have charge of such a major enterprise. This was certainly a subject close to his heart and it was to be his paramount interest when Churchill recalled him to Government in 1951.

Despite these appointments, it was Oxford life that engrossed him during the years following the end of the war. He saw much less of Churchill and his family, and did not stay again at Chartwell until early in 1947. In those years of restrictions and controls travel was difficult, and his life in that respect was a far cry from the luxurious progresses of pre-war times. He did visit Derek and Pamela Jackson, who had left England in disgust at its austerity, compounded by Socialist legislation and high taxation, and had found a gentler, more old-fashioned regime in southern Ireland; there Lindemann happily shared the comfort they had found, and complained as vociferously as they did about the drab conditions at home.

After five or six years the public had also wearied of the new regime, during which many of the hardships of war had continued – if not intensified – without the uplifting feeling of being in a battle for the nation's survival; and in October 1951 the Attlee Government fell. Churchill became Prime Minister once more.

Lindemann was by now wholly content with his way of life. He was in his mid-sixties and did not feel impatient to change his routine again. Nevertheless, Churchill strongly pressed him to join the Government and to resume his former position as Paymaster-General. 'I must have Prof,' he told his Cabinet colleagues, 'he is my adder. No,' he reflected, 'I can add: he is my taker away.'

Lindemann was greatly reluctant to return to full-time politics, but the call was too strong to resist: at heart he was a patriot and could not turn his back on duty; nor could he put aside his long-held feeling of loyalty to Churchill. Yet he believed that he could be just as useful as Churchill's personal assistant, and certainly did not want the full glare of a Cabinet post. At first he demurred, writing to the Prime Minister in rare terms of self-deprecation:

> As you know, I intended to resign in 1945 had we won the election. The arguments against switching now at the age of sixty-five from the peace of Oxford to the hurly-burly of political life are even stronger. I am sure I am quite unsuited to it; not only should I never be much good at it, but I am not avid for prizes and I dislike publicity.
>
> Here in Oxford I have a job which I understand and can do. The Physics School which I have built up in the course of 30 years is now coming into its own and I may still be able to produce work of permanent value. Furthermore my professorship is a life appointment and my rooms in Christ Church – the only home I have had for thirty years – go with it. I hope you will forgive me, therefore, if I decide not to sacrifice all this.[4]

That would seem to be a powerful case, on which he could quite properly have rested. Churchill was not in forgiving mood, however, and at length Lindemann decided that he would, after all, make the sacrifices required. Fortunately, they were not to be permanent.

Therefore he again became Paymaster-General, with particular responsibility for the country's atomic development. The Prime Minister, never entirely at home with economics, also asked him to resuscitate the Statistical Department. It was not to be quite the same: the circumstances were very different and the department was to be smaller and with a much less significant role than it had enjoyed in wartime. Donald MacDougall again headed it, but only three other economists joined him, although one of them, J. S. Fforde, was later to become Chief Cashier of the Bank of England. In addition there were two civil servants, one of whom had been a member of the wartime S Branch and who was to work as Lindemann's assistant.

Although atomic affairs would necessarily involve close co-operation with the Americans, Lindemann's duties were to be mainly domestic. Yet he had never lost the taste for airing his opinions (usually strongly held), whether or not they were in his brief, and one month after returning to power he gave an interesting synopsis of his views on *Weltpolitik* in a minute to Churchill in respect of the role of NATO:

> In considering whether we should accept large commitments in the Middle East the following points seem relevant.
>
> Now that we have lost India and Burma the freedom of the Suez Canal is an international rather than a specifically British interest. In

any event to sail through the Mediterranean will be difficult with enemy aircraft operating from Bulgaria unless fighter cover is provided. This would mean bases in Africa, Crete and Cyprus, all of which would have to be defended against airborne landings and bombing. It is doubtful whether this would be worthwhile merely in order to shorten the voyage from Britain to Australia by a couple of weeks.

Middle East oil is an immensely valuable asset. But we have already abandoned our Persian oil and the remainder is largely in American hands. Is it not for America rather than for Britain to defend it?

The only reason for holding the Middle East is to prevent another large accession of territory and manpower to the Communists. This falls under the Truman Doctrine and is more an American than a British responsibility.

For these reasons it would seem that the US should undertake the defence of the Middle East. With such grave dangers nearer home the UK in my view should not accept such a strain on its resources of manpower and shipping.[5]

These sentiments seem less imperialist than might have been expected from Lindemann, but probably reflect the fact that he had long been sadly aware of the economic weakness with which the war had saddled the country. In fact Britain's financial plight was about to come to a point of crisis, resulting in a remarkable battle in which Lindemann initially found himself in a corner fighting single-handedly, and in opposition to Churchill.

On 5 November 1951 the director of the Economic Section of the Cabinet Office, Robert Hall,[6] had been to see Lindemann in Christ Church to discuss the economic situation. Hall remembered the meeting partly because, as he described in his diary, 'Cherwell has a pocket slide rule which he constantly brings out to do little sums: it is a mannerism as he did the only one we wanted much in his head.'[7]

The situation had become extremely serious because of a run that had commenced on Britain's reserves. It had been the result largely of the abnormal situation caused by the Korean War, in which Britain was heavily engaged. Initially the sterling reserves had risen sharply – partly because the war had led to a speculative boom in commodity prices, particularly of the wool sold by Australia and New Zealand, and of various commodities produced by Malaya. Yet Britain's export balance had suffered from a significant amount of manufacturing capacity being turned over to rearming for the war, while at the same time imports of war materials had sharply increased. Then the commodity bubble had burst, and had caused the owners of the sterling that had piled up rapidly to draw down their reserves, while

Britain's exports were still more or less at a standstill. The balance of payments therefore turned sharply down; word of this got into the currency markets, and speculators began to sell the pound.

At this point, early in 1952, the Treasury – in the guise of Otto Clarke,[8] a larger-than-life former financial journalist, and then a senior Treasury official – prepared a paper recommending what were almost revolutionary measures. They included floating the pound, making it convertible into the dollar, and at the same time blocking most of the sterling balances held by overseas residents.

The persuasiveness of Clarke and his colleagues had worked its magic on the Governor of the Bank of England, and together they had swept up the Chancellor of the Exchequer, R. A. Butler. He wholeheartedly adopted the plan, which to preserve secrecy had been given the codename Robot. As Donald MacDougall recalled:

It came as a great shock when, on 22nd February, Butler suddenly informed a small group of ministers (including Prof) that the reserves would fall very soon to a critically low level, and proposed revolutionary changes in our external arrangements.[9]

Although the Prime Minister had himself selected Butler, he appeared to believe that his Chancellor needed help. Churchill had therefore appointed Sir Arthur Salter, Lindemann's old adversary on the hustings, as Minister of State to give economic support and advice. In making this appointment he had rather curiously described Salter as 'the best economist since Jesus Christ', although with what degree of irony is not recorded. At any rate Churchill did not always hang on Salter's words: at one Cabinet meeting Salter was describing, at some length, the state of reserves of commodities, or 'buffer stocks', when the Prime Minister turned to his neighbour at the table and asked:

'*What's* he talking about?'
'Buffer stocks, Prime Minister.'
'Oh. I thought he said "butter scotch".'

Despite the violent opposition to Robot of his own advisers, Butler now presented it to the Cabinet. The situation had become so grave that it was deemed prudent to take the exceptional step of postponing by a week the Budget, which was imminent, so as to clarify the best way forward. Robot, if implemented, would be a tremendous gamble. If it failed, it would almost certainly involve a collapse of the pound and the disintegration of complicated technical exchange arrangements with leading European countries – at a politically difficult moment, when Britain was trying to persuade the French to accept West German rearmament. There was also the risk that the Conservatives would forfeit, for a long time, the support of the electorate.

Lindemann alone stood out against the plan:

He at once voiced opposition. Temperamentally averse to unquantified economic arguments expressed in emotive and rhetorical terms, he was even more averse to them if they were deployed by high Civil Servants, about whose intellectual habits he could be acid . . . Towards bankers he affected an aristocratic disdain. A rich but financially careful man, he can seldom have had much to do with them. They were tradespeople, well enough versed in their commercial pursuits but otherwise ill-educated and not to be trusted with much responsibility in the field of national economic policy. Central bankers were not very different, in his mind, to commercial bankers. He knew little of them and was not disposed to make much effort to understand what they were trying to say.[10]

Drawing as much on common sense as on economics expertise, Lindemann suggested that the situation was not nearly so bad as to warrant such a measure, and that a sharp hike in interest rates in the Budget would do the trick – if not, they would at least have time to think again. He also said that once the pound had floated it would fall, which would make matters even worse. On 26 February he sent a warning to the Prime Minister, saying that the proponents of Robot were:

Prepared to gamble on a scheme that will cause heavy unemployment and rising living costs at home, great offence to our allies in Europe and the United States, probably the break up of the sterling area and perhaps the Commonwealth, and a reversion to anarchy in international relationships.

Apart from political consequences Britain would certainly come out second best in this sort of world; for in the last resort our customers could do without our cars and cloth, but we cannot do without their food.

Lindemann then proposed alternative measures, saying that they should 'raise the Bank Rate and introduce a really courageous budget that will show the speculators that we are determined to put our house in order and destroy their hope that the pound will fall any further'. He concluded:

If we follow this policy resolutely I believe we can round the corner, earn universal respect and get a chance to start the long steady task of building up our reserves and making Britain strong again. The other plan proposed, with its floating rate of exchange for the pound and all the dangers implied in convertibility, means a reckless leap in the dark involving appalling political as well as economic risks at home and abroad in the blind hope that the speculators will see us through.[11]

Undaunted by being in a minority of one, he remained inflexible, and by determination and sheer persistence succeeded in winning the Cabinet round. Robot was postponed, and later abandoned; Lindemann's measures were implemented in the Budget, and the country recovered strongly to move into a period, at least for some years, of sustained prosperity.

It is not perhaps surprising that the newspapers began to speculate that it was Lindemann who was in effect the Chancellor, rather than Butler. Anthony Howard, Butler's biographer, referred to Lindemann's position at this time:

A far more serious challenge to Rab's authority was posed by Churchill's eventual success in prevailing on another Oxford figure, this time the physicist, Lord Cherwell, to join his new Cabinet as Paymaster-General . . . given that his function had always been to provide a one-man, all-purpose brains trust for his patron, it was not only the Opposition who wondered whether he was not to be the new Chancellor in fact while Rab held the office only in name. This suspicion was, if anything, reinforced when Cherwell in November not only became an additional member of the seven-man Ministerial Advisory Committee appointed to supervise the Treasury but actually moved into the Chancellor's traditional private apartments above No. 11 Downing Street.[12]

In fact Butler preferred to remain in his own house, in nearby Smith Square, and consequently offered Lindemann the Chancellor's lodgings, as he did not have a London base of his own. Lindemann did not play the role of 'Chancellor in fact', but it lent itself as a possibility to those who continued to believe that he was the ever-influential – and, to some, over-influential – *éminence grise*. Churchill did, however, continue to seek his advice and elucidation on a wide variety of subjects, and Butler's niece, then Jane Portal, who at that time worked as a private secretary at 10 Downing Street, remembers the two of them walking alone round and round the garden at No. 10, deep in conversation, while Lindemann answered

Churchill's questions or explained complicated subjects in the way that the Prime Minister had always found so useful.[13]

It was just before the Robot battle broke out that Lindemann accompanied Churchill and the Foreign Secretary, Anthony Eden, to the United States to meet President Truman. Their objective was to persuade the Americans to supply Britain with one million tons of steel, at that time in extremely short supply, so that Britain could manufacture goods for export.

When they arrived they were entertained by Truman on the presidential yacht *Williamsburg*, moored on the Potomac River. It was a small dinnerparty, and afforded another occasion for Churchill to call on Lindemann and his slide-rule to perform for the President's benefit the charade that he particularly enjoyed. The Prime Minister therefore announced that he had consumed on average a quart of alcoholic drinks each day for sixty years and asked Lindemann to calculate, if it were all poured into the diningroom, how high it would rise. Out came the slide-rule as Lindemann asked the President for the measurements of the yacht's dining-saloon; then came the lightning calculation. Dean Acheson, the American Secretary of State, who was also present, recorded that Churchill's 'vast disappointment, when, instead of drowning us all in Champagne and brandy, the flood came only up to our knees, provided the high point of the performance'.[14]

The other major battle that Lindemann had to fight while Paymaster-General involved his role as adviser to the Prime Minister on Britain's development as a nuclear power. Even during the war there had been difficulties with the Americans over collaboration on nuclear projects, and their faith had recently been severely tried by the passing of nuclear secrets to the Russians by the atomic physicist Klaus Fuchs – and, shortly before Churchill returned to power, by the defection of 'The Missing Diplomats', Guy Burgess and Donald MacLean, to Moscow in May 1951. Now Britain had decided to build her own atomic bombs, and reactors for civil use, and Lindemann wanted American support. He also urged that the development should be carried out as quickly and efficiently as possible.

The project had got off to a very good start under the previous Government, but it had been placed under the control of the Ministry of Supply, which was traditionally in charge of armaments. Lindemann felt very strongly that the Civil Service, to which (his prejudice reinforced by experience) he had an aversion, was entirely the wrong body to control atomic research and development. His dislike of the ministry's performance was intensified in 1949 when the nation was shocked to learn that the Russians had exploded their first atomic bomb, three years, as it turned out, before Britain was to do so.

Lindemann believed it essential for Britain to develop her own nuclear capability, but he had first to ensure that there would be help and co-operation from the Americans. Early in 1950 he sent a minute the Prime Minister:

> I believe there is some idea that the Americans may offer close co-operation on condition that we undertake not to produce bombs in England, but only in Canada. This proposal I consider unacceptable . . . From the political point of view an agreement to refrain from making atomic bombs would in my opinion be equivalent to accepting the rank of a definitely second-class power, fit only to supply auxiliary forces . . . I should be sorry to see England sink to the provincial level which such utter dependence on the US for the main modern weapon of war would imply. I think, having been a partner from the very start, that England may claim to be in a rather exceptional position.
>
> The subject, as you see, bristles with difficulties. The only thing in my view is to begin by getting the closest possible alliance with the United States and the most intimate co-operation possible in the field of atomic bombs. If we concentrated all work on this subject in a quasi-autonomous body . . . I think the Americans might agree to resume closer co-operation. This, I am sure, would be in the interests of both nations in peace as it was in war.[15]

During the last months of the Labour Government, Lindemann had taken action by introducing, with the compliance of the Shadow Cabinet, a motion in Parliament urging the transfer of atomic development from the Ministry of Supply to a more flexible organisation. He might therefore have expected the matter to go forward smoothly when the Conservatives returned to power and he was given responsibility for advising the Prime Minister on atomic matters.

Unfortunately, from Lindemann's point of view, Churchill had appointed as Minister of Supply in the new Government Duncan Sandys, Lindemann's erstwhile opponent in the arguments over V-weapons, and he at once proved quite unwilling to contemplate the removal of the project from his new empire. Lindemann's argument was that the best scientists would not join the project, or remain with it, if they were subject to the dead hand of the Civil Service, with its poor employment conditions and rates of pay. He also felt that civil servants were wholly lacking in the experience and drive needed for a project of such importance and complexity. He proposed instead an Atomic Energy Authority, to be independent of the Ministry of Supply.

Sandys did not agree. Nor, more importantly, did the Prime Minister. So, for the first time in his long association with Churchill, Lindemann found himself having formally to oppose him in Cabinet, and to introduce papers, urging the need to take the atomic energy project out of the hands of the Civil Service, in opposition to Churchill's wishes. Writing to the Prime Minister in September 1952, he said:

> I sincerely hope you and the Cabinet will accept my advice. After all I have been more or less closely connected with the subject for eleven years now; indeed I doubt whether there is anyone else who has had such a long and continuous experience of the matter. But whether or not my advice is accepted I wish to have it on record that I have done my best to get this most necessary change made.[16]

All his life Lindemann had maintained an independent voice, and it is to his credit that he put his belief in what was right for the country above his loyalty to, and affection for, the man who had appointed him to his post.

The need for a resolution of the battle for control of Britain's atomic-energy programme was made more urgent by the fact that the practical use of her atomic power was no longer far in the distance – Britain's first atomic bomb was exploded at the Montebello Islands off Australia in October 1952. At length, after long months of lobbying, Lindemann won the day, and the Atomic Energy Authority came into being on 1 January 1954; he was to serve on it until he died:

> The establishment of the Atomic Energy Authority was won single-handedly by Cherwell. There was no aid from outside, and within, relentless opposition. It must be regarded as his political monument.[17]

Sure in the knowledge that he had achieved victory in a matter which he regarded as vital to Britain's interests, and which went to the very core of the country's place among the powers of the world, Lindemann at last felt able to insist on leaving the Government. He had always retained his sense of obligation as Dr Lee's professor, believing, as he put it, that the chair was the substance and politics the shadow. So he resigned at the end of October 1953 and returned to Oxford.

Before he did so, as Paymaster-General, he made a number of journeys overseas in support of British atomic interests. On these visits he never failed to attract the attentions of the press, but he consistently declined to respond to their interest or to engage with them in genial banter. For example, in the autumn of 1953 he talked with President Eisenhower in America, and went to Australia to discuss uranium supplies with the Commonwealth Government. As he set off for Australia from Heathrow, he was surrounded by reporters, but would tell them nothing of his plans:

Asked how long he would be in Colombo he replied: 'I don't know.'

He replied 'That is possible' when asked if he would be going on to the Woomera Atomic Exploration site in Australia.

Then he turned away and, followed – at a respectful distance – by Harvey, walked towards his aeroplane.[18]

When he returned to Christ Church after his second term in Government, Lindemann was nearing seventy and had acquired a certain venerability. Within a month of leaving office he had received the high distinction of becoming a Companion of Honour, although he tried to decline it, protesting that it was a political honour for which he was not qualified.

At Oxford he was now treated in a rather affectionate manner, albeit from a distance. Tall, but slightly stooping, he maintained about him – as ever – an uncommunicative air, with a manner that caused both undergraduates and dons to feel that here was someone definitely not to be trifled with. Nevertheless his presence after dinner in Hall was eagerly awaited. Christ Church has a fine and comfortable common room, adorned with pictures of former members of 'The House' – Viceroys on one wall and Prime Ministers on another. Lindemann would arrive to join his colleagues and their guests and the post-prandial atmosphere would be agreeable: icy intellectual prejudices melted by the warm glow of High Table. He would not sit down at the bridge tables, which were put out after dinner on most evenings, but was almost always affable and took care to make his colleagues' guests feel at ease.

There were, it is true, occasional contretemps, and they were inevitable if someone was rash enough to speak slightingly of Churchill. On one occasion a senior Australian soldier was a guest in the common room. He had a distinguished war record and had subsequently become a respected politician. He did not hear the name of the tall, sallow latecomer to the room and, while talking, innocently made some disparaging remark about Churchill. He might as well have pulled the tail of a cobra. The temperature rapidly descended, the genial hubbub ceased and the glasses of port were gripped, motionless, by donnish fingers. Lindemann turned at once on the soldier with blatant ill humour, and the Australian responded in kind. It all became rather awkward, and one of Lindemann's friends among the dons quickly steered him away towards the bridge at the other end of the room; not, however, before Lindemann announced with icy clarity: 'You can always hear the chains clanking, with those people!'

It is rather strange that he did not play bridge, as it might be supposed that he had the ability, with almost unparalleled memory and mental alacrity, to play at a high level. Yet he always maintained that he could not play the game, and that were he to do so he would agonise over his mistakes and be kept awake at night. Oddly he did enjoy playing Lexicon (a word-making game similar to Scrabble). Perhaps that was to please Churchill, as the two were reported, by the press at least, to play late into the evening when Lindemann inhabited 11 Downing Street, and the Prof was credited with being a past master at the game.

In fact he did on rare occasions play bridge: Lord Zuckerman recalls playing both bridge and *vingt-et-un* with him, describing him as a 'kibitzer', i.e. a meddler or onlooker. On one occasion in the common room Lindemann reluctantly took over the hand of a don who was called to the telephone, but after a short time he insisted on withdrawing. His colleagues cried: 'We know why you won't go on, Prof: you've made 1/9d and you're frightened of losing it.'

He need not have worried too much about the standard of play. One newly arrived don recalled appearing for the first time in the common room and being asked – firmly – to partner the dean, who was a fanatical bridge player. As a preliminary to this intellectual feast, Dean Lowe announced to his young partner that he always played a 'shaded no trump'. Anxious to please, the youthful don acquiesced, without having the slightest idea, even – or perhaps especially – after several hands, what a 'shaded no trump' was. Subsequent enquiries elicited the information that no one else had any idea, either. The young don was then drawn into conversation with Lindemann: 'he talked about his hobby, Prime Numbers, and he talked about functionals. I listened and nodded, but I'd no idea what functionals were.'[19]

Lindemann often brought intellectual puzzles to share with his colleagues, and after those at High Table had dined well, and had graduated to nuts, snuff and Barsac, conversation with him would consist of such subjects as the three fundamental reasons why religion would appear to be valid – claimed to be that the sun is hotter than the earth, so the earth must have been separately heated at a date much later than the sun; the fact that moving bodies have not come together into one mass, as theory would suggest; and that as uranium is continually halving itself, there ought to be none left.[20]

He still saw a few old friends, and was always welcomed by their children, and not only because he was a good 'tipper', safe for a pound where others might give ten shillings. To them also he would take intellectual problems, even if of more juvenile subject matter. One of his favourites involved mental arithmetic concerning a group of ladies spring-cleaning a church, some of whom could kiss the vicar; another was the better-known puzzle of cannibals and missionaries on either side of a river. To children he seemed a curious mixture of being distant but friendly. One such, a ten-year-old when she first knew the Prof, recalled her childhood memories:

He seemed a very private person. He was very good company and had a lot of charm. He had an odd sort of squeaky giggle, and was very good fun really, but in a buttoned up sort of way. He never had heart to hearts with us children, and I don't think he ever opened his inner thoughts to my father, who was a very good friend of his. He used to watch us playing tennis, and there would be a lot of commentary and criticism. I never thought of him as being old. He was one of those people who never seem to change, and who always seem much the same. I think he was probably one of those people who got to look quite old quite early on, and then just went on looking the same for twenty years.[21]

His conversation was not, however, always harmless, and it was sometimes unexpected. He continued from time to time to attend dinners and meetings at Wadham College, where he had remained a Fellow. One young don who used to see him there remembers him well:

I'd heard it said that he was agreeable to those whom he liked, but he didn't seem so on first acquaintance. He was always polite, but distant, and he seemed rather formidable. He was a large man with strong opinions. You felt that you had to be on your best behaviour. We had an excellent estates bursar, said to be the best in Oxford, who did a great deal for the college and the university finances. Cherwell used to express decisive, strong views at meetings of the Governing Body. Our bursar thought they were nonsense, but he could hardly say so to the Paymaster-General. He had to bite back his opinions.

I sat next to him at dinner occasionally. It was a mixed pleasure. He had a fund of stories of a rather crude kind. He would insist on telling them at High Table, and it was rather embarrassing. They were really fourth form stories. I don't think that he was aware of their effect, but he didn't strike me as being sensitive to people's feelings. On the other hand I think perhaps that he was trying to be jovial, to be one of the boys.[22]

By the 1950s journeys had once again become reasonably simple and Lindemann began to travel more often. He still insisted on the best available service, and Sir Roy Harrod recounted an occasion when this subject cropped up at Christ Church:

I recall his complaining in Common Room of the Golden Arrow on the ground that it had no second class. There was a chorus of voices,

'Oh, but Prof, you surely never travel second class.' 'No, but I mean that one has to have one's servant in with one.'[23]

By now he had become rather deaf, although it seemed to be the sort of deafness – quite common – that did not prevent him hearing adverse comments from the far end of a room. He could not get a hearing aid to help him and found it too much effort trying to hear people speak in a crowded room, so he gave up going to parties, and to the theatre. He was as short-sighted as ever in one eye, but continued to read by holding the page very close to his face, or if necessary by using a magnifying glass: reading glasses were not considered acceptable, any more than were wrist-watches, which he had long considered effeminate on a man.

It is perhaps no wonder that he now suffered from frailty: the strain of his life during the war had taken its toll, and notwithstanding the quality of the ingredients of his food – milk from his own cows; the very best olive oil – he ate practically nothing by normal standards. A day's intake would usually consist of about ten to twelve ounces of food. Lunch was typically pea soup, scrambled eggs and butter; dinner was often pea soup – again – and pancakes, potatoes, butter and green salad. There was not much variation from this, a meagre diet to support a man of six foot, who even then undertook quite a lot of work.

One venture that he championed gave him at last an opportunity to build a bridge between the arts and science. He had long been brooding on the continued divergence between the two disciplines, and one evening in 1949 he had a talk with R. H. Dundas, a senior Christ Church figure who taught Greek history, and with whom Lindemann had clashed in the past. Lindemann asked him who was the professor of archaeology in the university, saying that he would like to talk to him. Dundas arranged for that incumbent, Professor Christopher Hawkes, to dine at Christ Church, together with Stanley Robinson, a celebrated collector of Greek coins. Lindemann brought along to dinner one of his young researchers at the Clarendon, Teddy Hall, with whom he had discussed the idea, and to whom he had suggested that they could develop something to 'make the arts people sit up and think, and which would help them with their problems'. Lindemann had taken to Hall, a rich Old Etonian, who worked at the laboratory without pay. 'Well, Hall,' he had said, 'what do you think of making an honest woman of science?' – by which he meant marrying it to the arts.[24]

At dinner Lindemann put forward his idea: to use the methods of physics to date works of art, and thereby to discover more accurate information about their history than was provided by the guesswork of museum curators, about whom Lindemann had caustic comments to make, concerning their similarity to civil servants. Lindemann further suggested to Hawkes that Hall should run a laboratory for the purposes that he had explained.

All went according to plan, and Hall in due course produced, from his own funds, an X-ray spectrometer for examining works of art. In 1949 he was working with this at the Clarendon, experimenting with some blue-and-white pottery that he had persuaded a rather doubtful Ashmolean Museum to lend him, at about the time that Lindemann received a telephone call from one of the trustees of the British Museum.

It transpired that Dr Oakley, a senior curator of the Natural History Museum, wanted help with some bones about which some questions had arisen, and Lindemann had seemed the obvious man to approach. He at once arranged for three of the curators to go and see Hall at the Clarendon Laboratory, and they duly did so, it having first been decreed that for twenty-four hours it would become part of the British Museum, thereby enabling them to take their precious cargo to Oxford without being in breach of trust.[25]

The bones, which had been found forty years earlier at Piltdown in Sussex, were examined using the techniques that the laboratory had devised, and after a time were found to be a few hundred years old and parts of the skull of an orang-utan – not, as had been claimed, the 'Missing Link' in human evolution. The first major success of 'archaeometry' had been achieved. The publicity this case received was a boost to Lindemann's ideas, and caused many laymen in Oxford to think that 'there was something in science' after all. At length, with the support of the university vice-chancellor, Maurice Bowra, a dedicated laboratory was established, with the title 'Research Laboratory for Archaeology and the History of Art'. It has done valuable work ever since: one of Hall's particular successes there was to be the dating of the 'Turin Shroud'.

For a relatively long period Lindemann saw little of the Prime Minister, although he emerged from Oxford to accompany Churchill on two visits to America in 1953 and 1954, where he again met President Eisenhower. In 1955 the two old friends met more often. Lindemann stayed at Chartwell five times that year, and in April accompanied Churchill on a holiday to Syracuse. The plan had been for Churchill to paint and rest in the sun, but there was no sun and it rained incessantly. For Lindemann this was to prove a blessing. For long hours, while the skies were grey, he had to entertain his ageing patron; he did so with the help of Churchill's former private secretary, Jock Colville. During the weeks of their holiday Lindemann was able to plant in Churchill's mind the seed of an idea that he had long yearned to develop: that of creating in Britain a series of technical colleges along the lines of the Massachusetts Institute of Technology.

In this he had been inspired originally by the German model of the *Technische Hochschule*, such as the one that he himself had attended at Darmstadt, and all his adult life Lindemann had felt that Britain suffered from the lack of such institutions. He believed more than ever that in the post-war world the Government should make a great effort to develop new universities to meet industry's need for intelligent and scientifically trained employees. He had mentioned this in the past to Churchill, to little avail, but now at last he found a ready audience.

He had made his case the previous year when he had been awarded the Messel Medal by the Society of Chemical Industry, and had given a speech explaining the vital need, as he saw it, for technical universities, no doubt recalling the success that Germany had achieved by addressing the same point nearly a hundred years earlier:

> It is true that in six or seven of our universities we have departments of chemical engineering . . . but this is not nearly enough for a great country which depends to such a vital extent upon paying for its food and raw materials by exporting manufactures of various sorts and kinds . . .
>
> A young man abroad who has a bent for applied science and decides to devote his life to technological pursuits – and what nobler aim could he have – enters one of these great institutions straight from school as he would enter a university in this country . . .
>
> Unhappily this process is ruled out in this country. Technological universities which flourish elsewhere simply do not exist here . . . In my view it is quite wrong to confine teaching in the higher branches of technology to the ordinary universities . . .
>
> It is no use, in this connexion, refusing to face one of the obstacles which stand in the way, namely the ridiculous intellectual snobbery concerning technology which unhappily pervades this country. For some reason it is considered in many influential circles that technological competence is not really on a par socially or intellectually with a knowledge of the older subjects. It would be really amusing (if it were not so tragic) to see how arts men, whose knowledge of the rudiments of technology is not even up to the standard of '1066 and all that' have the impudence to look down upon people who know far more about the arts subjects than the arts men do technology. They seem to consider it quite natural and normal not to know how soda is made or how electricity is produced provided they have once learnt

something – which they have usually forgotten – about the mistresses of Charles II or the divagations of Alcibiades.[26]

The establishment, populated by people such as his detractor C. P. Snow, was unenthusiastic. In the words of Lindemann's former scientific adviser:

Far from carrying out Prof's ideas, 'they' (Snow et al) turned Battersea Poly, for example, once famous for its metallurgy, into Surrey University in order to turn out the 'Whole Man', who turned out to be wholly useless.[27]

To the Government minister responsible for the matter, Lindemann said:

I agree it is a good thing if they should chance to be geographically near a university, but I want to see them able to stand on their own feet, and have the status of universities in their own right. I should like to give the colleges complete freedom and set them up as an insti- tution of university rank with rights and privileges of their own . . . We want more people properly trained in the fundamentals of the various sciences but who, in addition, are versed in their application. These are the 'officer-class' in industry who are relatively more scarce than the 'NCOs' who get their training at the ordinary technical colleges.[28]

The holiday in Syracuse did result in the conception of a college at one of the older universities. It was not what Lindemann was striving for, but he felt that if it could be given a sufficient degree of importance and substance, at least it would make headway with the establishment. Churchill gave his blessing to the use of his name for fundraising, and Jock Colville led the campaign to establish what was to become Churchill College, Cambridge. What Lindemann thought about the choice of what he called 'the Eastern Zone', rather than Oxford, is not clearly recorded.

He continued to make speeches from time to time in the House of Lords, and their content was invariably cogent and often laced with dry wit. However, his inability to make himself heard was a serious handicap in that forum, and he never overcame it. He was deeply knowledgeable and tech- nically qualified to speak on a large number of subjects, but he concentrated on scientific and economic issues, although occasionally his distaste for the political direction in which the world was moving shone through in icy sarcasm. His politics were founded on logic and a sense of justice, and he therefore found the accelerating shift of influence from the western powers to the Third World wholly undesirable, and believed that it would cause no end of trouble.

His scorn for this trend reached a peak when the Egyptians seized the Suez Canal in 1956. This event set families, friends and large numbers of people throughout the country at loggerheads with one another; petrol rationing was introduced, there was a severe run on the sterling reserves and international tension rose alarmingly. The Prime Minister's wife was soon saying mournfully that she felt as though the Suez Canal was flowing through the middle of her drawing room. For Lindemann it was the United Nations Organisation that was the real culprit; he felt that its actions betrayed its charter and that it was biased against the West. His speech in Parliament in the debate on the Middle East exemplified his political outlook:

The system by which every nation or pseudo-nation has an equal vote, no matter what its form of Government, stage of civilisation, or what part it is able to take in enforcing a judgment, is of course perfectly ludicrous. Any petty dictator can cancel out the vote of the democratically-elected president of a great world power. The most civilised countries on the planet are equated to tiny states many of whose inhabitants are fetishists who cannot even read or write.

In the old days, Egypt would not have ventured, in breach of all treaties and agreements, to confiscate British and French property and to throw the world's shipping into disarray. Now they know that they will find support in the United Nations to prevent any action from being taken. Even the Yemen, whose tribesmen have been quarrelling and fighting with those in the Aden Protectorate for generations, has discovered that it can find many anti-English votes at the United Nations and is trying to put the blame on England. Everywhere these wretched little pseudo-nations, banking on the irresponsible antics of the United Nations Assembly, are seizing the opportunity to make trouble. Instead of being an agent for peace, it is the world's great trouble-maker.[29]

In 1956 Lindemann received two further honours: the Hughes Medal, from the Royal Society, and a viscountcy. He was reputed to feel that the award of the Hughes Medal was very slightly overdue, and rather in the nature of a 'leaving present'. The latter tribute, however, pleased him, especially as it came not on Churchill's recommendation but on that of his successor as Prime Minister, Anthony Eden. At Christ Church, Lindemann made a typical comment, half in jest, when he said that it was a very satisfactory award, as it 'puts me above all those damned science barons'. The Oxford versifiers soon got to work:

> *And now a greater honour yet:*
> *He gets a leg up in Debrett.*
> *For he becomes a nobler lord*
> *Than Ernest Baron Rutherford.*
> *At last his lordship's cup is full*
> *Up to the brim with Papal Bull.*

He was now – at seventy – past the retiring age for a professor and, although he was a life tenant of his chair, he wanted to go. He could justifiably reflect that if the Atomic Energy Authority was his political monument, the Clarendon Laboratory was an unquestioned tribute to his success in the field of science, and he can only have contemplated it with satisfaction. By now he had come to dislike lecturing, saying that it bored him and that he was not interested in the undergraduates and did not know them by name. His lingering worry, that if he retired he would have to leave the rooms that had been his home for so long, was allayed when Christ Church made the unique gesture of saying that he could stay in them for the rest of his days.

In 1956 he stood down as professor of experimental philosophy. His heart had begun to give him a little trouble, but otherwise he seemed well, and his days were spent in peaceful intellectual pursuits in the surroundings that he loved.

The summer day of 2 July 1957 was hot and still. In the evening, formal as ever in grey suit and hat, Lindemann went for a walk in Christ Church Meadow. He had made arrangements to go to Wimbledon two days later with a colleague and his wife, and had been following the matches on the television that he had installed in his rooms. On his return he complained of feeling ill, but when a doctor arrived there seemed to be nothing particularly wrong. Whether or not he had some premonition, he immediately made some very substantial, last-minute alterations to his will and sent out urgently to find witnesses.

He went to bed much earlier than usual. From his rooms he would have heard the distant chiming of the bells and the slight evening breeze rustling the leaves of the tall elms, the quiet sounds gentle on the air. As he lay in bed his mind might have traced the path of a life of the most unusual breadth, passed in extraordinary times. Back through the recent battles in Government, and his success at last with Britain's nuclear future; to his years of comparative rest after the war; and then to the war itself, six years of unrelenting work by the side of the country's greatest leader, as England fought off the threat to her survival and saw her enemies utterly vanquished, one of them by an elemental power that he had not wished to contemplate.

Then back through his years in the wilderness with Churchill, seeing so plainly the threat that few would acknowledge, yet living in a world of ease that had now vanished. He might have felt himself once more spinning towards the earth in his flimsy, noisy aeroplane – entirely confident that his solution was correct – and landing unharmed, with the answer to the airmen's fears safe in his pocket notebook. Before that, the trumpets and the laughter of Berlin, and dear Professor Nernst, and wondering at the discoveries of the age and his own part in bringing them about. At last he would find again the sun and happiness of his childhood, the pleasure of his father's company and the joy of being with him in his garden laboratory. The thoughts of his life's journey would have given him pleasure, richly deserved.

He died shortly after midnight.

NOTES

1. *Family Origins*

1. Oliver Lyttelton, Viscount Chandos (1884–1968). Held various ministerial offices, 1940–54.
2. Commemorative article for fifty years of the Pirmasens Water Works, 1879–1929.
3. Lindemann Papers.
4. Archives of the Norman Lockyer Observatory Society, Sidmouth.
5. *Monthly Notices of the Royal Astronomical Society*, February 1932.
6. Mrs Ian Kirkpatrick papers. John Vickers to author.

2. *Schooled in Germany*

1. Kurt Mendelssohn, *The World of Walther Nernst*.
2. Birkenhead Papers.
3. Mendelssohn, op. cit.
4. Robert Purrington, *Physics in the Nineteenth Century*.
5. Ibid.
6. Mendelssohn, op. cit.
7. *Obituary Notices of Fellows of the Royal Society*, Vol. IV, 1942–1944, p. 101.
8. Ibid.
9. 'Unscheinbar' here means 'inconspicuous'. Nernst's 'Wärmetheorie' became known as 'The Third Law of Thermodynamics'.
10. Birkenhead Papers. Sir Thomas Merton to Earl of Birkenhead.
11. Ibid. H. E. Watson to Earl of Birkenhead.
12. Birkenhead Papers. Charles Lindemann to Earl of Birkenhead.
13. Later Sir Henry Tizard, FRS.
14. Sir Henry Tizard, Autobiographical Notes.

15. Later Sir Alfred Egerton, FRS.
16. *Nature*, Vol. 180, 21 September 1957, Lord Cherwell obituary.
17. Earl of Birkenhead, *The Prof in Two Worlds*.
18. Mehta, *The Solvay Conferences on Physics*.
19. Clarendon Laboratory Archive.
20. Mendelssohn, op. cit.
21. Birkenhead Papers. Professor Derek Jackson to Earl of Birkenhead.
22. Ibid.
23. Later Lord Rayleigh.
24. See Roy Harrod, *The Prof*.
25. Lindemann Papers.
26. Ibid.
27. Ibid.
28. Niels Bohr. Danish scientist, founder of theoretical atomic physics.
29. Lindemann to *Nature*, 28 December 1913. *Nature*, Vol. 92.
30. H. G. J. Moseley, in *Nature*, 5 January 1914.
31. Quoted in J. L. Heilbron, *H. G. J. Moseley*.
32. Lindemann Papers.
33. Ibid.
34. Lewis Carroll, *Alice's Adventures in Wonderland*.

3.*War and Wings*

1. Earl of Birkenhead, *The Prof in Two Worlds*, p.57.
2. Robert A. Millikan, *Autobiography*.
3. *The Times*, 7 July 1914.
4. W. S. Churchill, *The World Crisis*. Mist enveloped the parishes only for a time: writing of the period after the war, Churchill noted the 'dreary steeples of Fermanagh and Tyrone' emerging once more.
5. Large placards appeared, bearing the news '*Russland mobilisiert sich*' ('Russia mobilises').
6. Lady Egerton, *Diary*. She was Ruth Cripps, daughter of the first Lord Parmoor. Alfred Egerton (1886–1959), Reader in Thermodynamics, Oxford, 1921–36; FRS 1926; knighted 1943; Secretary of the Royal Society, 1938–48.
7. Ibid.
8. Lindemann Papers.
9. *Phil. Mag.* (6), 29, 127.
10. *Mon. Not. Roy. Astr. Soc.*, 75. no. 3.
11. George Batchelor, *The Life and Legacy of G. I. Taylor*.
12. Ibid.

13. Lindemann Papers.

14. *Fifty Years at Farnborough*: Lord Cherwell contribution.

15. Batchelor, op. cit.

16. Major F. M. Green, *The Chudleigh Mess.*

17. Birkenhead, op. cit., p.66.

18. Professor R. V. Jones, FRS, *Notes Rec. R. Soc.* 41 (1987).

19. Per Sir William Farren, quoted in Constance Babington Smith, *Testing Time.*

20. Birkenhead, op. cit.

21. Sir George Thomson, FRS, interviewed in *The Lindemann Enigma*, BBC, 1961.

22. Batchelor, op. cit.

23. Lindemann Papers.

24. Kurt Mendelssohn Papers, Bodleian Library, Oxford.

25. Lindemann Papers.

26. *Royal Society Biographical Notes*: Lord Cherwell; Sir William Farren contribution.

27. *Fifty Years at Farnborough*: Lord Cherwell contribution.

28. Ibid: Sir William Farren contribution.

29. Ibid.

30. Lindemann Papers.

31. Constance Babington Smith, *Testing Time.*

32. *Fifty Years at Farnborough*: Lord Cherwell contribution.

33. Reported in *The Aeroplane*, 1916.

34. Later Sir Richard Southwell, FRS.

35. Richard Southwell, *Aeronautical Progress.*

36. Dr Darrol Stinton, MBE, *Flying Qualities and Flight Testing of the Aeroplane.*

37. *Reports & Memoranda. No. 618.*

38. *Fifty Years at Farnborough*, supra.

39. Lindemann Papers.

40. Lord Moran, *The Struggle for Survival*, p.765.

41. Professor R. V. Jones, *Lindemann Centenary Papers* (London, The Royal Society, 1987).

42. G. M. B. Dobson, FRS. Later a noted meteorologist; meteorological adviser to the Central Flying School after 1913.

43. *Fifty Years at Farnborough*, supra.

44. Lindemann Papers.

45. Sir William Deakin to author.

46. *Official History of the War in the Air.*

4. *Fresh Wind in Oxford*

1. Gerard Manley Hopkins, *Duns Scotus' Oxford*.
2. Evelyn Waugh, *Brideshead Revisited*, London: Chapman & Hall, 1945.
3. Max Beerbohm, *Zuleika Dobson*. An Oxford love story set in the late nineteenth century.
4. In 1877; a paper on the seat of the electromotive force in an electric circuit. Such industry calls to mind the university philosopher who published in 1936 an article entitled 'Meaning'; nothing further was heard from him until, thirty years later, he published another article entitled 'The Meaning of Meaning'.
5. Professor T. C. Keeley, *Notes Rec. Roy. Soc. Lond.* 53 (3), p.334
6. *Roy. Soc. Proc.* XCIXA (1921), Clifton Obituary, p.vii.
7. Quoted by Professor Brebis Bleaney, *Eur J. Phys. 9* (1988).
8. Mrs Kathrin Baxandall to author.
9. Lindemann Papers.
10. Birkenhead Papers. Tizard to Birkenhead.
11. Lindemann Papers. Lindemann to his father, 19 November 1913.
12. Lindemann Papers.
13. Ibid.
14. Keble: an Oxford college built in Victorian redbrick; celebrated at one time for divinity and for success at rowing.
15. Lindemann Papers.
16. Charles Dickens, *Little Dorrit*.
17. Later Sir George Thomson, FRS. See chapter 3.
18. For the Clarendon Laboratory.
19. Note on the Theory of Magnetic Storms. Published in the *Philosophical Magazine*, December 1919.
20. Marshal Joffre, French hero of the First World War.
21. Marquess Curzon, chancellor of Oxford University, and erstwhile holder of numerous great offices of state.
22. Field Marshal Sir Henry Wilson. Later murdered by the IRA.
23. Ved Mehta, *Up at Oxford*, p.105. See also Jack Morrell, *Science at Oxford 1914–1939*, p.97 et seq.
24. Quoted in Roy Harrod, *The Prof*, p.56.
25. Quoted in Harrod, op. cit.
26. Quoted in Morrell, op. cit., p. 401.
27. Clarendon Laboratory Archive: T. C. Keeley to the Clarendon research physicist A. J. Croft.
28. Clarendon Laboratory Archive: Douglas Roaf to T. C. Keeley.
29. Lindemann Papers.

30. Morrell, op. cit., p.393.
31. Quoted in Morrell, op. cit., p.390 (see pp.387 et seq.).
32. Ibid., p.389.
33. Later Sir Cyril Hinshelwood.
34. Later G. M. B. Dobson, FRS.
35. *Proc. Roy. Soc.* A103 (1923), p. 339.
36. Probably also an explanation for the story, handed down over the generations, of how the crashing and crackling of the Great Fire of London was heard sixty miles away in Oxford.
37. Birkenhead Papers. James Tuck to Earl of Birkenhead, 1961.
38. *Phil. Mag.* 6th series (38), 173.
39. See infra, and note 42.
40. See Professor Brebis Bleaney, *Notes Rec. R. Soc. Lond.* 48 (2), 1994.
41. For example: 'A Theory of Meteors' (1922), *Roy. Soc. Procs.* A 102; 'A Note on the Temperature of the Air at Great Heights' (1923), *Roy. Soc. Procs.* A 103; 'Note on the Photography of Meteors' (1923), *Mon. Not. R. Astr. Soc.* 83, 3.
42. Later Sir Thomas Merton, FRS. Spectroscopy as a discipline has now been made redundant by the development of laser technology.
43. 'The Possibility of Separating Isotopes', *Phil. Mag.* 6.
44. Morrell, op. cit., p.396.
45. *Biog. Memoirs Roy. Soc.* v. 16.
46. Later Professor D. A. Jackson, FRS.
47. Morrell, op. cit., p.397.
48. Professor R. V. Jones. Later professor of natural philosophy at Aberdeen University. For his valuable work in the Second World War, see his *Most Secret War*.
49. Clarendon Laboratory Archive.
50. Lindemann Papers.
51. *Phil. Mag.* 6th series (37), 523.
52. *Eur. J. Phys.* 9 (1988).
53. Professor Brebis Bleaney to author.
54. Lindemann Papers.

5. *New Dimensions*
1. Later Sir John Masterman. Provost of Worcester College and University vice-chancellor.
2. F. E. Smith, 1st Earl of Birkenhead.
3. Lord Tweedsmuir, *Memory Hold the Door*. John Buchan, later Lord Tweedsmuir, was a writer, soldier, lawyer and politician.

4. Later Lt Col G. H. M. Cartwright. He was originally from Australia, and became a well-known figure in cricketing circles.

5. Birkenhead Papers.

6. Lindemann Papers.

7. Earl of Birkenhead, *The Prof in Two Worlds*, p.128.

8. G. H. Hardy, the leading English pure mathematician of his time.

9. W. R. Merton to author.

10. Later Viscount Simon. He was to hold all the great offices of state except that of Prime Minister.

11. C. M. Bowra, *Memories, 1898–1939*.

12. Ibid.

13. Lady Mosley to author.

14. Diana Mosley, *A Life of Contrasts*.

15. 'Kaye and Laby' Physics Tables.

16. Lindemann Papers.

17. Ibid.

18. R. V. Jones, in *Biog. Memoirs Roy. Soc.*, W. L. S. Churchill, 1966.

19. At this time Churchill was out of office, but he became chancellor of the Exchequer later in 1924.

20. Lindemann Papers. Quoted in Sir Martin Gilbert, *Winston S. Churchill*, Vol. V Companion, part 1, p. 140. Lindemann also sent him J. B. S. Haldane's *Daedalus, or Science and the Future*, which foreshadowed the modern science of cloning. See Gilbert, op. cit.

21. *Nash's Pall Magazine*, 24 September 1924.

22. Lindemann Papers. And see Gilbert, op. cit., Vol. V, p. 49 et seq.

23. Lindemann Papers.

24. Lindemann's interest in relativity was expressed in his article 'The philosophical aspect of the theory of relativity', *Mind*, Vol. XXIX (New Series, No. 116), October 1920, pp. 437–45.

25. Lindemann Papers.

26. Lindemann Papers, and quoted in Gilbert, op. cit., Vol.V Companion 1922–29, p.684.

27. See also Gilbert, op. cit., Vol. V Companion, part 2, pp.241, 266, 273.

28. Lindemann Papers.

29. Sarah Churchill, *A Thread in the Tapestry*, pp.37–8.

30. Lindemann Papers.

31. Ibid.

32. Roy Harrod, *The Prof*.

33. Ibid.

34. A party at an Oxford college. Derived from *Gaude*, Latin for 'Rejoice'.

35. Quoted in Birkenhead, op. cit.

36. Birkenhead Papers.

37. *Macbeth*, I. vii. 10. The adage being that 'the cat wouldst sup milk, but durst not get its feet wet'.

38. Birkenhead Papers.

39. Birkenhead, op. cit., p.117.

40. Lindemann Papers.

41. See *Qty. J. Maths.* (Oxford), 4, 319; 17, 65; 20, 65.

42. Lord Randolph Churchill, at one time Chancellor of the Exchequer.

43. Now in the museum at Farnborough.

44. Harrod, op. cit. p.111.

45. *Oxford Times*, 1965 interview with James Harvey. Lindemann became Lord Cherwell in 1941.

46. Clarendon Laboratory Archive.

47. Lindemann Papers.

48. Birkenhead Papers.

49. Quoted in Gilbert, op. cit.

50. Thomas Jones, *A Diary with Letters, 1931–1950*.

51. Lindemann Papers, and quoted in Gilbert, op. cit.

52. Clarendon Laboratory Archive.

53. Ibid.

54. See chapter 2.

55. *Daily Telegraph*, 1954.

56. B. Cohen, *Albert Einstein*. See also Albrecht Folsing, *Albert Einstein*. Einstein himself was entirely confident of his theory. Asked what he would do if the predicted effect were not observed, he replied: 'I would be greatly surprised.' Pressed on what he might think if his prediction was not confirmed, or was even refuted, he said: 'In that case I'd have to feel sorry for God, because the theory is correct.'

57. *New York Times*, 10 November 1919.

58. Lindemann Papers.

59. Jack Morrell, *Science at Oxford 1914–1939*, p.409.

60. Quoted in Harrod, op. cit., p.57.

61. Winston S. Churchill, *Marlborough*.

62. Winston S. Churchill, *The Second World War*, vol. ii, p.65.

6. *Lindemann's List*

1. F. E. Simon (1893–1956). Son of a rich Berlin merchant, and cousin of the composer Felix Mendelssohn. Succeeded Lindemann at the Clarendon, but died after one month in office. Extremely learned and able, yet fond of practical jokes, kindly and humorous ('I define a

pedestrian as a man with two cars, a wife and a daughter'). Holder of the Iron Cross, the CBE and a knighthood.

2. Mrs Kathrin Baxandall to author.

3. Lindemann Papers.

4. Arnold Sommerfeld (1868–1951). Professor of theoretical physics, University of Munich, 1906–31.

5. *Privatdozen*: an academic rank or qualification.

6. Lindemann Papers.

7. Kurt Mendelssohn (1906–80). Cousin of Franz Simon, to whom he was principal assistant in Breslau. A leading low-temperature physicist, he was also an expert on Chinese pots, and bought for a low price a valuable one from Harrods, which the store, unaware of its value, was using as an ashtray for its customers. Later a Fellow of the Royal Society.

8. Jack Morrell, *Science at Oxford 1914–1939*, p.404.

9. Dr Monica Mendelssohn to author.

10. Dr Kurt Mendelssohn, *The Coming of the Refugee Scientists, New Scientist*, 26 May 1960.

11. Morrell, op. cit., p.406.

12. Mrs Kathrin Baxandall to author.

13. *Frontkämpfer*: someone who had served the Fatherland on the front line in the First World War. The distinction brought certain privileges.

14. Quoted in Nicholas Kurti, CBE, *Biog. Memoirs. Roy. Soc.* v. 46, pp. 299–315 (2000).

15. Dr John Sanders to author. Re. Simon, see *Biog. Memoirs. Roy. Soc.* v. 4, p.247.

16. Birkenhead Papers.

17. Lindemann Papers.

18. Mrs Mariele Kuhn-Oser to author.

19. Mendelssohn, op. cit.

20. Ibid.

7. *Alarm Call*

1. See Hansard, House of Commons Debates, Vol. 270, col. 632, 10 November 1932.

2. Hansard., November 1934.

3. Rauschning, *Hitler' Speaks*, p. 18.

4. Sir Arnold Wilson, DSO, MP (1884–1940). Soldier, explorer, civil administrator, author. Killed over Germany as an air gunner, aged fifty-five, in May 1940.

5. Lindemann Papers. Roy Harrod, *The Prof,* p.43.

6. Professor C. E. M. Joad, later famous as a member of the BBC's *Brains Trust* programme.

7. Lord Lloyd of Dolobran. Later Secretary of State for the Colonies.

8. Lindemann Papers.

9. Ibid.

10. *The Times*, 8 August 1934.

11. Hansard, July 1934.

12. Ibid.

13. Ibid.

14. For the report of the 1934 air exercises, see *The Aeroplane*, summer 1934.

15. H. E. Wimperis, director of scientific research at the Air Ministry since 1934.

16. A. P. Rowe (1898–1976). He became secretary of the Tizard Committee, and during the war chief superintendent of the Telecommunications Research Establishment at Malvern, there introducing the celebrated 'Sunday Soviets'.

17. Huge concave surfaces cut into cliffs on the south coast, mainly sited to pick up sound waves from the direction of France.

18. A. P. Rowe, *One Story of Radar*.

19. R. A. (later Sir Robert) Watson-Watt (1892–1973). The moving force behind the development of radar.

20. Lindemann Papers.

21. Ronald Clark, *Tizard,* p.15.

22. Professor Thomas Wilson, *Churchill and the Prof*, p.35.

23. Lindemann Papers.

24. P. M. S. (later Lord) Blackett, FRS (1897–1974). Nobel Prizewinner, 1948; President of the Royal Society, 1965–70.

25. Lindemann Papers.

26. Post Office Radio Report No. 233, Part V, 3 June 1932, 'The Further Development of Transmitting and Receiving Apparatus for Use at Very High Radio Frequencies'.

27. For an authoritative account of these developments, see Sir Robert Watson-Watt, *Three Steps to Victory*.

27. Sir Robert Watson-Watt: *Three Steps to Victory*.

28. Louis Blériot. The aircraft pioneer who made the first cross-Channel flight, from Calais to Dover, on 25 July 1909.

29. *Saturday Review*, November 1934.

30. *Infrared Physics,* Vol. 1, 1961, pp.153–4.

31. For relevant details of CSSAD minutes and background, see especially Tizard Papers, and Sir Martin Gilbert, *Winston S. Churchill*, Vol. V Companion, part III.

32. See Lord Blackett's obituary of Sir Henry Tizard, *Nature*, 5 March 1960.
33. Clark, op. cit.
34. Quoted in Gilbert, op. cit., p.58.
35. Lindemann Papers; and quoted in Gilbert, op. cit.
36. Churchill Papers, CHAR 2/269. Quoted in Gilbert, op. cit., pp.169–70.
37. Watson-Watt, op. cit., p.147.
38. Siting specification for CH – 'RDF' Stations, quoted in B. T. Neale, *CH – The First Operational Radar*.
39. See e.g. C. P. Snow, *Science in Government*.
40. Birkenhead Papers. Sir Robert Watson-Watt to Earl of Birkenhead.
41. Clark, op. cit.
42. PRO.CAB. 21/426. Quoted in Gilbert, op. cit., p.193.
43. Clark, op. cit.

8. *Professors for Parliament*

1. Lindemann Papers.
2. Ibid.
3. Ibid.
4. Ibid.
5. Osbert Lancaster, 'Drayneflete Revealed'.
6. Rather in the manner of P. G. Wodehouse's Sir Roderick Glossop, Buzzard had many members of the *haut monde* among his clientele; they included, for example, Sir Jock Delves Broughton, whom Buzzard advised to go to Kenya, as a cure for headaches. Broughton accepted the advice, and in Kenya became a central figure in the notorious saga of the murder of Lord Erroll.
7. *Oxford Magazine*, 18 February 1937.
8. Ibid.
9. Lindemann Papers. Letter to Fowey Montmorency, 30 October 1936.
10. Lady Mosley to Sue Lawley; BBC, *Desert Island Discs*.
11. W. S. Churchill, speech to Oxford Union, 30 October 1936.
12. Harold Nicolson, *Diaries and Letters*, Vol. 1, 9 December 1936.
13. Lindemann Papers.
14. Mrs Kathrin Baxandall to author.
15. Lindemann Papers. Letter to Harcourt Johnstone, MP, 4 March 1937.
16. *The Times*, 7 March 1937.
17. Lindemann Papers.
18. Birkenhead Papers. Sir John Masterman to Lord Birkenhead.
19. Ibid. Lady Townsend to Lord Birkenhead.

9. *While England Slept*

1. Article: 'The Legendary "Prof",' by Jan Bronowski. Bronowski (1908–1974) was a pioneer of 'operational research' in the Second World War, and a writer of renown in science, literature and poetry. He did not accept the idea of a separation between the scientific and the human aspirations of man, in a manner similar to Lindemann.

2. Lindemann had arranged with Jan Masaryk, the Czechoslovak minister in London and son of the first President of Czechoslovakia, for the Clarendon Laboratory to take charge of some radium belonging to the Czech Government.

3. Diana Mosley, *A Life of Contrasts.*

4. Ibid.

5. Lady Soames to author.

6. Ibid.

7. Ibid.

8. Lindemann Papers.

9. See R. W. Thompson, *Churchill and Morton.*

10. Sir Martin Gilbert, *In Search of Churchill.*

11. Churchill Papers, CHAR 2/304.

12. Ibid.

13. Ibid.

14. Ibid.

15. Stephen Roskill, *Hankey, Man of Secrets*, pp.260–2.

16. Ibid.

17. Ibid.

18. Sir John Simon was regarded by many as a gelatinous individual, of high intelligence – he was at one time the highest-paid barrister in England – but with few friends. Douglas Jerrold wrote: 'I first saw Sir John Simon at the opening of the Liberal election campaign in 1923. He followed Mr Asquith and Lord Grey, and froze the hall in five minutes' (*Georgian Afternoon*, p.328). A popular ditty about him ran: 'Sir John Simon / Is not like Timon / Timon hated mankind / Simon doesn't mind.'

19. Roy Jenkins, *Churchill*, p.505.

20. Sir John Slessor, *The Central Blue*, p.153. Such emotions reflected Louis MacNeice's poem of 1938, 'Autumn Journal': 'What we mean is Hodza, Henlein, Hitler, / The Maginot Line, / The heavy panic that cramps the lungs and presses / The collar down the spine'.

21. R. J. Overy, *The Road to War.*

22. At the same time the appeasers were doing all they could to foster good

relations with the Germans, whom they believed must ultimately behave like reasonable men. Consequently in November 1937 Lord Halifax, then Lord President of the Council, accepted an invitation, channelled through the editor of *The Field* magazine, to visit a hunting exhibition in Germany. Halifax was ostensibly invited in his capacity as Master of the Middleton Foxhounds: the invitation was, among other things, 'to shoot foxes' – an unusual invitation for an MFH. When Eden, the Foreign Secretary, heard of the invitation he was incensed, feeling that Halifax would in effect be, as he put it, 'running after Hitler'. When he met Chamberlain to raise the issue, Eden became so heated that Chamberlain famously ended the discussion by telling him to 'go home to bed and take an aspirin'. In the event Halifax met the Führer in his eyrie at Berchtesgaden, and was afterwards to say of Hitler that 'he struck me as very sincere'. Their meeting nearly got off to a rocky start when Halifax, getting out of his car, began to hand his coat to Hitler, mistaking him – dressed as he was in brown coat and black trousers – for a footman.

23. Leopold Amery, *My Political Life.*
24. Lindemann Papers.
25. Bolton King was due to go with him to the USA.
26. Lindemann Papers.
27. Ibid.
28. CHAR 25/14. Winston Churchill to Sir Kingsley Wood, 9 June 1938. Also quoted in Sir Martin Gilbert, *Winston S. Churchill*, Vol. V, pp.946–7.
29. CHAR 25/14. Sir Kingsley Wood to Churchill, 24 June 1938.
30. Ibid., Sir Kingsley Wood to Winston Churchill, 23 July 1938.
31. Ibid., Winston Churchill to Sir Kingsley Wood, 26 July 1938.
32. CHAR 25/15B.
33. CHAR 25/14.
34. Ibid.
35. Ibid.
36. Basil Collier, *The Battle of Britain.*
37. CHAR 25/14.
38. Lindemann Papers.
39. Now Sir Edward Maitland Wright. Lindemann Papers.
40. Lindemann Papers.
41. See *Nature*, 15 September 1945.
42. Professor R. V. Jones, in the BBC television documentary *The Secret War.*
43. CHAR. Churchill to Sir Kingsley Wood, 21 June 1939. Quoted in Gilbert, op. cit., p.1076.

44. E. G. Bowen, *Radar Days*.
45. Ronald Clark, *Tizard*.
46. Sir Edward Spears, *Prelude to Victory*. Spears was a soldier, Conservative MP and wartime liaison officer.
47. Amery, op. cit.
48. Both the Parliamentary Report and Harold Nicolson's diary give Robert Boothby the credit for this rallying cry; however, there is little doubt that Amery spoke these words, and the question remains whether Boothby did also. When questioned on this point, Boothby replied: 'Well, we both did.' (Lord Boothby: conversation with the author.) Such a coincidence seems unlikely; Boothby's memory of the moment had no doubt faded.
49. Quoted in *The Memoirs of Lord Ismay*, p.98. Hastings Ismay was soon to be Deputy Secretary of the War Cabinet. See chapter II.

10. *To the Admiralty*

1. Quoted in Sir Martin Gilbert, *Winston S. Churchill*, Vol V, p.1113.
2. Ibid., Vol. VI, p.7.
3. PRO.ADM1/ 10459.
4. T. C. Keeley Memoir, Clarendon Laboratory Archive.
5. Churchill Papers, CHAR 19/3.
6. Ibid.
7. Ibid.
8. PRO.ADM1/10459.
9. CHAR 19/3. 30 September 1939.
10. Ibid.
11. Ibid.
12. LP.F41/8.
13. A Student of Christ Church, and an eminent economist; biographer of Lord Keynes. Later Sir Roy Harrod.
14. Roy Harrod, *The Prof*, p.181.
15. G. D. A. MacDougall, *Memoirs of an Economist*, p.21. MacDougall, later Sir Donald MacDougall, CBE, in time became a 'Treasury Mandarin', carrying out significant work for the Government, the United Nations and the EEC.
16. H. W. Robinson, *In on the Ground Floor*.
17. Dr Cyril Martin to author.
18. R. V. Jones, *Most Secret War*, p.80.
19. Quoted in *Biog. Memoirs Roy. Soc.*: Winston S. Churchill.
20. Robinson, op. cit.

21. MacDougall, op. cit., p.23.

22. Lindemann Papers.

23. Ibid.

24. Ibid.

25. PRO.ADM.205/2, and see Gilbert, op. cit., Vol. VI, p.83.

26. Lindemann Papers, F95/6.

27. Earl of Birkenhead, *The Prof in Two Worlds*, p.214.

28. Harrod, op. cit., pp.187–8.

29. Ibid.

30. MacDougall, op. cit., pp.21–2.

31. 1st Baron Stamp, economist. Killed with his son in an air-raid, 1941. His paper was printed for the War Cabinet, 7 February 1940.

32. LP.H107/4.

33. And of those who could not escape. Professor Victor Goldschmidt, writing to Francis Simon in September 1945, said: 'Of the 1000 Jews arrested in Norway the same day as me and deported to Auschwitz, only 10, including me, are alive today' (Letter, 23 September 1945).

34. PRO.CAB.65/11.

35. Lindemann Papers.

36. Later Sir Millis Jefferis. In August 1940 Churchill wrote of him: 'I regard this officer as a singularly capable and forceful man who should be brought forward to a higher position.' Quoted in Gilbert, op. cit., Vol. VI, p.746. Lindemann was to champion Jefferis and his department in their frequent battles with more orthodox minds.

37. Antony Croft, *Oxford's Clarendon Laboratory*.

38. LP.B130/2.

39. Quoted in Sir John Colville, *Downing Street Diaries, 1939–55*. The report was passed on by George Binney, later knighted and awarded the DSO for gallantry in bringing cargoes of special steels from Sweden to Scotland, under the noses of the Germans.

40. House of Commons Debates, 8 May 1940.

41. Ibid.

42. *The Ironside Diaries, 1937–40*, pp.301–2.

11. *At the Centre*

1. Quoted in C. I. Hamilton, *Twentieth Century British History*, Vol. 12, no. 2 (2001).

2. Ibid.

3. See *War in History*, Vol. 2 (2) 1995, p.209.

4. Winston S Churchill, *The Second World War*, Vol. II, p.15.

5. Major General Sir Hastings Ismay, knighted 1940, later Lord Ismay. Chief of staff to the Minister of Defence, and Deputy Secretary to the War Cabinet, 1940–5.
6. Professor Lord Briggs to author.
7. Sir John Colville, *The Fringes of Power*, p.125.
8. Sir Martin Gilbert, *Winston S. Churchill*, Vol. VI, p.593.
9. Ibid.
10. Sir John Colville, *Diary*, 15 June 1940, Churchill College, Cambridge.
11. Sir John Colville, *Action This Day*, p.49.
12. Lindemann Papers, F64/17.
13. Sir Martin Gilbert, *Winston S. Churchill*, op. cit., Vol.I, p.420; Vol. II, p.338.
14. Lindemann Papers, F107/3.
15. C. J. Martin to author.
16. C. J. Martin to author; H. W. Robinson to author.
17. Professor Thomas Wilson, *Churchill and the Prof*, p.17.
18. G. D. A MacDougall, *The Prime Minister's Statistical Section*, p.4, incl. in *Lessons of the British War Economy*, ed. D. N. Chester, 1951.
19. Ibid.
20. Lindemann Papers, H39/8.
21. Sir Donald MacDougall to author.
22. Harrod, *The Prof*, p.199.
23. For these details the author is grateful to Mr H. W. Robinson, the member of S Department who dealt with the case.
24. Robinson, *In on the Ground Floor*.
25. Sir Donald MacDougall, *Don and Mandarin*, p.29.
26. Harrod, op. cit., p.199.
27. Sir Donald MacDougall to author. Such dangers call to mind Squire Mytten felling 1,000 acres of his famous ancient oak woods to pay for his profligate lifestyle.
28. Sir Donald MacDougall to author.
29. Germany was at that time under stringent British blockade.
30. Lindemann Papers, H26.
31. C. J. Martin to author.
32. Wilson, op. cit., p.9.
33. Later Sir Bryan Hopkin, CBE.
34. Sir Bryan Hopkin to author.
35. Sir Donald MacDougall to author.
36. Lindemann Papers, F154. Lindemann to Prime Minister, 9 March 1942.
37. Lindemann Papers, H97.
38. Of the innumerable comments about the war in North Africa, one of

the most engaging concerned General Wavell, who led the successful campaign to drive the Italians out of Cyrenaica. At Wavell's old school, Summer Fields, Oxford, among other items of school business and news of Old Boys, it was announced that: 'Wavell *ma*. has done well in Africa.'

39. PRO.W.P. (43), 8 January 1943.
40. Professor Thomas Wilson to author; and see Wilson, op. cit., pp.100–4.
41. C J. Martin to author.
42. Description by the historian A. J. P. Taylor, and see Earl of Birkenhead, *The Prof in Two Words*, p.215.
43. Robinson, op. cit., p.115.
44. Ibid.
45. Wilson, op. cit., p.15.
46. PRO.CAB 21/1366.
47. Quoted in Ronald Lewin, *Churchill as Warlord*.
48. H. W. Robinson, op. cit., pp. 135–6. Herbert Robinson was responsible for preparing the information and the charts.
49. Lewin, op. cit.
50. Ismay, *Memoirs*, p.172.
51. Beaverbrook Papers.
52. PRO.PREM 7/2.
53. Col. R. S. Macrae, *Winston Churchill's Toyshop*.
54. Quoted in *Biog. Memoirs Roy. Soc.*: Winston S. Churchill.
55. W. R. Merton to author.

12. *Out of House and Home*

1. Sir Charles Webster and Dr Noble Frankland, *The Strategic Air Offensive Against Germany 1939–1945*, Vol. i, p.145 (the official history).
2. Sir Arthur Bryant, *The Turn of the Tide*, p.213.
3. Earl of Halifax, *Fullness of Days*.
4. Churchill to Minister of Aircraft Production, 8 July 1940.
5. R. V. Jones, *Most Secret War*, p.210.
6. Said variously to be by Professor D. L. Hammick, FRS, a don at Oriel College, or by Robin Barrington-Ward, of *The Times*.
7. Sir Alexander Cadogan, *Diaries*, ed. Professor David Dilks, p.575.
8. Sir John Colville, *The Fringes of Power*, p.398.
9. Sir Henry Channon, *Chips: The Diaries of Sir Henry Channon*, ed. Robert Rhodes James.
10. An Oxford University magazine.
11. Dennis Rosborough to author.
12. Ralph Hochuth, *Soldiers*.

13. Dennis Rosborough to author.
14. Sir Geoffrey Cox, *Countdown to War*, p.189. Cox was a pioneer of television journalism and started *News at Ten*.
15. Frank Pakenham, a 'Student' (don) at Christ Church. Later Earl of Longford, and famous as a prison reformer.
16. Lindemann Papers, G237.
17. Ibid.
18. Webster and Frankland, op. cit., Vol. i, p.178.
19. See the Butt Report: *The Strategic Air Offensive Against Germany*, Vol. iv, App. 13.
20. Professor Thomas Wilson, *Churchill and the Prof*, p.66.
21. Lindemann Papers, and quoted in Winston S. Churchill, *The Second World War*, Vol. iv, p.250.
22. Portal Papers, Christ Church Archive, Oxford.
23. Ibid.
24. Ibid.
25. Sir Charles Portal, known as 'Peter', later Viscount Portal of Hungerford. In General Ismay's view, easily the best leader of any of the services during the war.
26. Air Staff Directive XI, 30 October 1940, paras 3 and 4(iii).
27. Dennis Richards, *Portal*, p.301.
28. Quoted in John Terraine, *The Right of the Line*, p.290.
29. Portal Papers. Portal to Churchill, 25 September 1941.
30. Air Staff to Bomber Command, 14 February 1942.
31. Hon. Lady Mosley, see chapter 6.
32. Lady Mosley to author.
33. Sir George Harvie-Watt, *Most of My Life*.
34. Channon, op. cit.
35. House of Commons Debates, 25 February 1942: Hansard, Vol. 316.
36. Webster and Frankland, op. cit., Vol. i, p.331.
37. Ibid., Vol. iii, p.22.
38. Later Lord Snow, novelist and politician. See *Science and Government* and *A Postscript*.
39. Dr Noble Frankland, co-author of the official history, op. cit., has helpfully advised the author on these points, although the conclusions drawn are entirely the author's, for which he accepts full responsibility.
40. Extract from the report by the Police President of Hamburg on the raids on Hamburg in July and August 1943. The July raid, when the RAF used 'Window' (see chapter 13) for the first time, was appropriately codenamed Operation Gomorrah.
41. Jones, op. cit., p.303.

42. Wilson, op. cit., p.90.
43. See H. W. Robinson, *In on the Ground Floor*.
44. Later Lord Zuckerman.
45. *Royal Society Notes*, A342.
46. University of East Anglia, Zuckerman Papers, 2/1/7.
47. Lindemann Papers, G193.
48. Blackett, *Operational Research*, Brassey's Annual, 1953.
49. Solly Zuckerman, *From Apes to Warlords*, p.146.
50. Lindemann Papers, F155/14; G193/3. Tizard to Lindemann, 15 April 1942.
51. Ibid.
52. Portal Papers. Sir Henry Tizard to Sir Archibald Sinclair, 20 April 1942.
53. *Biog. Memoirs Roy. Soc.* P. M. S. Blackett, p.64.
54. See *The Advancement of Modern Science*, Vol. IV.
55. Lindemann Papers, G200/12.
56. A. P. Rowe, 'Scientists at War', *Time and Tide*, Vol. 42, 6 April 1961.
57. S. Zuckerman, op. cit., p.143.
58. Webster and Frankland, op. cit., p.336.
59. Lindemann Papers, G189–205. Lindemann to Air Vice-Marshal Bottomley.
60. *The Spectator*, April 1961.
61. *New Statesman*, April 1961.
62. Richards, op. cit.
63. Lord Zuckerman to Earl of Birkenhead, 2 May 1961.
64. Air Staff Directive xvi, Appendix 'A' 1.
65. Webster and Frankland, op. cit.
66. Interrogation of Albert Speer by Combined Intelligence Objectives Sub-Committee, 18 July 1945.
67. Albert Speer, *Inside the Third Reich*, p.381.
68. Wilson, op. cit., p.90.
69. Webster and Frankland, op. cit., Vol. iii, p.224.
70. Quoted in Webster and Frankland, op. cit., Vol. iii, p.112.
71. Lindemann Papers, G193/9. Lindemann to Tizard, 22 April 1942.
72. Speer, op. cit., p.388.

13. *Science at War*

1. Basil Collier, *The Defence of Britain*, p.157.
2. Lindemann Papers, G335/1; F107/17.
3. Winston S. Churchill, *The Second World War*, vol. II, p.339.
4. R. V. Jones, *Most Secret War*, ch. 11.

5. Lindemann Papers, G335/1.

6. Churchill, op. cit.

7. Jones, op. cit, p.100.

8. Tizard Papers, Imperial War Museum.

9. Jones, op. cit., p.109.

10. Lindemann Papers

11. Portal Papers, Christ Church Archive, Oxford.

12. Ronald Clark, *Tizard*, p.236.

13. *Radio Counter Measures Periodical*, Report No. 8.

14. Lindemann Papers, and quoted in Alfred Price, *Instruments of Darkness*, pp.34–5.

15. Churchill, op. cit., p.338.

16. Quoted in Jones, op. cit., p.181.

17. Hugh Seely, created Lord Sherwood in order to add to the Government's strength in the House of Lords. 'He was a tiny little man, very *chetif*. When someone asked Churchill what name Seely would take as a peer, and was told 'Sherwood', Churchill added with his ever-ready wit: *'Down* in the forest something stirred . . .' (Hon. Lady Mosley to author).

18. Jones, op. cit. p.319.

19. See *Nature*, 23 January 1960: F. Brundrett on Sir Henry Tizard.

20. For the reasons behind the codename H2S, see Jones, op. cit., p.294.

21. Lindemann Papers, F153. Lindemann was referring to Air Chief Marshal Sir Wilfred Freeman.

22. Sir Bernard Lovell, OBE, FRS. Later director of the Jodrell Bank Experimental Station.

23. Birkenhead Papers. Philip Dee to Lindemann, 14 April 1946.

24. H. E. Bufton, a very successful airman, who had piloted the dramatic flight in search of the Knickebein beams on 21 June 1940.

25. Sir Charles Webster and Dr Noble Frankland, *The Strategic Air Offensive Against Germany, 1939–1945*, Vol. i, p.248.

26. Dudley Saward, *Bomber Harris*, p.202.

27. Professor R. V. Jones, *The Times*, 8 April 1961.

28. Churchill, op. cit., Vol. IV, pp.257–9; Vol. V, p.459.

29. Ibid.

30. Jones, op. cit.

31. Derek Jackson was an exceptionally able radar operator, and a very brave and much-decorated officer. Extremely rich and of independent and humorous mind, he was no respecter of persons. On one occasion, at his fighter base, after he had returned from a mission, a rather pompous Air Commodore asked him how he'd got on. 'Well, thank

you, sir,' replied Jackson, 'We got three and a half.' 'Oh well done,'
said the Air Commodore, and, after a pause, 'Half, eh? What was the
half for?' 'Oh, that, sir, that was one of ours – doesn't really count!'

32. *Infrared Physics*, Vol. 1, 1961, p.161.
33. Jones, op. cit., p.294.
34. Lindemann Papers, G342/8. Lindemann to Churchill, 11 September 1942.
35. Air Staff Directive XIV, 9 March 1941.
36. Admiral Dönitz, *Memoirs*.
37. Portal Papers. Air Chief Marshal Joubert to chief of the Air Staff.
38. Portal Papers. Lindemann to Churchill, 4 June 1942.
39. Ibid.
40. PRO.CAB. AU (43) (99). Lindemann Papers.
41. Sir Roy Harrod Papers, British Library.
42. Lindemann Papers, F 255/2.
43. Quoted in *Biog. Memoirs Roy. Soc.* R. V. Jones, Winston S. Churchill.
44. Sir Bernard Lovell, *Echoes of War*.
45. Captain Stephen Roskill, *The War at Sea*. Quoted in Ronald Lewin, *Churchill as Warlord*, p.186.
46. Dr Noble Frankland, CB, CBE, DFC. See Webster and Frankland, op. cit., Vol. iii, p.100.

14. *Follow My Leader*

1. General Sir Ian Jacob, *Diary*. General Jacob, an 'ascetic intellectual', was part of the famously efficient office of the Minister of Defence that fed the Prime Minister with facts, figures and plans.
2. Ibid.
3. For details of this meeting, see Theodore Wilson, *The First Summit*, which has a comprehensive bibliography on the subject.
4. Lindemann Papers, F256 5–10. Lindemann to Churchill, for War Cabinet meeting.
5. Lindemann Papers, H181/4.
6. See Nathan I. White, *Harry Dexter White*, and J. M. Blum, *The Morgenthau Diaries*.
7. Blum, op. cit. p.327.
8. Ibid, p.351, 354.
9. Lord Moran, *The Struggle for Survival*.
10. White, op. cit., p.362.
11. Lindemann Papers, F 209/22.
12. T. H. O'Brien, *Civil Defence*, HMSO, 1955, p.665.

13. 'V' stood for *Vegeltung*, meaning retaliation.
14. PRO.C.O.S. (43) 259 (O).
15. Marshal of the Royal Air Force Viscount Trenchard, generally regarded as the founder of the RAF.
16. Lindemann Papers, G410/1.
17. Ibid.
18. Lindemann Papers, G410.
19. Ibid.
20. 10th Meeting of Defence Committee (Operations), 25 October 1943. Lindemann Papers, G417/2.
21. Lindemann Papers, G417/5.
22. Lindemann Papers, G418/2. Lindemann to Churchill, 1 November 1943.
23. Lindemann Papers, G420/13.
24. Lindemann Papers, G421.
25. Ibid.
26. Ronald Lewin, *Churchill as Warlord*, p. 205.
27. Birkenhead Papers.
28. Lindemann Papers G415/7. Lindemann to Churchill, 15 August 1944.
29. Birkenhead Papers. William Merton to Lord Birkenhead.
30. Lindemann Papers G420/23. Photographs of the V1 launch pads resembled ski-shaped ramps and became known as 'ski sites'.
31. Lindemann Papers, F256.
32. James Leasor, *War at the Top. Diaries of Sir Leslie Hollis*, p.72. Lindemann's claim about one casualty per bomb was made to the Defence Committee (Operations) on 22 December 1943.

15. *Heavy Metal*

1. *Roosevelt and Churchill, Secret Correspondence*, Doc. 465, p.606.
2. Harold Nicolson, *Public Faces*, 1932, p.17.
3. Margaret Gowing, *Britain and Atomic Energy 1939–45*, p.38.
4. *New York Times*, 29 April 1939.
5. P. G. Wodehouse, *Right Ho, Jeeves*, 1937.
6. Supplement to *Nature*, 23 April 1938.
7. Later Sir James Chadwick, and a notable contributor to Britain's atomic development during the war years.
8. Quoted in A. Weale, *Science and the Swastika*, pp.115–16.
9. Jean Medawar and David Pyke, *Hitler's Gift*, p.213.
10. Spencer Weart, *Leo Szilard, Collected Works*.
11. Ibid., p.55.

12. PRO.AB 1/37.
13. Quoted in Winston S. Churchill, *The Second World War*, Vol. I, p.301.
14. R. V. Jones, *Reflections on Intelligence*, p.242.
15. PRO.AB 1/106.
16. PRO.AB 8/113. Professor Franz Simon, *Diary*.
17. Quoted in Gowing, op. cit., p.40.
18. Quoted in Ronald Clark, *The Birth of the Bomb*, p.87.
19. Ibid., p.41.
20. Quoted in Weale, op. cit. p.177.
21. Lindemann Papers.
22. PRO.AB 1/106.
23. Antony Croft, *Oxford's Clarendon Laboratory*.
24. This committee, the Sub-Committee on the Uranium Bomb, was officially called the M.A.U.D. Committee, but was usually referred to simply as MAUD. The name had resulted from a telegram that Niels Bohr had sent to Otto Frisch when Denmark was overrun by the Germans, which had ended: 'Tell Cockroft and Maud Ray Kent.' All sorts of ingenious theories had been propounded for the meaning of Maud Ray, but it was not until after the war that the explanation was found to be that Maud Ray was the name of the nanny who had looked after Bohr's children, and who lived in Kent. A similar confusion was recounted by the actor David Niven, who, before returning to England on leave during the war, had telegraphed his Danish girlfriend saying: 'Arriving with Secret Weapon'; he consequently found himself confronted on arrival at the girl's house by two men from the Secret Service.
25. PRO.AB 1/106.
26. PRO.CAB 126/329.
27. Quoted in Gowing, op. cit., p.106.
28. Minute from Sir John Anderson to Churchill, 30 July 1942. Quoted in Gowing, op. cit., App. 3.
29. PRO.CAB 126/183.
30. PRO.PREM 3/65. Quoted in Harris and Paxman, *A Higher Form of Killing*, p.101.
31. Broadcast from the headquarters of Grand Admiral Dönitz, 'Announcement by the High Command of the Armed Forces', 9 May 1945.
32. War Cabinet Paper (45), April 1945. Lindemann Papers, F257.
33. Ibid.
34. Lindemann Papers, H207.

16. *Home from the Hill*

1. J. G. Crowther, *Statesmen of Science*, p.369.
2. Birkenhead Papers.
3. Earl of Birkenhead; *The Prof in Two Worlds*, p.270.
4. Lindemann Papers; quoted in Birkenhead, op. cit., p.277.
5. Lindemann Papers. Cherwell to Churchill, 29 November 1951.
6. Later Lord Roberthall.
7. Robert Hall, *Diaries*.
8. Sir Richard Clarke, known as 'Otto', journalist with the *Financial News*, 1933–9; Under-Secretary at the Treasury, 1945–55.
9. Sir Donald MacDougall, *Don and Mandarin*, p.85.
10. J. S. Fforde, *Bank of England 1945–58*, p.440.
11. Lindemann Papers, J122.
12. Anthony Howard, *Rab, The Life of R. A. Butler*, p.181.
13. Lady Williams of Elvel to author.
14. Quoted in Sir Martin Gilbert, *Winston S. Churchill*, Vol. viii. p.673.
15. Lindemann Papers, J97.
16. Lindemann Papers, J122/99.
17. Birkenhead, op. cit., p.315.
18. Associated Press, 16 September 1953.
19. Dr Maurice Scott to author.
20. For a similar conversation at Churchill's table, see Charles Eade, editor of the *Sunday Dispatch*, note of a luncheon, 6 March 1941. Quoted in Sir Martin Gilbert, *Winston S. Churchill, War Papers*, Vol. 3.
21. Lady Juliet Townsend to author.
22. Dr John Bamborough to author.
23. Roy Harrod, *The Prof*, p.90.
24. Professor Hall to author; and see *Archaeometry* 28, 2 (1986), 131–2.
25. Professor Edward Hall, CBE, *Memoirs*.
26. *Chemistry and Industry*, 31 July 1954.
27. W. R. Merton to author.
28. Lord Zuckermann Papers, University of East Anglia. Lindemann to Lord President of the Council.
29. House of Lords debate on the Middle East, 10 April 1957. Hansard, Vol. 202, col. 1218.

SELECT BIBLIOGRAPHY

Unpublished Papers and Diaries

Birkenhead Papers: Private Collection.
Chamberlain Collection: Birmingham University Library.
Cherwell Archive: Nuffield College, Oxford.
Clarendon Laboratory Archive: Clarendon Laboratory, Oxford.
Colville Papers: Churchill Archive Centre, Churchill College, Cambridge.
Churchill Papers: Churchill Archive Centre, Churchill College, Cambridge.
Croft, Antony, *Oxford's Clarendon Laboratory*, 1986.
Hall, Professor E. T., Memoirs, private collection.
Inskip Papers: Churchill Archive Centre, Churchill College, Cambridge.
Papers of Sir Henry Tizard: Imperial War Museum.
The Zuckerman Archive: University of East Anglia.

Published works

Babington Smith, Constance, *Testing Time*, London: Cassell, 1961.
Batchelor, George, *The Life and Legacy of G. I. Taylor*, Cambridge: Cambridge University Press, 1996.
Birkenhead, Earl of, *The Prof in Two Worlds*, London: Collins, 1961.
Blackett, P. M. S., *Studies of War: Nuclear and Conventional*, Edinburgh: Oliver & Boyd, 1962.
Blum, J. M., *From the Morgenthau Diaries*, Boston: Houghton Miflin, 1959–1967.
Bowen, E. J., *Radar Days*, Bristol: A. Hilger, 1987.
Charmley, John, *Chamberlain and the Lost Peace*, London: Curtis, 1989.
Churchill, Sarah, *A Thread in the Tapestry*, André Deutsch: London, 1967.
Churchill, Winston S. *The Second World War, 1939–1945*, London: Cassell, 1950–1955.

Clark, Ronald, *The Birth of the Bomb*, London: Phoenix House, 1961.

Clark, Ronald, *Einstein: The Life and Times*, London: Hodder & Stoughton, 1973.

Clark, Ronald, *Tizard*, London: Methuen, 1965.

Cox, Geoffrey, *Countdown to War*, London: William Kimber, 1988.

Dilks, David, *The Diaries of Sir Alexander Cadogan, O.M., 1938–1945*, London: Cassell, 1971.

Dönitz, Admiral Karl, *Memoirs: Ten Years and Twenty Days*, London: Weidenfeld & Nicolson, 1959.

Egerton, Ruth, *Sir Alfred Egerton F.R.S., 1886–1959: A Memoir with Papers*, Curwen Press, 1963.

Frayn, Michael, *Copenhagen*, London: Methuen, 1998.

Gilbert, Martin, *In Search of Churchill*, London: HarperCollins, 1994.

Gilbert, Martin, and Churchill, Randolph S., *Winston S. Churchill*, London: Heinemann, 1966–1988.

Gowing, Margaret, *Britain and Atomic Energy 1939–1945*, London: Macmillan, 1964.

Harrod, Roy, *The Prof: A Personal Memoir of Lord Cherwell*, London: Macmillan, 1959.

Harvie-Watt, G. S. *Most of My Life*, London: Springwood Books, 1980.

Heilbron, J. L., *H. G. J. Moseley: The Life and Letters of an English Physicist, 1887–1915*, Berkeley: University of California Press, 1974.

Hinsley, F. H., *British Intelligence in the Second World War*, Keele: University of Keele, 1985.

Ismay, Lord, *Memoirs*, London: Heinemann, 1960.

Johnson, J. A., *The Kaiser's Chemists*, Chapel Hill: University of North Carolina Press, 1990.

Jones, R. V., *Most Secret War*, London: Hamish Hamilton, 1978.

Jones, R. V., *Reflections on Intelligence*, London: Hamish Hamilton, 1989.

Jones, Thomas, *A Diary with Letters 1931–1950*, Oxford: Oxford University Press, 1954.

Kennedy, John, *The Business of War*, London: Hutchinson, 1957.

Lewin, Ronald, *Churchill as Warlord*, London: Batsford, 1973.

Lewis, Julian, *Changing Direction: British Military Planning for Post-War Strategic Defence, 1942–1947*, London: Sherwood, 1988.

Lindemann, F. A., *The Physical Significance of the Quantum Theory*, Oxford: Clarendon Press, 1932.

Lindemann, F. A., *Physics and Philosophy*, Oxford: Oxford University Press, 1955.

Lovell, Bernard, *Echoes of War: The Story of H2S Radar*, Bristol: A. Hilger, 1991.

MacDougall, Sir Donald, *Don and Mandarin: Memoirs of an Economist*, London: John Murray, 1987.

Macrae, R. S., *Winston Churchill's Toyshop*, Kineton: Roundwood Press, 1971.

Medawar, Jean, and Pyke, David, *Hitler's Gift: Scientists Who Fled Nazi Germany*, London: Richard Cohen, 2000.

Mehra, Jagdish, *The Solvay Conferences on Physics*, Dordrecht: D. Reidel, 1975.

Mendelssohn, Kurt, *The World of Walther Nernst*, London: Macmillan, 1973.

Millikan, Robert A., *The Autobiography of Robert A. Millikan*, London: Macdonald, 1951.

Morrell, Jack, *Science at Oxford 1914–1939*, Oxford: Clarendon Press, 1997.

Nicolson, Harold, *Public Faces*, London: Constable, 1932.

O'Brien, T. H., *Civil Defence*, London: HMSO, 1955.

Overy, R. J., *The Road to War*, London: Macmillan, 1989.

Parker, R. A. C., *Chamberlain and Appeasement*, Basingstoke: Macmillan, 1993.

Price, Alfred, *Instruments of Darkness*, London: Kimber,. 1967.

Purrington, Robert D., *Physics in the Nineteenth Century*, New Brunswick: Rutgers University Press, 1997.

Raleigh, W. A. and Jones, H. A., *The Official History of the War in the Air*, Oxford: Clarendon Press, 1922–1937.

Richards, Denis, *Portal of Hungerford*, London: Heinemann, 1977.

Richardson, Charles, *From Churchill's Secret Circle to the BBC: The Biography of Lieutenant General Sir Ian Jacob*, London: Brassey's, 1991.

Robinson, H. W., *In on the Ground Floor*, Fountain Hills, Arizona: IMS Press, 1996.

Roskill, S. *Hankey, Man of Secrets*, London: Collins, 1970–1974.

Rowe, A., *One Story of Radar*, Cambridge: Cambridge University Press, 1948.

Saward, Dudley, *Bomber Harris*, London: Sphere, 1985.

Slessor, Sir John, *The Central Blue*, London: Cassell, 1956.

Snow, C. P. *Science and Government*, Oxford: Oxford University Press, 1961.

Southwell, Richard, *Aeronautical Progress: 1914–1930*, London: Institute of Civil Engineers, 1931.

Swinton, Earl of, *Sixty Years of Power*, London: Hutchinson, 1966.

Terraine, John, *The Right of the Line: The Royal Air Force in the European War, 1939–1945*, London: Hodder & Stoughton, 1985.

Watson-Watt, R. A., *Three Steps to Victory*, London: Odham's Press, 1957.

Webster, Sir Charles, and Frankland, Dr Noble, *The Strategic Air Offensive Against Germany 1939–1945*, London: HMSO, 1961.

Wheeler-Bennett, John (ed.), *Action This Day: Working With Churchill*, London: Macmillan, 1968.

Wilson, Theodore, *The First Summit: Roosevelt and Churchill at Placentia Bay, 1941*, London: Macdonald, 1970.

Wood, D., *Narrow Margin*, Shrewsbury: Airlife, 1990.

Zuckerman, Solly, *From Apes to Warlords*, London: Hamish Hamilton, 1978.

ACKNOWLEDGEMENTS

My gratitude is due to Lord Blake, who encouraged and guided me at the earliest stages of my work on this book.

I am grateful also to Lindemann's nephew, John Vickers, for providing me with information about the family.

My thanks are due to Dr John Sanders, Archivist of the Clarendon Laboratory, and to Dr Stuart Young, who worked for Lindemann in the 1950s, both of whom offered me invaluable help with detailed aspects of science. I would also like to thank Professor David Dilks and Sir Martin Gilbert for their advice and for taking the time to read parts of the draft text.

I also acknowledge the support that I have had from the Royal Society, and the help that I have received there from Susan Moss. I am also grateful for the encouragement offered by Professor Roger Cowley and his staff at the Clarendon Laboratory in Oxford.

Others whose assistance was most welcome include some of those who worked for Lindemann, whether at Oxford or in his Statistical Department. They include Sir Bryan Hopkin, Dr Cyril Martin, Sir Donald MacDougall, William Merton, Professor Jack Parkinson, Herbert W. Robinson, Dennis Rosborough, Gordon Rosborough, Maurice Scott, and the late Professor Thomas Wilson.

I have also received guidance and information from others who knew or were associated with Lindemann at Oxford. They include Lord Armstrong of Ilminster, John Bamborough, Dr Robert Berman, Professor Brebis Bleaney, Teddy Burn, George Cawkwell, the late Lord Dacre, the late Professor Edward Hall, Dr Paul Kent, Dr J. F. A. Mason, Sir Edward Maitland Wright, and Dr J. M. Wright.

In researching Lindemann's pioneering work in aeronautics, I was helped particularly by John Gratton and Dr Darrol Stinton, who provided me with theoretical and practical knowledge of aircraft spin; by Brian Kervell; by

Peter Trevett and Pam Turner at QinetiQ; and by Louise Weymouth at Marconi plc.

I am indebted to close relatives of scientists whom Lindemann helped to leave Nazi Germany and to start a new life in Oxford: Mrs Kathrin Baxandall, Dr Monica Mendelssohn, and Mrs Mariele Kuhn-Oser.

I would like to thank the following for their kind assistance: Professor Lord Briggs, James Bristow, Anthony Brotherton-Ratcliffe, Hon Lady Bonsor, Lord Charles Cecil, the Earl of Crawford and Balcarres, Anne Chisholm, Lady Margaret Colville, Anne de Courcy, Sir William Deakin, Dr Noble Frankland, Henry Gillett, Jeffie Hall, Lady Harrod, Alistair Horne, Virginia Howard, Dr Stuart Jones, Reginald Lane of the Sid Vale Heritage Centre, Violet Liddle, Dr Julian Lock, Sir Anthony Montague Browne, Hon Lady Mosley, Lady Antonia Pinter, Charles Ponsonby, Lady Soames, Lady Juliet Townsend, Hugo Vickers, Gerald White of the Norman Lockyer Observatory Society, Lady Williams of Elvel and Patricia Woodifield.

Librarians and their colleagues have been very patient with my enquiries, and my special thanks are due to Melanie Aspey of the Rothschild Archive; Gill Bennett at the Foreign and Commonwealth Office; Dr Victoria Child and her colleagues at Nuffield College Library; Dr Judith Curthoys at Christ Church Library; Kenneth Dunn at the Scottish National Library; Deirdre Sharp at the University of East Anglia; Roderick Suddaby at the Imperial War Museum; the staff at the Churchill Archive, and at the Radcliffe Science Library.

I would like to thank Sally Back, Jan Coleman and Clare Jones for their efficiency in matters of administration.

I am also very grateful to James Gill at PFD, and to Will Sulkin and Jörg Hensgen at Jonathan Cape, for their guidance in the preparation of this book.

INDEX

Abyssinia 241
Academic Assistance Council 119–20
Acheson, Dean 324
Adlon Hotel, Berlin 28, 72
Admiralty 44, 51, 53, 182, 183–203, 209, 276
ADR (Air Defence Research) Committee 173–4, 175, 176–7, 185, 270
aerial mines 142–3
Aeronautical Research Committee 128
Aeronautics, Advisory Committee for 60
Air Council 76
air defence
    concerns at deficiencies in 172
    drive for research programme in 173–4
    interception demonstration 179–80
Air Ministry 79, 134–6, 145, 167, 170–1, 171–2, 175, 186, 259
Air Research Council 82
Aircraft Production, Ministry of 213, 251, 292
Akers, William 310
Alamogordo, nuclear test at 311
Alsace 3, 4
American Physical Society 297
Amery, Leopold 172, 181
Anderson, Sir John 310–11
Anderson, Squadron Leader Charles 167
Anglo-American co-operation on atomic research 311
Anglo-Persian Oil Company 235
anthrax bomb 312
anti-Semitism 92, 117, 153, 300
appeasement 130, 133, 171, 172–3, 177–8, 183, 347–8
Archaeology and the History of Art, Research Laboratory for 331
Arms, Schull 307
Army Council 55
Asquith, Raymond 70
Aston, Francis W. 49, 80, 81, 84, 303
ASV (Air to Surface Vessel) radar 267, 269
Athenia, sinking of 183
'Atlantic Charter', declaration of 279
atomic bomb 297–311
    production of ('Tube Alloys') 308–12
Atomic Energy Authority 325, 326, 335
Austria, *Anschluss* in 177, 298
Ayr, Professor 236

Baden-Baden 8
Baedeker, Karl 70
Baldwin, Stanley 108, 130, 133, 167, 177
Balfour, Arthur James 53
Bank of England 321
Barrington-Ward, Robin 236
Bateman, H. M. 185
Battersea Polytechnic 333
Battle of Britain 229
Battle of the Atlantic 274–8
Bavaria 2, 4–5
Bavarian Academy of Science 119
Baxandall, Kathrin 68, 116
Beaverbrook, Lord 222, 223, 226, 233, 243, 262
Becquerel, Henri 20
Beecham, Sir Thomas 78
Belgian Congo 302
Berkeley, Earl and Countess of 85, 155
Berlin 22–40, 229
Bernal, Desmond 247, 249–50
Bethmann-Hollweg, Chancellor Theobald 41
Binney, Sir George 350
Birkenhead, (F. E. Smith), 1st Earl of 41, 50, 88, 90, 94, 99, 226, 235
Birmingham University 267, 304
Bismarck, Chancellor Otto von 42, 47
Blackett, Patrick 137–8, 143, 146, 249, 251, 274
Blair Lodge School 12–14
Blenheim Palace 89–90
Bletchley Park 206, 259, 277
Board of Trade 212
Bohr, Niels 38, 298, 299, 300, 304, 311–12
Bomber Command 230–1, 270, 272, 276
    Air Staff directive to 255
    bomb-aiming accuracy 231, 237–8
    bomber numbers, shortage of 256
    bombing efficiency calculations 247–53
    Dresden, saturation raids on 245, 257
    effects of bombing on Germany 254–6
    general attacks on industrial populations 243–4
    Hamburg, raids of 244–5
    Mannheim, area bombing of 239
    night operations over Germany 265–6
    Pathfinder Force 269
    strategic bombing 239–40, 244–6
Bone, Professor 131